Mickey & Billy Ed Murray

JOURNEYS
THROUGH
BOOKLAND

Tournament
T. M. GRANT '09

Journeys Through Bookland

A New and Original Plan for Reading, Applied to the World's Best Literature for Children

BY

Charles H. Sylvester
AUTHOR OF *English and American Literature, Etc.*

VOLUME SIX

BELLOWS-REEVE COMPANY
CHICAGO

R0120337486

CONTENTS

For classification of selections, see the index at the end of Volume X.

ILLUSTRATIONS

Title-page and halftone decorations by Mrs. Thomas Wood Stevens.

Initial letters, tailpieces and other decorations by Mrs. Thomas Wood Stevens, Frederick Grant and Miss Edith Virden.

THE RISE OF ROBERT BRUCE[1]

SIR WALTER SCOTT[2]

ROBERT the Bruce was a remarkably brave and strong man; there was no man in Scotland that was thought a match for him. He was very wise and prudent, and an excellent general; that is, he knew how to conduct an army, and place them in order for battle, as well or better than any great man of his time. He was generous, too, and courteous by nature; but he had some faults, which perhaps belonged as much to the fierce period in which he lived as to his own character. He was rash and passionate, and in his passion he was sometimes relentless and cruel.

Robert the Bruce had fixed his purpose to attempt once again to drive the English out of Scotland, and he desired to prevail upon Sir John the Red Comyn, who was his rival in his pretensions to the throne, to join with him

1. Robert Bruce was born in July, 1274. During the early part of his life he was sometimes to be found on the side of the English and sometimes on the side of the Scotch, but as he grew older his patriotic spirit was roused, and he threw himself heart and soul into the cause of his native land. As late as the year 1299, after the Scotch patriot Wallace had been defeated, Bruce was in favor with the English King Edward, but in February, 1306, occurred the event with which Scott's narrative opens.

2. The following interesting account of some of the incidents in the life of Bruce is abridged from Scott's *Tales of a Grandfather*, a series of historical stories which Scott wrote for his little grandson.

in expelling the foreign enemy by their common efforts. With this purpose, Bruce posted down from London to Dumfries, on the borders of Scotland, and requested an interview with John Comyn. They met in the church of the Minorites in that town, before the high altar. What passed between them is not known with certainty; but they quarrelled, either concerning their mutual pretensions to the crown, or because Comyn refused to join Bruce in the proposed insurrection against the English; or, as many writers say, because Bruce charged Comyn with having betrayed to the English his purpose of rising up against King Edward. It is, however, certain that these two haughty barons came to high and abusive words, until at length Bruce, who I told you was extremely passionate, forgot the sacred character of the place in which they stood, and struck Comyn a blow with his dagger. Having done this rash deed, he instantly ran out of the church and called for his horse. Two gentlemen of the country, Lindesay and Kirkpatrick, friends of Bruce, were then in attendance on him. Seeing him pale, bloody, and in much agitation, they eagerly inquired what was the matter.

"I doubt," said Bruce, "that I have slain the Red Comyn."

"Do you leave such a matter in doubt?" said Kirkpatrick. "I will make sicker!"—that is, I will make certain.

Accordingly, he and his companion Lindesay rushed into the church, and made the matter

BRUCE KILLS COMYN

certain with a vengeance, by despatching the wounded Comyn with their daggers. His uncle, Sir Robert Comyn, was slain at the same time.

This slaughter of Comyn was a rash and cruel action; and the historian of Bruce observes that it was followed by the displeasure of Heaven:

for no man ever went through more misfortunes than Robert Bruce, although he at length rose to great honor.

After the deed was done, Bruce might be called desperate. He had committed an action which was sure to bring down upon him the vengeance of all Comyn's relations, the resentment of the King of England, and the displeasure of the Church, on account of having slain his enemy within consecrated ground. He determined, therefore, to bid them all defiance at once, and to assert his pretensions to the throne of Scotland. He drew his own followers together, summoned to meet him such barons as still entertained hopes of the freedom of the country, and was crowned king at the Abbey of Scone, the usual place where the kings of Scotland assumed their authority.

The commencement of Bruce's undertaking was most disastrous. He was crowned on the twenty-ninth of March, 1306. On the eighteenth of May he was excommunicated by the Pope, on account of the murder of Comyn within consecrated ground, a sentence which excluded him from all benefits of religion, and authorized any one to kill him. Finally, on the nineteenth of June, the new king was completely defeated near Methven by the English Earl of Pembroke. Robert's horse was killed under him in the action, and he was for a moment a prisoner.

But he had fallen into the power of a Scottish knight, who, though he served in the English army, did not choose to be the instrument of putting Bruce into their hands, and allowed him to escape. The conquerors executed their prisoners with their usual cruelty.

Bruce, with a few brave adherents, among whom was the young Lord of Douglas, who was afterward called the Good Lord James, retired into the Highland mountains, where they were chased from one place of refuge to another, often in great danger, and suffering many hardships. The Bruce's wife, now Queen of Scotland, with several other ladies, accompanied her husband and his few followers during their wanderings. There was no other way of providing for them save by hunting and fishing. It was remarked that Douglas was the most active and successful in procuring for the unfortunate ladies such supplies as his dexterity in fishing or in killing deer could furnish to them.

Driven from one place in the Highlands to another, starved out of some districts, and forced from others by the opposition of the inhabitants, Bruce attempted to force his way into Lorn; but he was again defeated, through force of numbers, at a place called Dalry. He directed his men to retreat through a narrow pass, and placing himself last of the party, he fought with and slew such of the enemy as attempted to press hard on them. A father and two sons, called M'Androsser, all very strong men, when they saw Bruce thus protecting the retreat of his followers, made a vow that they would either kill this redoubted champion, or make him prisoner. The whole three rushed on the king at once. Bruce was on horseback, in the strait pass we have described, between a precipitous rock and a deep lake. He struck the first man who came up and seized his horse's rein such a blow with his sword, as cut off his hand and freed the bridle. The man bled to death. The other brother had grasped Bruce in the meantime by the leg, and was attempting to throw him from horseback. The king, setting spurs to his horse, made the animal suddenly spring forward, so that the Highlander fell under the horse's feet, and, as he was endeavoring to rise again, Bruce cleft his head in two with his sword. The father, seeing his two sons thus slain, flew desperately at the king, and grasped him by the mantle so close to his body that he could not have room to wield his long sword. But with the heavy pommel of that weapon, or, as others say, with an iron hammer which hung at his saddle-bow, the king struck his third assailant so dreadful a blow, that he dashed out his brains. Still, however, the Highlander kept his dying grasp on the king's mantle; so that, to be freed of the dead body, Bruce was obliged to undo the brooch, or clasp, by which it was fastened, and leave that, and the mantle itself, behind him.

At last dangers increased so much around the brave King Robert, that he was obliged to separate himself from his queen and her ladies; for the winter was coming on, and it would be impossible for the women to endure this wandering life when the frost and snow should set in.

So Bruce left his queen, with the Countess of Buchan and others, in the only castle which remained to him, which was called Kildrummie. The king also left his youngest brother, Nigel Bruce, to defend the castle against the English; and he himself, with his second brother Edward, who was a very brave man, but still more rash and passionate than Robert himself, went over to an island on the coast of Ireland, where Bruce and the few men who followed his fortunes passed the winter of 1306. In the meantime, ill luck seemed to pursue all his friends in Scotland. The castle of Kildrummie was taken by the English, and Nigel Bruce, a beautiful and brave youth, was cruelly put to death by the victors. The ladies who had attended on Robert's queen, as well as the queen herself, and the Countess of Buchan, were thrown into strict confinement, and treated with the utmost severity.

It was about this time that an incident took place, which, although it rests only on tradition in families of the name of Bruce, is rendered probable by the manners of the times. After receiving the last unpleasing intelligence from Scotland, Bruce was lying one morning on his wretched bed, and deliberating with himself whether he had not better resign all thoughts of again attempting to make good his right to the Scottish crown, and, dismissing his followers, transport himself and his brothers to the Holy Land, and spend the rest of his life in fighting against the Saracens; by which he thought, perhaps, he might deserve the forgiveness of

Heaven for the great sin of stabbing Comyn in the church at Dumfries. But then, on the other hand, he thought it would be both criminal and cowardly to give up his attempts to restore freedom to Scotland while there yet remained the least chance of his being successful in an undertaking, which, rightly considered, was much more his duty than to drive the infidels out of Palestine, though the superstition of his age might think otherwise.

While he was divided between these reflections, and doubtful of what he should do, Bruce was looking upward to the roof of the cabin in which he lay; and his eye was attracted by a spider, which, hanging at the end of a long thread of its own spinning, was endeavoring, as is the fashion of that creature, to swing itself from one beam in the roof to another, for the purpose of fixing the line on which it meant to stretch its web. The insect made the attempt again and again without success; at length Bruce counted that it had tried to carry its point six times, and been as often unable to do so. It came into his head that he had himself fought just six battles against the English and their allies, and that the poor persevering spider was exactly in the same situation with himself, having made as many trials and been as often disappointed in what it aimed at. "Now," thought Bruce, "as I have no means of knowing what is best to be done, I will be guided by the luck which shall attend this spider. If the insect shall make another effort to fix its thread, and shall be successful, I will venture a seventh time to try my fortune in Scotland; but if the spider shall fail, I will go to the wars in Palestine, and never return to my native country more."

While Bruce was forming this resolution the spider made another exertion with all the force it could muster, and fairly succeeded in fastening its thread to the beam which it had so often in vain attempted to reach. Bruce, seeing the success of the spider, resolved to try his own fortune; and as he had never before gained a victory, so he never afterward sustained any considerable or decisive check or defeat. I have often met with people of the name of Bruce, so completely persuaded of the truth of this story, that they would not on any account kill a spider, because it was that insect which had shown the example of perseverance, and given a signal of good luck, to their great namesake.

Having determined to renew his efforts to obtain possession of Scotland, notwithstanding the smallness of the means which he had for accomplishing so great a purpose, the Bruce removed himself and his followers from Rachrin to the island of Arran, which lies in the mouth of the Clyde. The king landed and inquired of the first woman he met what armed men were in the island. She returned for answer that there had arrived there very lately a body of armed strangers, who had defeated an English officer, the governor of the castle of Brathwick, had killed him and most of his men, and were now amusing themselves with hunting about the island. The king, having caused himself to be guided to the woods which these strangers most frequented, there blew his horn repeatedly.

Now, the chief of the strangers who had taken the castle was James Douglas, one of the best of Bruce's friends, and he was accompanied by some of the bravest of that patriotic band. When he heard Robert Bruce's horn, he knew the sound well, and cried out, that yonder was the king, he knew by his manner of blowing. So he and his companions hastened to meet King Robert, and there was great joy on both sides; while at the same time they could not help weeping when they considered their own forlorn condition, and the great loss that had taken place among their friends since they had last parted. But they were stout-hearted men, and looked forward to freeing their country in spite of all that had yet happened.

The Bruce was now within sight of Scotland, and not distant from his own family possessions, where the people were most likely to be attached to him. He began immediately to form plans with Douglas how they might best renew their enterprise against the English. The Douglas resolved to go disguised to his own country, and raise his followers in order to begin their enterprise by taking revenge on an English nobleman called Lord Clifford, upon whom Edward had conferred his estates, and who had taken up his residence in the castle of Douglas.

Bruce, on his part, opened a communication with the opposite coast of Carrick, by means of one of his followers called Cuthbert. This person had directions, that if he should find the countrymen in Carrick disposed to take up arms against the English he was to make a fire on a headland, or lofty cape, called Turnberry, on the coast of Ayrshire, opposite to the island of Arran. The appearance of a fire on this place was to be a signal for Bruce to put to sea with such men as he had, who were not more than three hundred in number, for the purpose of landing in Carrick and joining the insurgents.

Bruce and his men watched eagerly for the signal, but for some time in vain. At length a fire on Turnberry-head became visible, and the king and his followers merrily betook themselves to their ships and galleys, concluding their Carrick friends were all in arms and ready to join with them. They landed on the beach at midnight, where they found their spy Cuthbert alone in waiting for them with very bad news. Lord Percy, he said, was in the country with two or three hundred Englishmen, and had terrified the people so much, both by actions and threats, that none of them dared to think of rebelling against King Edward.

"Traitor!" said Bruce, "why, then, did you make the signal?"

"Alas," replied Cuthbert, "the fire was not made by me, but by some other person, for what purpose I know not; but as soon as I saw it burning, I knew that you would come over, thinking it my signal, and therefore I came down to wait for you on the beach to tell you how the matter stood."

King Robert's first idea was to return to Arran after this disappointment; but his brother Edward refused to go back. He was, as I have told you, a man daring even to rashness. "I will not leave my native land," he said, "now that I am so unexpectedly restored to it. I will give freedom to Scotland, or leave my carcass on the surface of the land which gave me birth."

Bruce, also, after some hesitation, determined that since he had been thus brought to the mainland of Scotland, he would remain there, and take such adventure and fortune as Heaven should send him.

Accordingly, he began to skirmish with the English so successfully, as obliged the Lord Percy to quit Carrick. Bruce then dispersed his men upon various adventures against the enemy, in which they were generally successful. But then, on the other hand, the king, being left with small attendance, or sometimes almost alone, ran great risk of losing his life by treachery or by open violence.

At one time, a near relation of Bruce's, in whom he entirely confided, was induced by the bribes of the English to attempt to put him to death. This villain, with his two sons, watched the king one morning, till he saw him separated from all his men, excepting a little boy, who waited on him as a page. The father had a sword in his hand, one of the sons had a sword and a spear, and the other had a sword and a battle-axe. Now, when the king saw them so well armed, when there were no enemies near, he began to call to mind some hints which had been given to him, that these men intended to murder him. He had no weapons excepting his sword; but his page had a bow and arrow. He took them both from the little boy, and bade him stand at a distance; "for," said the king, "if I overcome these traitors, thou shalt have enough of weapons; but if I am slain by them, you may make your escape, and tell Douglas and my brother to revenge my death." The boy was very sorry, for he loved his master; but he was obliged to do as he was bidden.

In the meantime the traitors came forward upon Bruce, that they might assault him at once. The king called out to them, and commanded them to come no nearer, upon peril of their lives; but the father answered with flattering words, pretending great kindness, and still continuing to approach his person. Then the king again called to them to stand. "Traitors," said he, "ye have sold my life for English gold; but you shall die if you come one foot nearer to me." With that he bent the page's bow, and as the old conspirator continued to advance, he let the arrow fly at him. Bruce was an excellent archer; he aimed his arrow so well that it hit the father in the eye, and penetrated from that into his brain, so that he fell down dead. Then the two sons rushed on the king. One of them fetched a blow at him with an axe, but missed his stroke and stumbled, so that the king with his great sword cut him down before he could recover his feet. The remaining traitor ran on Bruce with his spear; but the king, with a sweep of his sword, cut the steel head off the villain's weapon, and then killed him before he had time to draw his sword. Then the little page came running, very joyful of his master's victory; and the king wiped his bloody sword, and, looking upon the dead bodies, said, "These might have been reputed three gallant men, if they could have resisted the temptation of covetousness."

After the death of these three traitors, Robert the Bruce continued to keep himself concealed in his own earldom of Carrick, and in the neighboring country of Galloway, until he should have matters ready for a general attack upon the English. He was obliged, in the meantime, to keep very few men with him, both for the sake of secrecy, and from the difficulty of finding provisions. Now, many of the people of Galloway were unfriendly to Bruce. They had heard that he was in their country, having no more than sixty men with him; so they resolved to attack him by surprise, and for this purpose they got two hundred men together, and brought with them two or three bloodhounds. These animals were trained to chase a man by the scent of his footsteps, as foxhounds chase a fox, or as beagles and harriers chase a hare. Although the dog does not see the person whose trace he is put upon, he follows him over every step he has taken. At that time these bloodhounds, or sleuthhounds (so called from *slot*, or *sleut*, a word which signifies the scent left by an animal of chase), were used for the purpose of pursuing great criminals. The men of Galloway thought themselves secure, that if they missed taking Bruce, or killing him at the first onset, and if he should escape into the woods, they would find him out by means of these bloodhounds.

The good King Robert Bruce, who was always watchful and vigilant, had received some information of the intention of this party to come upon him suddenly and by night. Accordingly, he quartered his little troop of sixty men on the side of a deep and swift-running river, that had very steep and rocky banks. There was but one ford by which this river could be crossed in that neighborhood, and that ford was deep and narrow, so that two men could scarcely get through abreast; the ground on which they were to land on the side where the king was, was steep, and the path which led upward from the water's edge to the top of the bank, extremely narrow and difficult.

Bruce caused his men to lie down to take some sleep, at a place about half a mile distant from the river, while he himself, with two attendants, went down to watch the ford, through which the enemy must needs pass before they could come to the place where King Robert's men were lying. He stood for some time looking at the ford, and thinking how easily the enemy might be kept from passing there, provided it was bravely defended, when he heard at a distance the baying of a hound, which was always coming nearer and nearer. This was the bloodhound which was tracing the king's steps to the ford where he had crossed, and the two hundred Galloway men were along with the animal, and guided by it. Bruce at first thought of going back to awaken his men; but then he reflected that it might be only some shepherd's dog. "My men," said he, "are sorely tired; I will not disturb their sleep for the yelping of a cur, till I know something more of the matter."

So he stood and listened; and by and by, as the cry of the hound came nearer, he began to hear a trampling of horses, and the voices of men, and the ringing and clattering of armor, and then he was sure the enemy were coming to the river side. Then the king thought, "If I go back to give my men the alarm, these Galloway men will get through the ford without opposition; and that would be a pity, since it is a place so advantageous to make defence against them." So he looked again at the steep path, and the deep river, and he thought that they gave him so much advantage, that he himself could defend the passage with his own hand, until his men came to assist him. His armor was so good and strong, that he had no fear of arrows, and therefore the combat was not so very unequal as it must have otherwise been. He therefore sent his followers to waken his men, and remained alone by the bank of the river.

In the meanwhile, the noise and trampling of the horses increased; and the moon being bright,

Bruce beheld the glancing arms of about two hundred men, who came down to the opposite bank of the river. The men of Galloway, on their part, saw but one solitary figure guarding the ford, and the foremost of them plunged into the river without minding him. But as they could only pass the ford one by one, the Bruce, who stood high above them on the bank where they were to land, killed the foremost man with a thrust of his long spear, and with a second thrust stabbed the horse, which fell down, kicking and plunging in his agonies, on the narrow path, and so prevented the others who were following from getting out of the river. Bruce had thus an opportunity of dealing his blows at pleasure among them, while they could not strike at him again. In the confusion, five or six of the enemy were slain, or, having been borne down the current, were drowned in the river. The rest were terrified, and drew back.

But when the Galloway men looked again, and saw they were opposed by only one man, they themselves being so many, they cried out that their honor would be lost forever if they did not force their way; and encouraged each other, with loud cries, to plunge through and assault him. But by this time the king's soldiers came up to his assistance, and the Galloway men retreated, and gave up their enterprise.

At another time King Robert and his foster brother were walking through a wood extremely weary and hungry. As they proceeded, however, in the hopes of coming to some habitation, they met in the midst of the forest with three men who looked like thieves or ruffians. They were well armed, and one of them bore a sheep on his back, which it seemed as if they had just stolen. They saluted the king civilly; and he, replying to their salutation, asked them where they were going. The men answered, they were seeking for Robert Bruce, for that they intended to join with him. The king answered, that if they would go with him he would conduct them where they would find the Scottish king. Then the man who had spoken changed countenance, and Bruce, who looked sharply at him, began to suspect that the ruffian guessed who he was, and that he and his companions had some design against his person, in order to gain the reward which had been offered for his life.

So he said to them, "My good friends, as we are not well acquainted with each other, you must go before us, and we will follow near to you."

"You have no occasion to suspect any harm from us," answered the man.

"Neither do I suspect any," said Bruce; "but this is the way in which I choose to travel."

The men did as he commanded, and thus they traveled till they came together to a waste and ruinous cottage, where the men proposed to dress some part of the sheep, which their companion was carrying. The king was glad to hear of food; but he insisted that there should be two fires kindled, one for himself and his foster brother at one end of the house, the other at the other end for their three companions. The men did as he desired. They broiled a quarter of mutton for themselves, and gave another to the king and his attendant. They were obliged to eat it without bread or salt; but as they were very hungry, they were glad to get food in any shape, and partook of it very heartily.

Then so heavy a drowsiness fell on King Robert, that, for all the danger he was in, he could not resist an inclination to sleep. But first, he desired his foster brother to watch while he slept, for he had great suspicion of their new acquaintances. His foster brother promised to keep awake, and did his best to keep his word. But the king had not been long asleep ere his foster brother fell into a deep slumber also, for he had undergone as much fatigue as the king. When the three villains saw the king and his attendant asleep, they made signs to each other, and rising up at once, drew their swords with the purpose to kill them both. But the king slept but lightly, and little noise as the traitors made in rising, he was awakened by it, and starting up, drew his sword, and went to meet them. At the same moment he pushed his foster brother with his foot, to awaken him, and he got on his feet; but ere he got his eyes cleared to see what was about to happen, one of the ruffians that were advancing to slay the king, killed him with a stroke of his sword. The king was now alone, one man against three, and in the greatest danger of his life; but his amazing strength, and the good armor which he wore, freed him once more

BRUCE AND THE PEASANT WOMAN

from this great peril, and he killed the three men, one after another. He then left the cottage, very sorrowful for the death of his faithful foster brother, and took his direction toward the place where he had appointed his men to assemble. It was now near night, and the place of meeting being a farmhouse, he went boldly into it, where he found the mistress, an old true-hearted Scotswoman, sitting alone. Upon seeing a stranger enter, she asked him who and what he was. The king answered that he was a traveler journeying through the country.

"All travelers," answered the good woman, "are welcome here, for the sake of one."

"And who is that one," said the king, "for whose sake you make all travelers welcome?"

"It is our rightful king, Robert the Bruce," answered the mistress, "who is the lawful lord of this country; and although he is now pursued and hunted after with hounds and horns, I hope to live to see him king over all Scotland."

"Since you love him so well, dame," said the king, "know that you see him before you. I am Robert the Bruce."

"You!" said the good woman, in great surprise; "and wherefore are you thus alone?—where are all your men?"

"I have none with me at this moment," answered Bruce, "and therefore I must travel alone."

"But that shall not be," said the brave old dame, "for I have two stout sons, gallant and trusty men, who shall be your servants for life and death."

So she brought her two sons, and though she well knew the dangers to which she exposed them, she made them swear fidelity to the king; and they afterward became high officers in his service.

Now, the loyal old woman was getting everything ready for the king's supper, when suddenly there was a great trampling of horses heard round the house. They thought it must be some of the English, and the good wife called upon her sons to fight to the last for King Robert. But shortly after, they heard the voice of the good Lord James of Douglas, and of Edward Bruce, the king's brother, who had come with a hundred and fifty horsemen to this farmhouse, according to the instructions that the king had left with them at parting.

Robert the Bruce was right joyful to meet his brother, and his faithful friend Lord James, and had no sooner found himself once more at the head of such a considerable body of followers, than forgetting hunger and weariness, he began to inquire where the enemy who had pursued them so long had taken up their abode for the night; "for," said he, "as they must suppose us totally scattered and fled, it is likely that they will think themselves quite secure, and disperse themselves into distant quarters, and keep careless watch."

"That is very true," answered James of Douglas, "for I passed a village where there are two hundred of them quartered, who had placed no sentinels; and if you have a mind to make haste, we may surprise them this very night, and do them more mischief than they have been able to do us during all this day's chase."

Then there was nothing but mount and ride; and as the Scots came by surprise on the body of

English whom Douglas had mentioned, and rushed suddenly into the village where they were quartered, they easily dispersed and cut them to pieces; thus, as Douglas had said, doing their pursuers more injury than they themselves had received during the long and severe pursuit of the preceding day.

The consequence of these successes of King Robert was, that soldiers came to join him on all sides, and that he obtained several victories, until at length the English were afraid to venture into the open country as formerly, unless when they could assemble themselves in considerable bodies. They thought it safer to lie still in the towns and castles which they had garrisoned, and wait till the King of England should once more come to their assistance with a powerful army.

When King Edward the First heard that Scotland was again in arms against him, he marched down to the Borders, with many threats of what he would do to avenge himself on Bruce and his party, whom he called rebels. But he was now old and feeble, and while he was making his preparations, he was taken very ill, and after lingering a long time, at length died on the sixth of July, 1307, at a place in Cumberland called Burgh upon the Sands, in full sight of Scotland, and not three miles from its frontier.

His hatred to that country was so inveterate that his thoughts of revenge seemed to occupy his mind on his death-bed. He made his son promise never to make peace with Scotland until the nation was subdued. He gave also very singular directions concerning the disposal of his dead body. He ordered that it should be boiled in a caldron till the flesh parted from the bones, and that then the bones should be wrapped up in a bull's hide, and carried at the head of the English army, as often as the Scots attempted to recover their freedom. He thought that he had inflicted such distresses on the Scots, and invaded and defeated them so often, that his very dead bones would terrify them. His son, Edward the Second, did not choose to execute this strange injunction, but caused his father to be buried in Westminster Abbey, where his tomb is still to be seen, bearing for an inscription, *Here Lies the Hammer of the Scottish Nation.*

Edward the Second was neither so brave nor so wise as his father; on the contrary, he was a weak prince, fond of idle amusements and worthless favorites. It was lucky for Scotland that such was his disposition. He marched a little way into Scotland with the large army which Edward the First had collected, and went back again without fighting, which gave great encouragement to Bruce's party.

Several of the Scottish nobility now took arms in different parts of the country, declared for King Robert, and fought against the English troops and garrisons. The most distinguished of these was the good Lord James of Douglas. Other great lords besides Douglas were now exerting themselves to destroy the English. Among them was Sir Thomas Randolph, whose mother was a sister of King Robert.

While Robert Bruce was gradually getting possession of the country, and driving out the English, Edinburgh, the principal town of Scotland, remained, with its strong castle, in possession of the invaders. Sir Thomas Randolph was extremely desirous to gain this important place; but the castle is situated on a very steep and lofty rock, so that it is difficult or almost impossible even to get up to the foot of the walls, much more to climb over them.

So while Randolph was considering what was to be done, there came to him a Scottish gentleman named Francis, who had joined Bruce's standard, and asked to speak with him in private. He then told Randolph that in his youth he had lived in the Castle of Edinburgh, and that his father had then been keeper of the fortress. It happened at that time that Francis was much in love with a lady who lived in a part of the town beneath the castle, which is called the Grassmarket. Now, as he could not get out of the castle by day to see his mistress, he had practiced a way of clambering by night down the castle rock on the south side, and returning at his pleasure; when he came to the foot of the wall, he made use of a ladder to get over it, as it was not very high at that point, those who built it having trusted to the steepness of the crag; and for the same reason, no watch was placed there. Francis had gone and come so frequently in this dangerous manner, that, though it was now long ago, he told Randolph he knew the road so well that he would undertake to guide a small party of men by night to the bottom of the wall; and as they might bring ladders with them, there would be no difficulty in scaling it. The great risk was, that of their being discovered by the watchmen while in the act of ascending the cliff, in which case every man of them must have perished.

Nevertheless, Randolph did not hesitate to attempt the adventure. He took with him only thirty men (you may be sure they were chosen for activity and courage), and came one dark night to the foot of the rock, which they began to ascend under the guidance of Francis, who went before them, upon his hands and feet, up one cliff, down another, and round another, where there was scarce room to support themselves. All the while, these thirty men were obliged to follow in a line, one after the other, by a path that was fitter for a cat than a man. The noise of a stone falling, or a word spoken from one to another, would have alarmed the watchmen. They were obliged, therefore, to move with the greatest precaution. When they were far up the crag, and near the foundation of the wall, they heard the guards going their rounds, to see that all was safe in and about the castle. Randolph and his party had nothing for it but to lie close and quiet, each man under the crag, as he happened to be placed, and trust that the guards would pass by without noticing them. And while they were waiting in breathless alarm they got a new cause of fright. One of the soldiers of the castle, willing

THE ASCENT TO THE CASTLE OF EDINBURGH

to startle his comrades, suddenly threw a stone from the wall, and cried out, "Aha, I see you well!" The stone came thundering down over the heads of Randolph and his men, who naturally thought themselves discovered. If they had stirred, or made the slightest noise, they would have been entirely destroyed; for the soldiers above might have killed every man of them, merely by rolling down stones. But being courageous and chosen men, they remained quiet, and the English soldiers, who thought their comrade was merely playing them a trick (as, indeed, he had no other meaning in what he did and said) passed on without further examination.

Then Randolph and his men got up and came in haste to the foot of the wall, which was not above twice a man's height in that place. They planted the ladders they had brought, and Francis mounted first to show them the way; Sir Andrew Grey, a brave knight, followed him, and Randolph himself was the third man who got over. Then the rest followed. When once they were within the walls, there was not so much to do, for the garrison were asleep and unarmed, excepting the watch, who were speedily destroyed. Thus was Edinburgh Castle taken in March, 1312.

It was not, however, only by the exertions of great and powerful barons, like Randolph and Douglas, that the freedom of Scotland was to be accomplished. The stout yeomanry and the bold peasantry of the land, who were as desirous to enjoy their cottages in honorable independence as the nobles were to reclaim their castles and estates from the English, contributed their full share in the efforts which were made to deliver the country from the invaders.

While Douglas, Randolph, and other true-hearted patriots, were taking castles and strongholds from the English, King Robert, who now had a considerable army under his command, marched through the country, dispersing such bodies of English as he met on the way.

Now when Sir Philip Mowbray, the governor of Stirling, came to London to tell the king that Stirling, the last Scottish town of importance which remained in possession of the English, was to be surrendered if it were not relieved by force of arms before midsummer, then all the English nobles called out it would be a sin and shame to permit the fair conquest which Edward the First had made, to be forfeited to the Scots for want of fighting. It was, therefore, resolved, that the king should go himself to Scotland, with as great forces as he could possibly muster.

King Edward the Second, therefore, assembled one of the greatest armies which a King of England ever commanded. There were troops brought from all his dominions. Many brave soldiers from the French provinces which the King of England possessed in France—many Irish, many Welsh—and all the great English nobles and barons, with their followers, were assembled in one great army. The number was not less than one hundred thousand men.

King Robert the Bruce summoned all his nobles and barons to join him, when he heard of the great preparations which the King of England was making. They were not so numerous as the English by many thousand men. In fact, his whole army did not very much exceed thirty thousand, and they were much worse armed than the wealthy Englishmen; but then, Robert, who was at their head, was one of the most expert generals of the time; and the officers he had under him were his brother Edward, his nephew Randolph, his faithful follower the Douglas, and other brave and experienced leaders, who commanded the same men that had been accustomed to fight and gain victories under every disadvantage of situation and numbers.

The king, on his part, studied how he might supply, by address and stratagem, what he wanted in numbers and strength. He knew the superiority of the English, both in their heavy-armed cavalry, which were much better mounted and armed than that of the Scots, and in their archers, who were better trained than any others in the world. Both these advantages he resolved to provide against. With this purpose, he led his army down into a plain near Stirling, called the Park, near which, and beneath it, the English army must needs pass through a boggy country, broken with water courses, while the Scots occupied hard, dry ground. He then caused all the ground upon the front of his line of battle, where cavalry were likely to act, to be dug full of holes, about as deep as a man's knee. They were filled with light brushwood, and the turf was laid on the top, so that it appeared a plain field, while in reality it was all full of these pits as a honeycomb is of holes. He also, it is said, caused steel spikes, called caltrops, to be scattered up and down in the plain, where the

English cavalry were most likely to advance, trusting in that manner to lame and destroy their horses.

When the Scottish army was drawn up, the line stretched north and south. On the south, it was terminated by the banks of the brook called Bannockburn, which are so rocky, that no troops could attack them there. On the left, the Scottish line extended near to the town of Stirling. Bruce reviewed his troops very carefully; all the useless servants, drivers of carts, and such like, of whom there were very many, he ordered to go behind a height, afterward, in memory of the event, called the Gillies' hill, that is, the Servants' hill. He then spoke to the soldiers, and expressed his determination to gain the victory, or to lose his life on the field of battle. He desired that all those who did not propose to fight to the last, should leave the field before the battle began, and that none should remain except those who were determined to take the issue of victory or death, as God should send it.

When the main body of his army was thus placed in order, the king posted Randolph, with a body of horse, near to the Church of Saint Ninian's, commanding him to use the utmost diligence to prevent any succors from being thrown into Stirling Castle. He then despatched James of Douglas, and Sir Robert Keith, the Mareschal of the Scottish army, in order that they might survey, as nearly as they could, the English force, which was now approaching from Falkirk. They returned with information, that

ON THE GILLIES' HILL

the approach of that vast host was one of the most beautiful and terrible sights which could be seen—that the whole country seemed covered with men-at-arms on horse and foot, that the number of standards, banners, and pennons (all flags of different kinds) made so gallant a show, that the bravest and most numerous host in

Christendom might be alarmed to see King Edward moving against them.

It was upon the twenty-third of June (1314) the King of Scotland heard the news, that the English army were approaching Stirling. He drew out his army, therefore, in the order which he had before resolved on. After a short time, Bruce, who was looking out anxiously for the enemy, saw a body of English cavalry trying to get into Stirling from the eastward. This was the Lord Clifford, who, with a chosen body of eight hundred horse, had been detached to relieve the castle.

"See, Randolph," said the king to his nephew, "there is a rose fallen from your chaplet." By this he meant, that Randolph had lost some honor, by suffering the enemy to pass where he had been stationed to hinder them. Randolph made no reply, but rushed against Clifford with little more than half his number. The Scots were on foot. The English turned to charge them with their lances, and Randolph drew up his men in close order to receive the onset. He seemed to be in so much danger, that Douglas asked leave of the king to go and assist him. The king refused him permission.

"Let Randolph," he said, "redeem his own fault; I cannot break the order of battle for his sake." Still the danger appeared greater, and the English horse seemed entirely to encompass the small handful of Scottish infantry. "So please you," said Douglas to the king, "my heart will not suffer me to stand idle and see Randolph perish—I must go to his assistance." He rode off accordingly; but long before they had reached the place of combat, they saw the English horses galloping off, many with empty saddles.

"Halt!" said Douglas to his men, "Randolph has gained the day; since we were not soon enough to help him in the battle, do not let us lessen his glory by approaching the field." Now, that was nobly done; especially as Douglas and Randolph were always contending which should rise highest in the good opinion of the king and the nation.

The van of the English army now came in sight, and a number of their bravest knights drew near to see what the Scots were doing. They saw King Robert dressed in his armor, and distinguished by a gold crown, which he wore over his helmet. He was not mounted on his great war-horse, because he did not expect to fight that evening. But he rode on a little pony up and down the ranks of his army, putting his men in order, and carried in his hand a sort of battle-axe made of steel. When the king saw the English horsemen draw near, he advanced a little before his own men, that he might look at them more nearly.

There was a knight among the English, called Sir Henry de Bohun, who thought this would be a good opportunity to gain great fame to himself, and put an end to the war, by killing King Robert. The king being poorly mounted, and having no lance, Bohun galloped on him suddenly and furiously, thinking, with his long spear, and his tall powerful horse, easily to bear him down to the ground. King Robert saw him, and permitted him to come very near, then suddenly turned his pony a little to one side, so that Sir Henry missed him with the lance-point, and was in the act of being carried past him by the career of his horse. But as he passed, King Robert rose up in his stirrups, and struck Sir Henry on the head with his battle-axe so terrible a blow, that it broke to pieces his iron helmet as if it had been a nutshell, and hurled him from his saddle. He was dead before he reached the ground. This gallant action was blamed by the Scottish leaders, who thought Bruce ought not to have exposed himself to so much danger, when the safety of the whole army depended on him. The king only kept looking at his weapon, which was injured by the force of the blow, and said, "I have broken my good battle-axe."

The next morning, being the twenty-fourth of June, at break of day, the battle began in terrible earnest. The English as they advanced saw the Scots getting into line. The Abbot of Inchaffray walked through their ranks bare-footed, and exhorted them to fight for their freedom. They kneeled down as he passed, and prayed to Heaven for victory. King Edward, who saw this, called out, "They kneel down—they are asking forgiveness." "Yes," said a celebrated English baron, called Ingelram de Umphraville, "but they ask it from God, not from us—these men will conquer, or die upon the field."

The English king ordered his men to begin the battle. The archers then bent their bows, and began to shoot so closely together, that the arrows fell like flakes of snow on a Christmas day. They killed many of the Scots, and might, as at Falkirk, and other places, have decided the victory; but Bruce, as I told you before, was prepared for them. He had in readiness a body of men-at-arms, well mounted, who rode at full gallop among the archers, and as they had no weapons save their bows and arrows, which they could not use when they were attacked hand to hand, they were cut down in great numbers by the Scottish horsemen and thrown into total confusion.

The fine English cavalry then advanced to support their archers, and to attack the Scottish line. But coming over the ground which was dug full of pits, the horses fell into these holes, and the riders lay tumbling about, without any means of defence, and unable to rise, from the weight of their armor. The Englishmen began to fall into general disorder; and the Scottish king, bringing up more of his forces, attacked and pressed them still more closely.

On a sudden, while the battle was obstinately maintained on both sides, an event happened which decided the victory. The servants and attendants on the Scottish camp had, as I told you, been sent behind the army to a place afterward called the Gillies' hill. But when they saw that their masters were likely to gain the day, they rushed from their place of concealment with such weapons as they could get, that they might have their share in the victory and in the spoil. The English, seeing them come suddenly over the hill, mistook this disorderly rabble for a new army coming up to sustain the Scots, and, losing all heart, began to shift every man for himself. Edward himself left the field as fast as he could ride. A valiant knight, Sir Giles de Argentine, much renowned in the wars of Palestine, attended the king till he got him out of the press of the combat. But he would retreat no further. "It is not my custom," he said, "to fly." With that he took leave of the king, set spurs to his horse, and calling out his war-cry of Argentine! Argentine! he rushed into the thickest of the Scottish ranks, and was killed.

Edward first fled to Stirling Castle, and entreated admittance; but Sir Philip Mowbray, the governor, reminded the fugitive sovereign that he was obliged to surrender the castle next day, so Edward was fain to fly through the Torwood, closely pursued by Douglas with a body of cavalry. An odd circumstance happened during the chase, which showed how loosely some of the Scottish barons of that day held their political opinions: As Douglas was riding furiously after Edward, he met a Scottish knight, Sir Laurence Abernethy, with twenty horse. Sir Laurence had hitherto owned the English interest, and was bringing this band of followers to serve

King Edward's army. But learning from Douglas that the English king was entirely defeated, he changed sides on the spot, and was easily prevailed upon to join Douglas in pursuing the unfortunate Edward, with the very followers whom he had been leading to join his standard.

Douglas and Abernethy continued the chase, not giving King Edward time to alight from horseback even for an instant, and followed him as far as Dunbar, where the English had still a friend in the governor, Patrick, Earl of March. The earl received Edward in his forlorn condition, and furnished him with a fishing skiff, or small ship, in which he escaped to England, having entirely lost his fine army, and a great number of his bravest nobles.

The English never before or afterward, whether in France or Scotland, lost so dreadful a battle as that of Bannockburn, nor did the Scots ever gain one of the same importance. Many of the best and bravest of the English nobility and gentry lay dead on the field; a great many more were made prisoners; and the whole of King Edward's immense army was dispersed or destroyed.

The English, after this great defeat, were no longer in a condition to support their pretensions to be masters of Scotland, or to continue, as they had done for nearly twenty years, to send armies into that country to overcome it. On the contrary, they became for a time scarce able to defend their own frontiers against King Robert and his soldiers.

Thus did Robert Bruce arise from the condition of an exile, hunted with bloodhounds like a stag or beast of prey, to the rank of an independent sovereign, universally acknowledged to be one of the wisest and bravest kings who then lived. The nation of Scotland was also raised once more from the situation of a distressed and conquered province to that of a free and independent state, governed by its own laws, and subject to its own princes; and although the country was after the Bruce's death often subjected to great loss and distress, both by the hostility of the English, and by the unhappy civil wars among the Scots themselves, yet they never afterward lost the freedom for which Wallace had laid down his life, and which King Robert had recovered, not less by his wisdom than by his weapons. And therefore most just it is, that while the country of Scotland retains any recollection of its history, the memory of those brave warriors and faithful patriots should be remembered with honor and gratitude.[3]

3. Three years after the Battle of Bannockburn, Bruce went over into Ireland to assist in establishing his brother Edward as king of the island. The Irish defended themselves so vigorously that the Scotch were compelled to retire, leaving Edward dead upon the field. For a number of years, Robert the Bruce reigned gloriously over Scotland, but toward the end of his life he fell a victim to leprosy and was compelled to live for two years in his castle at Cardross on the beautiful banks of the River Clyde. During this illness, Edward the Second of England died, and his son Edward the Third, a mere youth, came to the throne. The boy king determined to retrieve the losses that his father had sustained, but was prevented by Douglas, Randolph, and other loyal Scotch leaders, who distinguished themselves by almost incredible deeds of valor.

When the king was dying, he ordered that his heart should be taken

BRUCE AND THE SPIDER

BERNARD ARTON

For Scotland's and for freedom's right
  The Bruce his part had played,
In five successive fields of fight
  Been conquered and dismayed;
Once more against the English host
His band he led, and once more lost
  The meed for which he fought;
And now from battle, faint and worn,
The homeless fugitive forlorn
  A hut's lone shelter sought.

And cheerless was that resting place
  For him who claimed a throne:
His canopy, devoid of grace,
  The rude, rough beams alone;
The heather couch his only bed,—
Yet well I ween had slumber fled
  From couch of eider down!
Through darksome night till dawn of day,
Absorbed in wakeful thought he lay
  Of Scotland and her crown.

---

from his body, embalmed and given to Douglas to be by him carried to Palestine and buried in Jerusalem. Douglas caused the heart to be enclosed in a silver case, and proud of the distinction the king had shown him, started with a number of followers for Palestine. When he arrived in Spain, however, he was diverted from his original purpose and led to join with King Alphonso in an attempt to drive the Saracens from Granada. In a bitter fight with the Moors, Douglas was killed, and after the battle, his body was found lying across the silver case, as if his last object had been to defend the heart of Bruce. No further attempt was made to carry Robert's heart to Jerusalem, but it was returned to Scotland and buried in the monastery of Melrose.

BRUCE BEHELD A SPIDER

The sun rose brightly, and its gleam
  Fell on that hapless bed,
And tinged with light each shapeless beam
  Which roofed the lowly shed;
When, looking up with wistful eye,
The Bruce beheld a spider try

His filmy thread to fling
From beam to beam of that rude cot;
And well the insect's toilsome lot
Taught Scotland's future king.

Six times his gossamery thread
The wary spider threw;
In vain that filmy line was sped,
For powerless or untrue
Each aim appeared, and back recoiled
The patient insect, six times foiled,
And yet unconquered still;
And soon the Bruce, with eager eye,
Saw him prepare once more to try
His courage, strength, and skill.

One effort more, his seventh and last!
The hero hailed the sign!
And on the wished-for beam hung fast
That slender, silken line;
Slight as it was, his spirit caught
The more than omen, for his thought
The lesson well could trace,
Which even "he who runs may read,"
That Perseverance gains its meed,
And Patience wins the race.

THE HEART OF BRUCE

WILLIAM E. AYTOUN

It was upon an April morn,
  While yet the frost lay hoar,
We heard Lord James's bugle horn
  Sound by the rocky shore.

Then down we went, a hundred knights,
  All in our dark array,
And flung our armor in the ships
  That rode within the bay.

We spoke not as the shore grew less,
  But gazed in silence back,
Where the long billows swept away
  The foam behind our track.

And aye the purple hues decayed
  Upon the fading hill,
And but one heart in all that ship
  Was tranquil, cold, and still.

The good Lord Douglas paced the deck,
  And O, his face was wan!
Unlike the flush it used to wear
  When in the battle-van.

"Come hither, come hither, my trusty knight,
  Sir Simon of the Lee;
There is a freit lies near my soul
  I fain would tell to thee.

GAZED IN SILENCE BACK

"Thou know'st the words King Robert spoke
Upon his dying day:
How he bade take his noble heart
And carry it far away;

"And lay it in the holy soil
Where once the Saviour trod,

Since he might not bear the blessed Cross,
  Nor strike one blow for God.

"Last night as in my bed I lay,
  I dreamed a dreary dream:—
Methought I saw a Pilgrim stand
  In the moonlight's quivering beam.

"His robe was of the azure dye,
  Snow-white his scattered hairs,
And even such a cross he bore
  As good Saint Andrew bears.

"'Why go ye forth, Lord James,' he said,
  'With spear and belted brand?
Why do you take its dearest pledge
  From this our Scottish land?

"'The sultry breeze of Galilee
  Creeps through its groves of palm,
The olives on the Holy Mount
  Stand glittering in the calm.

"'But 'tis not there that Scotland's heart
  Shall rest by God's decree,
Till the great angel calls the dead
  To rise from earth and sea!

"'Lord James of Douglas, mark my rede!
  That heart shall pass once more
In fiery fight against the foe,
  As it was wont of yore.

"'And it shall pass beneath the Cross,
And save King Robert's vow;
But other hands shall bear it back,
Not, James of Douglas, thou!'

"Now, by thy knightly faith, I pray,
Sir Simon of the Lee,—
For truer friend had never man
Than thou hast been to me,—

"If ne'er upon the Holy Land
'Tis mine in life to tread,
Bear thou to Scotland's kindly earth
The relics of her dead."

The tear was in Sir Simon's eye
As he wrung the warrior's hand,—
"Betide me weal, betide me woe,
I'll hold by thy command.

"But if in battle-front, Lord James,
'Tis ours once more to ride,
Nor force of man, nor craft of fiend,
Shall cleave me from thy side!"

And aye we sailed and aye we sailed
Across the weary sea,
Until one morn the coast of Spain
Rose grimly on our lee.

And as we rounded to the port,
Beneath the watchtower's wall,
We heard the clash of the atabals,
And the trumpet's wavering call.

"Why sounds yon Eastern music here
  So wantonly and long,
And whose the crowd of armèd men
  That round yon standard throng?"

"The Moors have come from Africa
  To spoil and waste and slay,
And King Alonzo of Castile
  Must fight with them to-day."

"Now shame it were," cried good Lord James,
  "Shall never be said of me
That I and mine have turned aside
  From the Cross in jeopardie!

"Have down, have down, my merry men all,—
  Have down unto the plain;
We'll let the Scottish lion loose
  Within the fields of Spain!"

"Now welcome to me, noble lord,
  Thou and thy stalwart power;
Dear is the sight of a Christian knight,
  Who comes in such an hour!

"Is it for bond or faith you come,
  Or yet for golden fee?
Or bring ye France's lilies here,
  Or the flower of Burgundie?"

"God greet thee well, thou valiant king,
  Thee and thy belted peers,—
Sir James of Douglas am I called,
  And these are Scottish spears.

"We do not fight for bond or plight,
  Nor yet for golden fee;
But for the sake of our blessed Lord,
  Who died upon the tree.

"We bring our great King Robert's heart
  Across the weltering wave,
To lay it in the holy soil
  Hard by the Saviour's grave.

"True pilgrims we, by land or sea,
  Where danger bars the way;
And therefore are we here, Lord King,
  To ride with thee this day!"

The king has bent his stately head,
  And the tears were in his eyne,—
"God's blessing on thee, noble knight,
  For this brave thought of thine!

"I know thy name full well, Lord James;
  And honored may I be,
That those who fought beside the Bruce
  Should fight this day for me!

"Take thou the leading of the van,
  And charge the Moors amain;
There is not such a lance as thine
  In all the host of Spain!"

The Douglas turned towards us then,
  O, but his glance was high!—
'There is not one of all my men
  But is as bold as I.

"There is not one of all my knights
But bears as true a spear,—
Then onward, Scottish gentlemen,
And think King Robert's here!"

The trumpets blew, the cross-bolts flew,
The arrows flashed like flame,
As spur in side, and spear in rest,
Against the foe we came.

And many a bearded Saracen
Went down, both horse and man;
For through their ranks we rode like corn,
So furiously we ran!

But in behind our path they closed,
Though fain to let us through,
For they were forty thousand men,
And we were wondrous few.

We might not see a lance's length,
So dense was their array,
But the long fell sweep of the Scottish blade
Still held them hard at bay.

"Make in! make in!" Lord Douglas cried,—
"Make in, my brethren dear!
Sir William of Saint Clair is down;
We may not leave him here!"

But thicker, thicker grew the swarm,
And sharper shot the rain,
And the horses reared amid the press,
But they would not charge again.

HELD THE HEART ALOFT

"Now Jesu help thee," said Lord James,
"Thou kind and true Saint Clair!
An' if I may not bring thee off,
I'll die beside thee there!"

Then in his stirrups up he stood,
So lionlike and bold,

And held the precious heart aloft
  All in its case of gold.

He flung it from him, far ahead,
  And never spake he more,
But—"Pass thou first, thou dauntless heart,
  As thou wert wont of yore!"

The roar of fight rose fiercer yet,
  And heavier still the stour,
Till the spears of Spain came shivering in,
  And swept away the Moor.

"Now praised be God, the day is won!
  They fly o'er flood and fell,—
Why dost thou draw the rein so hard,
  Good knight, that fought so well?"

"O, ride ye on, Lord King!" he said,
  "And leave the dead to me,
For I must keep the dreariest watch
  That ever I shall dree!

"There lies, above his master's heart,
  The Douglas, stark and grim;
And woe is me I should be here,
  Not side by side with him!

"The world grows cold, my arm is old,
  And thin my lyart hair,
And all that I loved best on earth
  Is stretched before me there.

"O Bothwell banks! that bloom so bright
  Beneath the sun of May,
The heaviest cloud that ever blew
  Is bound for you this day.

"And Scotland! thou mayst veil thy head
  In sorrow and in pain:
The sorest stroke upon thy brow
  Hath fallen this day in Spain!

"We'll bear them back unto our ship,
  We'll bear them o'er the sea,
And lay them in the hallowed earth
  Within our own countrie.

"And be thou strong of heart, Lord King,
  For this I tell thee sure,
The sod that drank the Douglas' blood
  Shall never bear the Moor!"

The King he lighted from his horse,
  He flung his brand away,
And took the Douglas by the hand,
  So stately as he lay.

"God give thee rest, thou valiant soul!
  That fought so well for Spain;
I'd rather half my land were gone,
  So thou wert here again!"

We bore the good Lord James away,
  And the priceless heart we bore,
And heavily we steered our ship
  Towards the Scottish shore.

No welcome greeted our return,
  Nor clang of martial tread,
But all were dumb and hushed as death
  Before the mighty dead.

We laid our chief in Douglas Kirk,
  The heart in fair Melrose;
And woful men were we that day,—
  God grant their souls repose!

THE SKELETON IN ARMOR

HENRY W. LONGFELLOW

"Speak! speak! thou fearful guest!
Who with thy hollow breast
Still in rude armor drest,
Comest to daunt me!
Wrapt not in Eastern balms,
But with thy fleshless palms
Stretched, as if asking alms,
Why dost thou haunt me?"

Then, from those cavernous eyes
Pale flashes seemed to rise,
As when the northern skies
Gleam in December;
And, like the water's flow
Under December's snow,
Came a dull voice of woe
From the heart's chamber.

"I was a Viking[1] old!
My deeds, though manifold,
No Skald[2] in song has told,
No Saga[3] taught thee!

1. *Vikings* was the name given to the bold Norse seamen who in the eighth, ninth, and tenth centuries infested the northern seas. Tradition maintains that a band of these rovers discovered America centuries before Columbus.

2. A skald was a Norse poet who celebrated in song the deeds of warriors.

3. A saga is an ancient Scandinavian legend or tradition, relating mythical or historical events.

I WAS A VIKING OLD

Take heed, that in thy verse
Thou dost the tale rehearse,
Else dread a dead man's curse;
For this I sought thee.

"Far in the Northern Land,
By the wild Baltic's strand,

I, with my childish hand,
Tamed the gerfalcon;[4]
And, with my skates fast-bound,
Skimmed the half-frozen Sound,
That the poor whimpering hound
Trembled to walk on.

"Oft to his frozen lair
Tracked I the grisly bear,
While from my path the hare
Fled like a shadow;
Oft through the forest dark
Followed the werewolf's[5] bark,
Until the soaring lark
Sang from the meadow.

"But when I older grew,
Joining a corsair's[6] crew,
O'er the dark sea I flew
With the marauders.
Wild was the life we led;
Many the souls that sped,
Many the hearts that bled,
By our stern orders.

"Many a wassail-bout[7]
Wore the long Winter out;
Often our midnight shout
Set the cocks crowing,

4. A gerfalcon is a large falcon of Northern Europe.

5. According to a popular superstition, a werewolf is a man, who, at times, is transformed into a wolf. Such a wolf is much more savage than a real wolf, and is especially fond of human flesh. This superstition has at some time existed among almost all peoples.

6. *Corsair* is but another name for a pirate.

7. A wassail-bout is a drinking bout, or carouse.

As we the Berserk's[8] tale
Measured in cups of ale,
Draining the oaken pail,
Filled to o'erflowing.

"Once as I told in glee
Tales of the stormy sea,
Soft eyes did gaze on me,
Burning yet tender;
And as the white stars shine
On the dark Norway pine,
On that dark heart of mine
Fell their soft splendor.

"I wooed the blue-eyed maid,
Yielding, yet half afraid,
And in the forest's shade
Our vows were plighted.
Under its loosened vest
Fluttered her little breast,
Like birds within their nest
By the hawk frighted.

"Bright in her father's hall
Shields gleamed upon the wall,
Loud sang the minstrels all,
Chaunting his glory;
When of old Hildebrand
I asked his daughter's hand,
Mute did the minstrels stand
To hear my story.

---

8. *Berserk*, or *Berserker*, was the name given in heathen times in Scandinavia to a wild warrior or champion. The Berserkers, it is said, had fits of madness, when they foamed at the mouth and howled like

I WOOED THE MAID

"While the brown ale he quaffed,
Loud then the champion laughed.
And as the wind-gusts waft

beasts, rushing into battle naked and defenseless. It was believed that at such times they were proof against wounds either from fire or from steel.

The sea-foam brightly,
So the loud laugh of scorn,
Out of those lips unshorn,
From the deep drinking-horn
Blew the foam lightly.

"She was a Prince's child,
I but a Viking wild,
And though she blushed and smiled,
I was discarded!
Should not the dove so white
Follow the sea-mew's flight,
Why did they leave that night
Her nest unguarded?

"Scarce had I put to sea,
Bearing the maid with me,—
Fairest of all was she
Among the Norsemen!—
When on the white sea-strand,
Waving his armèd hand,
Saw we old Hildebrand,
With twenty horsemen.

"Then launched they to the blast,
Bent like a reed each mast,
Yet we were gaining fast,
When the wind failed us;
And with a sudden flaw
Came round the gusty Skaw,[9]
So that our foe we saw
Laugh as he hailed us.

9. The Skaw is the most northerly point of Denmark.

"And as to catch the gale
Round veered the flapping sail,
Death! was the helmsman's hail,
Death without quarter!
Mid-ships with iron keel
Struck we her ribs of steel;
Down her black hulk did reel
Through the black water!

"As with his wings aslant,
Sails the fierce cormorant,
Seeking some rocky haunt,
With his prey laden,
So toward the open main,
Beating to sea again,
Through the wild hurricane
Bore I the maiden.

"Three weeks we westward bore,
And when the storm was o'er,
Cloud-like we saw the shore
Stretching to lee-ward;
There for my lady's bower
Built I the lofty tower,[10]
Which, to this very hour,
Stands looking seaward.

"There lived we many years;
Time dried the maiden's tears;
She had forgot her fears,
She was a mother;

10. At Newport in Rhode Island is an old stone tower, which tradition says was built by the Norsemen when they visited this country. That is the tower to which Longfellow refers here.

Death closed her mild blue eyes,
Under that tower she lies;
Ne'er shall the sun arise
On such another!

"Still grew my bosom then,
Still as a stagnant fen!
Hateful to me were men,
The sunlight hateful!
In the vast forest here,
Clad in my warlike gear,
Fell I upon my spear,
O, death was grateful!

"Thus, seamed with many scars
Bursting these prison bars,
Up to its native stars
My soul ascended!
There from the flowing bowl
Deep drinks the warrior's soul,
Skoal![11] to the Northland! *skoal!*"
—Thus the tale ended.

11. *Skoal* is the customary salutation in Scandinavia when a health is drunk.

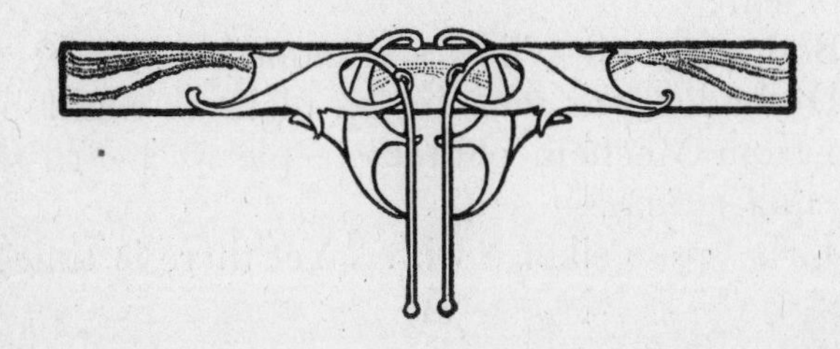

HOW THEY BROUGHT THE GOOD NEWS FROM GHENT TO AIX

ROBERT BROWNING

I sprang to the stirrup, and Joris and he;
I galloped, Dirck galloped, we galloped all three;
"Good speed!" cried the watch as the gate-bolts
undrew,
"Speed!" echoed the wall to us galloping
through.
Behind shut the postern, the lights sank to rest,
And into the midnight we galloped abreast.

Not a word to each other; we kept the great pace,—
Neck by neck, stride by stride, never changing
our place;
I turned in my saddle and made its girths tight,
Then shortened each stirrup and set the pique
right,
Rebuckled the check-strap, chained slacker the
bit,
Nor galloped less steadily Roland a whit.

'T was a moonset at starting; but while we drew
near
Lokerem, the cocks crew and twilight dawned
clear;
At Boom a great yellow star came out to see;
At Düffeld 't was morning as plain as could be;
And from Mecheln church-steeple we heard the
half-chime,—
So Joris broke silence with "Yet there is time!"

At Aerschot up leaped of a sudden the sun,
And against him the cattle stood black every one,
To stare through the midst at us galloping past;
And I saw my stout galloper Roland at last,
With resolute shoulders, each butting away
The haze, as some blind river headland its spray;

And his low head and crest, just one sharp ear
bent back
For my voice, and the other pricked out on his
track;
And one eye's black intelligence,—ever that
glance
O'er its white edge at me, his own master,
askance;
And the thick heavy spume-flakes, which aye and
anon
His fierce lips shook upward in galloping on.

By Hasselt Dirck groaned; and cried Joris,
"Stay spur!
Your Roos galloped bravely, the fault's not in
her;
We'll remember at Aix,"—for one heard the
quick wheeze
Of her chest, saw the stretched neck, and stag-
gering knees,
And sunk tail, and horrible heave of the flank,
As down on her haunches she shuddered and
sank.

So we were left galloping, Joris and I,
Past Looz and past Tongres, no cloud in the sky;

ROLAND GALLOPED ALONE

The broad sun above laughed a pitiless laugh;
'Neath our feet broke the brittle, bright stubble
like chaff;
Till over by Dalhem a dome-spire sprang white,
And "Gallop," gasped Joris, "for Aix is in
sight!"

"How they'll greet us!"—and all in a moment his roan
Rolled neck and croup over, lay dead as a stone;
And there was my Roland to bear the whole weight
Of the news which alone could save Aix from her fate,
With his nostrils like pits full of blood to the brim,
And with circles of red for his eye-sockets' rim.

Then I cast loose my buff-coat, each holster let fall,
Shook off both my jack-boots, let go belt and all,
Stood up in the stirrup, leaned, patted his ear,
Called my Roland his pet name, my horse without peer,—
Clapped my hands, laughed and sang, any noise, bad or good,
Till at length into Aix Roland galloped and stood.

And all I remember is friends flocking round,
As I sate with his head 'twixt my knees on the ground;
And no voice but was praising this Roland of mine,
As I poured down his throat our last measure of wine,
Which (the burgesses voted by common consent)
Was no more than his due who brought good news from Ghent.

When we read this poem, the first question that comes to us is "What *was* the 'good news from Ghent?'" But we find on looking up the matter that the whole incident is a fanciful one; Browning simply imagined a very dramatic situation, and then wrote this stirring poem about it. And surely he has made it all seem very real to us. We feel the intense anxiety of the riders to reach Aix on time—for we are given to understand in the last line of the third stanza that Aix must learn the news by a certain hour; we feel the despair of the two who are forced to give up the attempt, and the increased sense of responsibility of the only remaining rider; and we fairly hold our breath in our fear that the gallant Roland will not stand the strain.

The towns mentioned are real places, all of them in Belgium.

Does the poem seem to you somewhat rough and jerky? It is a ballad, and that fact accounts in part for its style, for ballads are not usually smooth and perfect in structure. But there is another reason for the jerkiness, if we may call it by so strong a name. Read the first two lines aloud, giving them plenty of swing. Do they not remind you of the galloping of a horse, with their regular rise and fall? A little poet might have attempted to write about this wild midnight ride in the same smooth, flowing style in which he would describe a lazy river slipping over the stones; but Browning was a great poet, and knew how to fit sound to sense. Other poets may excel him in writing of quiet, peaceful scenes, but no one who has ever written could put more dash and vigor into a poem than could Browning.

REMINISCENCES OF A PIONEER[1]

EDWIN D. COE

MY father left his old home in Oneida County, New York, in June, 1839, a young man in his twenty-fourth year. The beauty and fertility of the Rock River valley, in Wisconsin, had been widely proclaimed by participants in the Black Hawk War and in the glowing reports of Government engineers. In fact, the latter declared it to be a very Canaan of promise. As a consequence, hundreds of young people, restless and ambitious, and very many older ones whom the panic of the late 30's had separated from their business moorings, turned their thoughts and then their steps toward the new promised land.

When my father was rowed ashore from the steamer at Milwaukee, he could have taken up "government land" within the present limits of that city, but the bluffs and swamps of the future metropolis had no charms for him compared with the vision he had in mind of the Rock River country. So he crossed Milwaukee River on a ferry at the foot of Wisconsin Street, walked out on a sidewalk quavering on stilts until solid

1. From the Proceedings of the State Historical Society of Wisconsin, 1907.

ground was reached at Third Street, and then struck the trail for the west.

Along the shore of Pewaukee Lake, the traveler met a wolf which bristled and snarled but at last surrendered the right of way before the superior bluff, which was put up against him, backed by a "big stick." That night he stayed with a friend named Terry, who had come West the year before, and preëmpted a piece of land on the east shore rock, about seven miles above Watertown. The next morning he saw on the opposite bank a gently rising slope covered with stately maples and oaks; beneath were the grass and flowers of mid June, and the swift flowing river, clear as a spring brook, was in front, making the scene one of entrancing beauty. It was fully equal to his highest expectations, and he never rested until he had secured title to that particular block of land.

He at once prepared to build a log house, and, after a few days, the neighborhood was invited to the raising. Some men came eight and ten miles, and a big laugh went around when it was found that logs a foot and a half and two feet in diameter had been cut for the house. Four large ones were rolled together for a foundation, and then the inexperienced young man was told that for a house he needed to cut logs half as large, and they would return in a week and raise them. This they did, showing the kindly, helpful spirit of the early settlers.

In August my mother came and brought the household furniture from their Oneida County home, together with a year's provisions. The trip from Milwaukee to their log house, nearly forty miles, took nearly three days by ox team. She was delighted and happy with the building and its surroundings, and never faltered in her love for that first home in the West. A barrel of pork was among the supplies she had brought, and people came as far as twenty miles to beg a little of it, so tired were they of fresh meat from the woods, and fish from the river; and they never went away empty-handed, as long as it lasted.

They came, as I have said, in 1839, and I the year following. There is a vague, misty period at the beginning of every life, as memory rises from mere nothingness to full strength, when it is not easy to say whether the things remembered may not have been heard from the lips of others. But I distinctly recall some very early events, and particularly the disturbance created by my year-old brother, two years younger than myself, when he screamed with pain one evening and held his bare foot up, twisted to one side.

My mother was ill in bed, and the terrified maid summoned my father from outside, with the story that the baby's ankle was out of joint. He hurried in, gave it one look, and, being a hasty, impetuous man, he declared, "Yes, the child's ankle is out of joint; I must go for a doctor;" and in another moment he would have been off on a seven-mile tramp through the dark to Watertown. But the level-headed woman on the bed called out, "Wait a minute; bring me the child and a candle;" and a minute later she had discovered a little sliver which pricked him when he set his foot down, and extricated it between thumb and finger. "There," said she; "I don't think you need walk to Watertown to-night."

Indians were so numerous that I don't remember when they first came out of the haze into my consciousness, but probably in my third year. They were Winnebago and Pottawatomi, the river being a common inheritance of both tribes. In the winter of 1839–40, about thirty families of the former tribe camped for several weeks opposite our home and were very sociable and friendly. Diligent hunters and trappers, they accumulated fully a hundred dollars worth of otter, beaver, bear, deer, and other skins. But a trader came up from Watertown in the spring and got the whole lot in exchange for a four-gallon keg of whisky. That was a wild night that followed. Some of the noisiest came over to our house, and when denied admittance threatened to knock the door down, but my father told them he had two guns ready for them, and they finally left. He afterwards said that he depended more on a heavy hickory club which he had on hand than on the guns—it could be fired faster.

An ugly squaw whose nose had been bitten off years before in a fight, stabbed her brother that night, because he refused her more whisky. He had, according to custom, been left on guard, and was entirely sober. The next day the Indians horrified my mother by declaring that they

HALF A DOZEN INDIANS BOLTED IN

should cut the squaw into inch pieces if her brother died. They went down to Lake Koshkonong two days later, but he died the first day out. The squaw escaped and lived a lonely life for years after, being known up and down the river as "Old Mag."

At any time of the year we were liable to

receive visits from Indians passing to and fro between Lakes Horicon and Koshkonong. They would come into the house without ceremony further than staring into the windows before entering. Being used only to town life at the East, my mother was afraid of them, but she always carried a bold face and would never give them bread, which they always demanded, unless she could readily spare it.

One summer afternoon, when she had finished her housework and had sat down to sew, half a dozen Indians, male and female, suddenly bolted in and clamored for bread. She shook her head and told them she had none for them. When she came West she had brought yeast cakes which, by careful renewal, she kept in succession until the family home was broken up in 1880. Upon the afternoon referred to, she had a large pan of yeast cakes drying before the fireplace. Seeing them, the Indians scowled at her, called her a lying woman, and made a rush for the cakes, each one taking a huge bite. Those familiar with the article know how bitter is the mixture of raw meal, hops, and yeast, and so will not wonder that presently a look of horror came over the Indians' faces and that then they sputtered the unsavory stuff out all over the newly scrubbed floor. My mother used to say that if they had killed her she could not have kept from laughing. They looked very angry at first, but finally concluding that they had not been poisoned and had only "sold" themselves, they huddled together and went out chattering and laughing, leaving my mother a good share of her day's work to do over again.

One day I saw a big Indian shake her by the shoulder because she wouldn't give him bread. She was ironing at the time, and threatened him with a hot flat iron till he hurried out. Another came in one warm summer afternoon, shut the door behind him, and leaned against it, glowering at her. For once she was thoroughly frightened. He had with him a tomahawk, having a hollow handle and head, that could be used as a pipe. However, her wits did not desert her. Seeing the cat sleeping peacefully in the corner, she cried, "How did that cat get in here!" and catching up the broom she chased pussy around till she reached the door, when seizing the heavy iron latch she pulled it wide open, sending Mr. Indian into the middle of the room; she then pushed the door back against the wall and set a chair against it. The Indian stood still for a minute, then uttered a grunt and took himself off, probably thinking she was too dangerous a person for him to attempt to bully.

The Indians used to offer for sale venison, fish, and maple sugar, but the line was always drawn on the latter, for it was commonly reported that they strained the sap through their blankets. And you should have seen their blankets! About 1846 a company of civilized Oneidas, some of whom my father had known in the East, camped near by and manufactured a large number of handsome and serviceable baskets. From wild berries they would make dyes that never faded, and print them on the baskets with stamps cut from potatoes. Some of their designs were quite artistic. A small basket and a rattle which they gave my year-old sister showed their good will.

I soon learned to have no fear of the tribesmen, although sometimes a fleet of fifty canoes would be in sight at once, passing down the river to Koshkonong; but the first Germans who came to our parts nearly scared the life out of me. Their heavy beards, long coats, broad-visored caps, and arm-long pipes, made me certain that nothing less than a fat boy of five would satisfy their appetites; and whenever they appeared I would hunt my mother. They had bought a considerable tract of land about five miles from our place, and always wanted to know of us the road thither. The result was just such a "jabber match" as could be expected where neither side knew the other's tongue; but by pointing and motioning my mother was always able to direct them. Sometimes they wished to come in and make tea or coffee on our stove, and eat the luncheon of bread and meat that they had brought across the water. They would then always urge their food upon me, so I came to like their black bread very much and soon revised my first estimate of their character. All those people cut fine farms out of the heavy timber and died rich.

The first settlers were mostly Americans, from New York and New England; but before leaving the old farm we used to hear of English, Irish, Dutch, Norwegian, and Welsh settlements. The latter people enveloped and overflowed our own particular community and came to form a good portion of the population.

Besides the numerous nationalities on this front edge of advancing settlement, there were people of many and diverse individualities—the uneasy, the unlucky, the adventurous, the men without money but full of hope, the natural hunters, the trappers, the lovers of woods and solitudes, and occasionally one who had left his country for his country's good; all these classes were represented. But on the whole the frontier's people were an honest, kindly, generous class, ready to help in trouble or need of any kind.

If there was sickness, watchers by the bedside and harvesters in the field were promptly forthcoming. If a new house or barn was to be raised, every available man came. If a cow was mired, and such was often the case, her owner easily got all the help he wanted. Husking and logging and quilting bees were common, and in the autumn there were bees for candle-dipping, when the family supply of candles would be made for a year; and all such events would of course be followed by a supper, and perhaps a frolic. Visits among the women folk were all-day affairs; if the husbands were invited, it would be of an evening, and the call then would last till midnight with a supper at ten. There was a world of comfort and good cheer in those forest homes. I doubt if any child in modern palaces enjoys happier hours than were mine on winter evenings, when I rested on the broad stone hearth in front of the big fireplace, with its blazing four-foot log, the dog on one side and the cat on the other, while my father told stories that had to be repeated as the stock ran out, and I was gradually lulled to sleep by the soft thunder of my mother's spinning wheel. What could be more luxurious for any youngster?

I remember that when I was about six I saw my first apple. Half of it came to me, and I absorbed it as if to the manor born. What a revelation it was to a lad who could be satisfied with chokecherries and crab apples! In those times, when a visitor called it was common to bring out a dish of well-washed turnips, with plate and case knife, and he could slice them up or scrape them as he chose.

The woods abounded in wild fruits, which the women made the most of for the winter season. Berries, grapes, plums, and crab apples were all utilized. The latter were especially delicious for preserves. The boy who ate them raw off the tree could not get his face back into line the same day; but he would eat them. However, pumpkins were our main reliance for present and future pies and sauce; such pumpkins do not grow now in these latter days. There were two sugar bushes on our place, and a good supply of maple sugar was put up every spring. Many other dainties were added to our regular menu, and a boy with such a cook for a mother as I had, needed no sympathy from any one the whole world round.

The river was three hundred feet wide opposite our house, and about two feet deep, so teams could be driven across at ordinary stages, but foot passengers depended on our boat, a large "dugout." I remember how beautiful it was, when first scooped out from a huge basswood log, clean, white, and sweet-smelling. Strangers and neighbors alike would call across, "Bring over the boat;" and if they were going from our side they would take it over and leave the job of hollering to us. At five years of age I could pole it around very nicely.

One day, when I was first trusted to go in the boat alone, a stranger called over, and as my father was busy, he told me to go after him. The man expressed much wonderment, and some hesitancy to trusting himself to the skill and strength of a bare-footed boy of five; but I assured him I was a veteran at the business. He finally got in very gingerly, and sat down flat on the bottom. All the way over he kept wondering at and praising my work until I was ready to melt with mingled embarrassment and delight. At the shore he asked me unctuously how much he should pay. "Oh nothing," I said. "But let me pay you. I'd be glad to," said he. "Oh, no, we never take pay," I replied, and dug my toes into the sand, not knowing how to get out of the scrape, yet well pleased at his high estimate of my service. All the time he was plunging down first into one pocket of his barn-door trousers and then the other, till at last he fished out an old "bungtown" cent, which with muck

HE SAT DOWN FLAT ON THE BOTTOM

graciousness and pomposity he pressed upon me, until my feeble refusals were overcome. I took the coin and scampered away so fast that I must have been invisible in the dust I raised. Showing it to my father, I was told that I ought not to have taken it; but I explained how helpless I had been, and repeated word for word what the man had said, and, unintentionally, somewhat copied his tone and manner. The twinkle in my father's eye showed that he understood. That copper was my first-earned money; if it had only been put out at compound interest, I ought, if the mathematicians are right, to be now living in *otium cum dignitate*,[2] perhaps.

Steve Peck was one of the most notable of the marked characters above hinted at. He was a roistering blade, who captained all the harum-scarums of the section. Peck was a surveyor and had helped at the laying out of Milwaukee. Many were the stories told of his escapades, but space will not permit of their rehearsal here. He had selected a choice piece of land and built a good house; then he induced the daughter of an Aberdeen ex-merchant of aristocratic family but broken fortune, who had sought a new chance in the wilds of Wisconsin, to share them with him. But wife and children could not hold him to a settled life, and he sold out one day to a German immigrant, gave his wife a few dollars and disappeared, not to be seen or heard of in those parts again.

Another character was a man named Needham, who also was somewhat of a mystery. The women considered that he had been "crossed in love." He affected a sombre style, rather imitating the manners and habits of the Indians. His cabin was near the river, and he was a constant hunter. Many times when playing by

2. *Otium cum dignitate* is a Latin expression meaning *ease with dignity*.

the shore I would become conscious of a strange, noiseless presence, and looking up would see Needham paddling by, swift and silent. It always gave me the shudders and sent me to the house. One day, on coming home from school, I saw a great platter of red meat on the table. I asked who had killed the beef; it was a practice to share the meat with the neighbors, whenever a large animal was killed, taking pay in kind. I was told it was not beef, and being unable to guess was at last informed that it was bear meat, which Mr. Needham had left. As he had killed the animal near where I hunted the cows every night, the news gave me a sensation.

Uncle Ben Piper, the only gray-haired man in the community, kept tavern and was an oracle on nearly all subjects. He was also postmaster, and a wash-stand drawer served as post office. It cost twenty-five cents in those times to pass a letter between Wisconsin and the East. Postage did not have to be prepaid, and I have known my father to go several days before he could raise the requisite cash to redeem a letter which he had heard awaited him in the wash-stand drawer, for Uncle Ben was not allowed to accept farm produce or even bank script for postage.

An Englishman named Pease, who lived near us, had "wheels." He thought the Free Masons and the women were in league to end his life. Every night he ranged his gun and farm tools beside his bed, to help ward off the attack that he constantly expected. Nothing could induce him to eat any food that a woman had prepared.

In changing "work" with my father, which often occurred, he would bring his own luncheon and eat it by the fire during mealtime. But after my sister was born, he refused to enter the house; he told the neighbors that "women were getting too thick up at Cowe's." Pease had nicknames for all the settlers but one, and while very polite to their faces, he always applied his nicknames in their absence.

A man named Rugg lost caste with his neighbors because he dug and used a potato pit in an Indian mound from which he had thrown out a large number of human bones. Some of the bones were of gigantic size.

There were many good hunters among the settlers; the Smith brothers scorned to shoot a bird or squirrel except through the head. If there were sickness in the family of any neighbor, the Smiths saw that partridges, quail, or pigeons, properly shot, were supplied. Another Smith was a bee hunter, and a very successful one, too. Those were the days when the beautiful passenger pigeons at times seemed to fill the woods and the sky. Deer were very abundant; I have seen them eating hay with my father's cows; and in the spring and fall seasons the river was covered with wild ducks and geese.

Two events in my seventh year left a strong impression upon me. The first was an address by a colored man named Lewis Washington, a runaway slave, who had a natural gift of oratory and made many speeches in this state. I was so curious to see a genuine black man that I got too close to him when he was in the convulsion of putting on his overcoat, and caught a considerable thump. No harm was done, but he apologized very earnestly. I have read that his campaigning of the state was quite effective.

The other occurrence was the visit to Watertown of Herr Dreisbach with his famous menagerie. Our indulgent father took my brother and myself and a neighbor's daughter to see the "great instructive exhibition." It took our oxteam three hours to make the seven miles, and the elephant's foot-prints by the bridges, and the other impedimenta of the great show, which we passed, carried our excitement, which had been cruelly growing for three weeks, well-nigh up to an exploding climax. I was told not to lose my ticket, or I could not get in; and when the ticket taker seized hold of it, I held on until he finally yelled angrily, "Let go, you little cuss!" whereupon my father came to his rescue. The show on the whole was very satisfactory, except for the color of Columbus, the fine old elephant, which for some reason, probably from the show bills on the barns, I had expected to be of a greenish tint. I also had supposed that the lion would drag his chariot at least half a mile, with the driver in heroic pose, instead of merely two cars' length. Herr Dreisbach afterwards showed on Rock Prairie, in the open country, a few miles east of Janesville. People came from great distances to attend, even from as far as Baraboo, sometimes camping out two nights each way.

Our first public edifice was a log schoolhouse

CHASING THE GEESE TO GET A NEW QUILL

about twenty feet square. It was on the opposite side of the river, nearly a mile distant, but I began to attend school before I was fully five years old. One of the things I remember of one of my early teachers most distinctly is, that she used to hang a five-franc piece, tied with blue ribbon, around the neck of the scholar who had "left off at the head." I was occasionally favored, but my mother's satisfaction was greatly modified by her fear that I would lose the coin while taking it back the next day.

The teachers probably could not have passed a normal school examination, but they could do what our graduates now cannot do—that is, make and mend a quill pen. Those were all the pens we had, and many a time have I chased our geese to get a new quill. The teachers patiently guided our wobbling ideas from the alphabet to cube root. The lessons over, we were told to "toe the crack," and "make obeisance," and were then put through our paces in the fields of general knowledge. I still remember, from their drilling, the country, territory, county, and town in which we lived; that James K. Polk was president, that George M. Dallas was vice-president, and that Henry Dodge was governor. What ancient history that now seems!

Near the school lived a family named Babcock, with four well-grown boys. One of them used often to come over at noon to see one of the teachers. One noon, on running to the schoolroom after something that I wanted, I was horrified to see my loved teacher struggling to prevent the young fellow from kissing her. I felt very sorry for her, and on going home promptly reported the outrage to my mother. She evidently did not approve, but did not make as much of a demonstration over it as I had expected. I doubt now, if the teacher was as greatly in need of my sympathy as I then thought.

The Babcocks all went to the war, as I am told, and one of them became colonel of his regiment. He came home to be fatally and mysteriously shot one night on his way to his room in Chicago; the why and how were never revealed.

The winter after I was six years old I went to a school taught by a fine young man named Martin Piper, a relative of Uncle Ben's. The next summer he enlisted in the Mexican War with another of our young neighbors, John Bradshaw. I saw the volunteers from Watertown filling two wagons that carried them to Milwaukee, and I could not keep the tears back, for I feared I should never see John and Martin again. And so it was; they both perished at Vera Cruz.

My last winter's school was taught by my father. I remember that we used to cross the river, which only froze along the edges, on cakes of ice which he would cut out and pole across. The school closed in the spring with an "exhibition," consisting of declamations, dialogues, a little "play," and a spelling contest. The whole countryside was there, and about thirty of us youngsters were put up in the attic, which was floored over with loose boards, to make room for our elders. The only light we had was what percolated up through the cracks, and all that we could see of the exhibition was through them. As we hustled around, sampling them to see where we could see best, we made a good deal of disturbance. The best place, next the chimney, we were driven back from, for repeated burning had weakened the support. (The beam next to the chimney used to catch fire nearly every day, and we younger ones used to watch it and report to the teacher, who would calmly throw a dipper of water up and put the fire out for the time being.) A fat woman sat under the dangerous place that evening, and made a great outcry if we came near to enjoy the desirable outlook—stout people always seem fearful that something will fall on them. I remember also that her little girl, a pretty creature in curls and a pink dress, spoke "Mary had a little lamb," by having it "lined out" to her.

Our schoolhouse was so set in a noble grove of oaks, elms and maples with a heavy undergrowth, that we could not be seen from the road. Nearly every day droves of cattle went by, and we used to run up through the thicket to see them. It must have been an odd sight to the drovers to see a dozen or more little half-scared faces peering out of the brush, and no building in sight. They would often give us a noisy salute, whereupon we would scamper back, telling of our narrow escape from dangerous beasts and men.

The presidential election in the fall of 1848 aroused a good deal of interest, for Wisconsin had now become a state, and citizens could vote for national candidates. I was in Jonathan Piper's store one evening, with my father, when about a dozen men were present. A political discussion sprang up and grew hot, and finally a division was called for. Two or three voted for Zachary Taylor, the Whig candidate; one for Lewis Cass, the Democrat; and the rest for Martin Van Buren, Free Soiler. The State went with the lone voter, for Cass carried it by a small plurality.

Good health was the rule among the hard-working, plain-living pioneers, but plowing up the soil released the poison which nature seemed to have put there on guard, and every one at one time or another came down with the "shakes." However, the potent influence of sunshine, quinine, and cholagogue speedily won their way, and in a few years malaria had become a mere reminiscence.

In November, 1848, my parents moved to Beaver Dam, and thus our life in the Rock River country came to an end. The splendid primeval forest has now gone, and even before we left much of it had been converted into log heaps and burned. Every night scores of fires would gleam out where the finest hardwood logs, worth now a king's ransom, were being turned into smoke and ashes. Even the mills which that grand pioneer, Andrew Hardgrave, had built in 1844, to the great rejoicing of all the people, are gone, and the river flows on over its smooth limestone floor, unvexed as of old. But fine brick buildings have taken the place of the old log structures, and land brings at least twenty times as much per acre as then. Who can argue against that?

THE BUCCANEERS

DURING the seventeenth century there were a great number of pirates who committed serious ravages upon the settlements in the West Indies and upon the mainland adjacent, and whose expeditions extended even to the coasts of Chili and Peru. These men were called buccaneers; and the meaning of the word gives some intimation of the origin of the buccaneers themselves.

At an earlier day, many of the settlers in the island of Hispaniola, or Hayti, made their living by hunting cattle and preserving the meat by the *boucan* process. These hunters used to form parties of five or six in number, and arming themselves with musket, bullet bag, powderhorn and knife, they took their way on foot through the tangled forests of the country. When they killed one of the wild cattle, its flesh was cut into long strips and laid upon gratings, constructed of green sticks, where it was exposed to the smoke of a wood fire, which was fed by the fat and waste parts of the animals. The grating upon which the meat was laid was called a *boucan*, and the hunters were called *boucaniers*. Later these hunters were driven from Hayti by the Spaniards and took refuge in some of the neighboring islands, where they revenged themselves for some of the ill-treatment by preying upon the possessions of their oppressors wherever they could find them.

At the same time affairs in Europe brought France and England on the one hand, and Spain on the other, into collision; and as a result, the Spanish possessions in America became the object of French and English attacks. Accordingly, those two nations were inclined to look with a lenient eye upon the depredations committed by the buccaneers, so long as the property of the English and French was respected. As a natural consequence, many of the disreputable and daring characters of both nations joined themselves with the original buccaneers, whom they soon made as corrupt as themselves. Eventually these pirates increased so in number, and grew so daring in their operations that it was necessary for all nations to unite in putting them down; and by that time, the word *buccaneer* had come to mean *pirate* in its worst sense.

From time to time there arose among the buccaneers leaders whose successes brought a large following from men of other companies, and in one or two instances a particularly strong man gathered about him almost all the men who were willing to engage in such enterprises. At such times the pirates formed a very powerful organization, and none of the smaller cities were proof against their ravages. Whether the band was large or small, however, the method of operation was always practically the same.

Naturally there were preliminary meetings in

which a few men discussed plans and decided upon an expedition of some sort. Then a preliminary meeting was held at which the object of attack was determined, funds were raised, officers were elected, and the smaller details of the expedition were determined. Then articles of agreement were drawn up, signed by the buccaneers, and usually kept with remarkable exactness. In conformity with these agreements, the spoils of the expedition were distributed among the individuals according to rank, each individual of the ordinary class receiving one share of the plunder, while the officers were given from two to eight, according to their position and influence. It was customary, however, before any allotment was made to the individuals, to set aside a certain portion of the spoils to be distributed among those who had suffered some injury in the expedition, and in case any of the members died, that member's share was distributed to his heirs. Besides this, there were special rewards given to the first man who should sight a prize, to the first man to board a ship, and to other men who were noticeably brave and successful.

It was quite customary for two buccaneers to swear brotherhood each to the other, to make written agreements to stand by each other during life, to sign these agreements with their own blood; and then to keep these curious partnerships to the end. There are numerous touching accounts of the devotion with which a friend often followed the fortunes of his sworn brother.

In fact, the buccaneers usually dealt honestly and fairly with one another, and in the same way with the Indians, notwithstanding the fact that they were bloodthirsty, cruel and heartless in their treatment of the captives they made on their expeditions.

The usual place of meeting for the buccaneers was upon the west end of the island of Tortuga, which lies off the northern coast of Hayti, although the English pirates after 1654 met on the island of Jamaica. The traders and planters of these islands and of others in the vicinity were not averse to having the buccaneers among them, for no sooner had the latter returned from a successful expedition than they spent, with lavish hand, the money which they had made. While it is true that between these forays the pirates were given to the wildest excesses, and were anything but a desirable addition to a community, yet there are always plenty of people who are willing to profit by the wastefulness and dissipations of others. Many of the buccaneers, accordingly, had homes which they visited in the intervals of their cruises, where, although their business was well known, they were in a certain sense respected. However, before the pirates were wholly subdued, they had become less and less acceptable residents in any community, and finally were at enmity with every soul not in their own occupation.

That these buccaneers had a large amount of physical bravery, goes without saying; for only a man who feared nothing could undertake such apparently hopeless tasks as these wild plunderers carried to a successful conclusion. In fact many times they were successful for the reason that the vessels or towns they attacked deemed themselves secure from attack by so small a force as the pirates could muster. They were inured to hardship and willing to undergo any amount of pain and suffering, if they could but gather the riches for which they sought. The accounts of their adventures are filled with descriptions of daring deeds, which if undertaken in a better cause would have made the men famous for all time.

The beginning of these expeditions may be placed at about 1625, and the last important cruise of the pirates was made in 1688. After the latter date they gradually dispersed, and the buccaneers appeared no more. In 1664, Mansveldt, who was one of the ablest of the pirate chiefs, conceived the idea of forming an independent government with a flag of its own, and locating his capital at Santa Katalina. His early death prevented him from realizing his purpose; and though his successor, the famous Henry Morgan, attempted to carry out the plan, it met with such opposition from the Governor of Jamaica that it was definitely abandoned. It was under the leadership of this same Morgan that the buccaneers reached the height of their reputation, and executed their most daring and successful raids. Among Morgan's performances was the capture of the town of Puerto del Principe in Cuba, and the cities of Porto Bello,

Maracaibo and Gibraltar in South America. His greatest exploit, however, occurred in 1670, when at the head of the fleet of thirty-seven ships of all sizes manned by more than two thousand pirates, he captured the forts on the Chagres River, marched across the Isthmus of Panama, and after ten days of incredible hardship and suffering, fighting against a force of twenty-five hundred men, captured the city of Panama. After a stay of about three weeks he returned across the Isthmus.

So unsatisfactory in value were the spoils of this expedition, that Morgan was accused of embezzling some portion, and in consequence became very unpopular with his followers.

However, as this expedition was made against the Spanish, it received some approval from the English; and Morgan, abandoning his career as a pirate, accepted the lieutenant-governorship of Jamaica, and was subsequently made governor of that island, in which capacity he did much toward suppressing piracy in the Caribbean Sea.

We have two notable accounts of the deeds of the early buccaneers. One was published in 1678 in Amsterdam by John Esquemeling, who wrote from observation, as he was himself one of the pirates, and present at many of the conflicts which he describes. The second account is the journal of Basil Ringrose, who, as a pirate, took part in Sharp's voyage around South America, and was finally killed in a plundering raid.

CAPTAIN MORGAN AT MARACAIBO[1]

CAPTAIN Morgan had been so long absent from Maracaibo that he knew that the Spaniards had had sufficient time to fortify themselves strongly, and so hinder his departure from the lake. Without waiting to collect the full sum he had required from the inhabitants of Gibraltar, he demanded some of the townsmen as hostages, whom he might carry with him on his return journey, and whom he would release upon the full payment of the tribute he had levied.

Four persons who had been agreed upon were delivered to him as hostages for the sums demanded, and at last Morgan weighed anchor and set sail with great haste, directing his course toward Maracaibo.

Four days later, he arrived in front of the town and found things very much in the same condition as that in which they had been left, yet he was very much disturbed when he learned from an old man, who had been left alone and sick in the village, that three Spanish men-of-war were

1. This account of Henry Morgan's deeds at Maracaibo is taken from the narrative of John Esquemeling, but no attempt has been made to give a literal translation of his words. Morgan had passed through the Gulf of Venezuela, captured the town of Maracaibo and made his way through the narrow passage into the lake of the same name, where he captured and despoiled Gibraltar. At the opening of this sketch, he is in Lake Maracaibo, seeking an opportunity to return to the open sea.

lying at anchor in the entrance to the lake, waiting patiently for the return of the pirates. Moreover, the great castle that stood at the opening of the channel had been again repaired, provided with great guns and garrisoned by a strong force which was well supplied with ammunition.

Morgan was indeed in a dangerous predicament, for the passages leading out of the lake were narrow and tortuous. In order to learn just what force he had to meet, he sent his swiftest boat scouting through the inlet, while his ships remained within the lake.

The next day the boat came back, confirming what the old man had said and assuring Morgan that it had been so close to the Spanish ships that it was in great danger of being sunk by their shells The biggest ship carried forty guns, the second had thirty and the smallest twenty-four. As Morgan's largest ship did not carry more than fourteen small guns, the Spanish forces appeared much superior. In fact, every one thought that Morgan must lose all hope, considering the difficulty of his passing safely with his little fleet through these winding passages, amidst the great ships and by the strong fort. Moreover, there appeared no way of escape by land, and there was certainly no other outlet into the sea.

Captain Morgan, however, was not a man to be easily discouraged, and these terrible dangers left him wholly undaunted. In a spirit of bravado he boldly sent a Spanish prisoner to the admiral of the ships demanding of him a considerable tribute or ransom, threatening, in case the ransom was not promptly paid, to set the city of Maracaibo in flames and to destroy the whole Spanish fleet. After two days the Spaniard returned, bringing from the admiral a letter which read much as follows:

"To Captain Morgan, Commander of the Pirate Fleet:

Having understood by all our friends and neighbors that you have dared to attempt and commit hostilities in the countries, cities, towns and villages belonging to the dominions of his Catholic Majesty, my Sovereign Lord and Master, I let you understand by these lines that I have come here and have put into a very good state of defense that castle which you took out of the hands of a parcel of cowards; for I have again mounted the artillery which you spiked and made useless.

"My intent is to dispute with you your passage out of the lake and to follow and pursue you everywhere. Notwithstanding, if you be content to surrender with humility all that you have taken, together with the slaves and all other prisoners, I will let you pass freely and without trouble or molestation, providing you agree to return to your own country at once.

"But in case you make any resistance or opposition to my offers, I assure you I will utterly destroy you and put every man of you to the sword. This is my last and absolute resolution. Be prudent, therefore, and do not abuse my bounty. I have with me very good soldiers who desire nothing more ardently than to revenge on you and your people all the infamous cruelties and brutal acts that you have committed upon the Spanish nation in America.

"Dated on board the royal ship Magdalena, lying at anchor at the entry of Lake Maracaibo, this twenty-fourth day of April, Sixteen Hundred Sixty-nine.

Don Alonso del Campo y Espinosa."

As soon as Captain Morgan had received this letter, he called all his men together in the market place at Maracaibo, and after reading the contents both in French and in English, he requested the advice of his companions upon the whole matter, and asked whether they preferred to surrender all they had gained in order to obtain their liberty, or to fight for their possessions. With one voice they cried: "We will fight and spill the very last drop of blood in our veins rather than surrender the booty which we have captured at the risk of our lives."

Among those who shouted most loudly was one who pushed his way forward to Captain Morgan and said: "If you will take care of the rest, I, with only twelve men, will agree to destroy the biggest of those ships. I will take that vessel which we captured in the River of Gibraltar and make of her a fire ship. However, to conceal our purpose from the enemy, we will fill her decks with logs of wood standing erect and wearing hats and caps. We will put more of these logs at the portholes where they can be made to counterfeit cannon. At the stern we will hang out the English colors, and so make the enemy think that she is one of our largest ships well equipped for battle."

Everybody agreed to the sailor's proposal, but after all they were not fully satisfied nor fully relieved of their fears, and on the next day they tried again to come to some agreement with Don Alonso. Morgan sent him two messengers bearing the following propositions:

First, that he would quit Maracaibo without doing any damage to the town, or taking any ransoms.

Second, that he would set at liberty half of his slaves and all the other prisoners without ransom.

Third, that he would send home freely those four chief inhabitants of Gibraltar whom he held as hostages for the ransoms which had been promised.

Don Alonzo rejected these propositions instantly, considering it dishonorable to grant them. In return he sent back a message to the effect that if the pirates did not surrender themselves voluntarily into his hands within two days under the conditions of his letter, he would immediately come and force them to do it.

Deeply angered by this message, Captain Morgan put everything in order for fighting, resolving to get out of the lake by main force without surrendering anything. In the first place he commanded that all the slaves and the prisoners should be tied and guarded very closely. After this his men gathered all the pitch, tar and brimstone they could find in the town, and with them stocked the fire ship, which we have spoken of before. They mixed the powder, the brimstone and the tar with great quantities of palm leaves, and arranged everything so that it would burn quickly and furiously. They set their counterfeit cannon in proper position at the portholes, and under each fastened heaps of powder so that they would explode with great force and noise. In some of the portholes they fastened little native drums, and upon the decks they placed logs of wood dressed as men, wearing hats and coats and carrying swords and muskets.

When the fire ship was fully fitted out in this manner, they prepared to enter the passageway into the lake. The prisoners were all put into the great boat, and in another they placed all the plate, jewels and other rich things which they had acquired. In the same ship were placed the women and the wounded and suffering. The heavy goods and bulky merchandise were distributed among other vessels, each of which was manned by twelve well-armed sailors.

The fire ship was ordered to go ahead of the rest of the vessels, and at the earliest moment to grapple with the largest of the Spanish ships. Before starting, Morgan had exacted from each of his comrades an oath in which he vowed to defend himself and his comrades against the Spaniards, even to the last drop of his blood, and never under any circumstances to beg for quarter. In return for these pledges, Morgan promised his men that all should be very well rewarded if they were successful.

It was on the thirtieth day of April, 1669, that the buccaneers made their courageous start to find the Spanish. It was growing dark when Captain Morgan found the three ships riding at anchor in the middle of the passageway into the lake, and fearing to attack in the darkness, he ordered his vessels to come to anchor, resolved that if the Spanish attacked he would fight them from that position.

All that night the valiant captain and his men kept a careful and vigilant watch, for the Spanish were almost within gunshot. No sooner had daylight come, however, than the buccaneers weighed anchor and again set sail, starting their course for the Spanish vessels. The latter, seeing them come, themselves put on sail and moved to meet the attack. The fire ship in its place at the head of the line soon met the largest ship, and instantly grappled itself firmly to her side. Too late the Spaniards discovered their terrible danger, and although they made strenuous efforts to free themselves, they were unable to do so. The flames from the burning vessel seized upon the timber and rigging of the ship, and in a very short space of time consumed the stern of the vessel, leaving the fore part to sink into the sea, carrying with it the survivors.

The second Spanish ship, seeing that the pirates were successful in destroying the admiral's vessel, fled toward the castle, but being unable to escape, they sunk their vessel, preferring to lose their ship rather than fall into the hands of bloodthirsty pirates. A portion of the sunken ship extended above the shallow water and was set on fire. The third vessel was captured by the pirates, all of whom now gave their attention to the Spaniards who were swimming toward the shore from the two wrecked vessels. Many were overtaken, but none would ask for quarter, preferring to die rather than be given life by the pirates.

Rejoicing at their wonderful and almost unexpected victory, the buccaneers pushed rapidly to the shore and attacked the castle with great vigor, but the walls were strong and were defended with such skill that the assailants were driven back time and again. The pirates had nothing but small guns with them, and although they advanced close to the castle walls and kept up a constant fire, yet they were able to do very little damage. On the other hand, the Spaniards were well armed, and in the course of the day succeeded in killing and wounding no less than sixty of the pirates. Toward evening the buccaneers retired discouraged to their ships.

All that night the Spaniards labored hard to strengthen their castle and to put things in readiness for the renewal of the attack which they expected on the morrow. However, Captain Morgan did not continue his attack on the second day, but busied himself in taking prisoner such of the sailors as he could find in the water or on the shore, and trying to recover some of the riches that were lost in the two ships.

Among those whom he captured was the pilot of the second vessel. This man was a stranger among the Spanish, and from him Morgan gathered much information. By this means he discovered that the Spanish Council of State had sent six well-equipped men-of-war with instructions to drive the English pirates out of the seas, and to destroy as many of them as possible. This vigorous action was taken at the order of the Spanish monarch, who had frequently complained to the English of the depredations their subjects were committing on the Spanish possessions, but had never been given the least satisfaction. When, however, the ships arrived at Cartagena, two of the six were found to be too large for cruising along the shallow waters of the coast, and were returned to Spain. The remaining four sailed toward Campeche to seek out the English, but in the port of that city one of the ships was lost in a fierce gale, and only the three which Morgan had now captured remained to act against the pirates. The night before Morgan arrived, the admiral had given a banquet to all his people, and on that occasion he persuaded them neither to take nor to give quarter; and this was the reason why the sailors fought even in the presence of death by drowning. It seems that Don Alonso had been warned by a deserting negro that the buccaneers were building a fire ship, but he deemed it impossible

THE THIRD VESSEL WAS CAPTURED

that they should construct one that would menace the safety of his vessels.

More important information which the pilot gave, however, was that in the vessel which had been sunk by the fire ship, was a great quantity of gold and silver plate, together with other riches to the value of forty thousand pieces of eight.[2]

Morgan directed one of his ships to remain near the sunken vessel, drive away the native boats which prowled around in that vicinity, and try to recover the treasures. As for himself, the pirate returned to Gibraltar, where he transferred himself and his sailors to the larger and stronger ship which he had captured from the Spaniards.

When he was well established in this new ship, he sent word to the Spanish admiral, who had escaped on shore and who was assisting in the defense of the castle, that a large ransom must be paid or the town would be burned to the ground. The admiral flatly refused to pay a single dollar to Morgan; but the garrison, remembering how successful Morgan had always been and how fierce was his revenge, concluded to pay the ransom freely. Accordingly, after some discussion, it was agreed that the Spaniards should pay twenty thousand pieces of eight and deliver five hundred beeves on the following day. This was done, and the pirates salted the flesh of the cattle and stored it away for their voyage.

Notwithstanding Captain Morgan had promised to deliver the prisoners if the ransom was

2. The piece of eight was equivalent to about $1.25 of our money.

paid, he was so much in fear of destruction by shells from the castle as he was passing out of the lake that he told them he would release none of them until he was entirely out of range and safe in the open sea. In the meantime his men had recovered from the sunken ship fifteen thousand pieces of eight, besides much plate and valuable goods, such as the hilts of swords, and a great quantity of pieces of eight that had melted and run together from the heat of the burning vessel.

After thinking the matter over more fully, Morgan decided that it would not be safe even yet for him to attempt to pass the castle, and accordingly he called before him his prisoners and told them that unless the admiral and the garrison of the castle should promise him free passage out of the lake, he would hang every prisoner on the yards of his ship. Accordingly, the prisoners sent a deputation to Don Alonso beseeching and supplicating him to have pity on the prisoners, who with their wives and children were still on board the ship with Captain Morgan, and to give his word of honor to permit the buccaneers to pass freely; for if such a promise were not given, every one of those in captivity would surely be killed by the sword or hanged.

The reply of Don Alonso was characteristic of the brave leader. He said, "If you had been as loyal to your king in hindering the entry of these pirates as I shall be in preventing their going out, you had never brought this trouble

DIVIDING THE SPOILS

upon yourselves nor upon our nation, which has now suffered so much through your cowardice. In a word, I shall never grant your request, but shall endeavor to maintain to its fullest the respect which is due to my king."

In deep despair over the result of their interview, the Spaniards returned to their fellow-prisoners, and delivered to Captain Morgan the admiral's answer. Morgan replied simply—"If Don Alonso will not give me permission to pass, I must find a way of going without his consent."

In preparation for his dangerous voyage, Morgan gathered his men on shore, and required them to bring to him all the spoils, of whatever nature, they had taken on the cruise. When these were assembled, it was found that besides a huge quantity of merchandise and a large number of slaves, the buccaneers had acquired plate, jewels and money to the value of two hundred fifty thousand pieces of eight. All of this magnificent prize was divided among the buccaneers according to the agreements which had been made before they began the expedition. Each man was permitted to take his share with him upon his own vessel. Morgan made the distribution of his spoils at this time in order not to risk the loss of the entire treasure by the sinking of one ship, and in order that no one faction of his party might succeed in carrying off all the plunder.

After everything was in readiness for the voyage, Morgan perfected a little stratagem by which he hoped to make his escape more safely. He announced to all his men that on a certain night they would sail through the narrow channel, his own ship leading the way. On the day preceding that night the Spaniards in the castle observed great activity in the pirate fleet. Canoes and boats loaded with men left the ships and pulled to the shore some distance away from the castle and on the side away from the channel. Here, overhanging trees hid the boats from the onlookers in the castle so that the latter were not aware that when the boats returned from the shore the men, with the exception of one or two who rowed, were lying concealed in the bottoms of the boats. Not a one was landed on shore, although it appeared that Morgan was preparing to attack the castle from the land side. All day long the boats plied back and forth, apparently leaving men and returning empty to the ships. Expecting a heavy assault, the Spaniards moved their best guns and a greater part of their garrison to that side of the castle which faced the land, and thus left the water side comparatively harmless.

As soon as night came on, the pirates weighed anchor, and by the light of the moon, without setting their sails, they glided slowly out with the ebbing tide, which brought them down almost in sight of the castle. They then spread their sails as quietly and with as great haste as possible. The Spaniards saw them and opened fire, hastily moving their guns back to the water side; but a favorable wind blew the vessels past the danger point before the men in the castle could put their guns into position to do any great damage.

When Morgan was safely out of reach of the guns of the castle, he gave his prisoners a boat and sent them ashore, retaining, however, the hostages which he had demanded from the city of Gibraltar, because that place had not yet paid its ransom. Just as he was sailing away, Morgan fired seven great shells against the castle as a farewell message, but the Spaniards did not reply even with so much as a musket shot.

The day after their departure, the buccaneers were overtaken by a terrible tempest which forced them at first to cast anchor, but as the wind increased in force they were compelled to draw their anchor and to put out to sea. Here they were indeed in great danger, for if they were cast on shore, they certainly would receive no mercy from either the Spaniards or the Indians. Once more, however, fortune smiled on Captain Morgan, and after a day or two the wind ceased and the buccaneers went on their way rejoicing.

BRADDOCK'S DEFEAT

BENJAMIN FRANKLIN

NOTE,—When it became evident that the conflicting land-claims of the French and English in America would admit of no peaceable settlement, a convention of representatives from the colonies was called to consider a union of the colonies and to find ways of establishing friendly relations with the Indians, especially with the redoubtable Five Nations. This convention met at Albany in 1754, and adopted a plan of union which had been drawn up by Franklin. However, the plan, when submitted to the colonies and to the British government, pleased no one. The colonies rejected it because it gave too much power to the king, the king because it gave too much power to the colonies. Franklin's own account of what followed is here given:

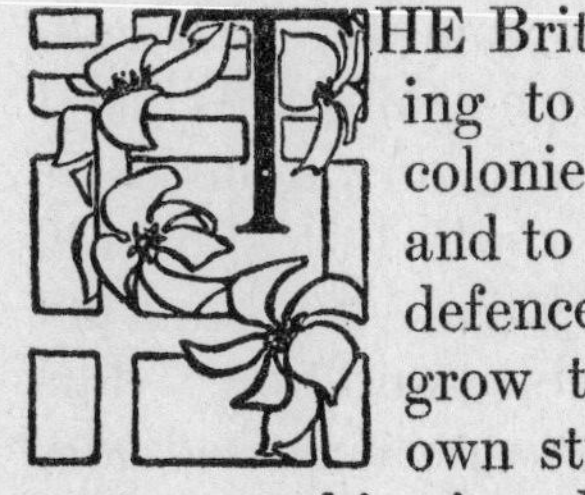

HE British government, not choosing to permit the union of the colonies as proposed at Albany, and to trust that union with their defence, lest they should thereby grow too military and feel their own strength, suspicions and jealousies at this time being entertained of them, sent over General Braddock with two regiments of regular English troops for that purpose. He landed at Alexandria, in Virginia, and thence marched to Fredericktown, in Maryland, where he halted for carriages. Our Assembly apprehending, from some information, that he had conceived violent prejudices against them, as averse to the service, wished me to wait upon him, not as from them, but as postmaster-general, under the guise of proposing to settle with him the mode of conducting with most celerity and certainty the despatches between him and the governors of the several provinces, with whom he must necessarily have continual correspondence, and of which they proposed to pay the expense. My son accompanied me on this journey.

We found the general at Fredericktown, waiting impatiently for the return of those he had sent through the back parts of Maryland and Virginia to collect wagons. I stayed with him several days, dined with him daily, and had full opportunity of removing all his prejudices, by the information of what the Assembly had before his arrival actually done, and were still willing to do, to facilitate his operations. When I was about to depart, the returns of wagons to be obtained were brought in, by which it appeared that they amounted only to twenty-five, and not all of those were in serviceable condition. The general and all the officers were surprised, declared the expedition was then at an end, being impossible, and exclaimed against the ministers for ignorantly landing them in a country destitute of the means of conveying their stores, baggage, etc., not less than one hundred and fifty wagons being necessary.

I happened to say I thought it was a pity they had not been landed rather in Pennsylvania, as in that country almost every farmer had his wagon. The general eagerly laid hold of my words, and said, "Then you, sir, who are a man of interest there, can probably procure them for us; and I beg you will undertake it." I asked what terms were to be offered the owners of the wagons; and I was desired to put on paper the terms that appeared to me necessary. This I did, and they were agreed to, and a commission and instructions accordingly prepared immediately. What those terms were will appear in the advertisement I published as soon as I arrived at Lancaster, which being, from the great and sudden effect it produced, a piece of some curiosity, I shall insert it at length, as follows:

"ADVERTISEMENT

"LANCASTER, April 26, 1755.

"Whereas, one hundred and fifty wagons, with four horses to each wagon, and fifteen hundred saddle or pack horses, are wanted for the service of his Majesty's forces now about to rendezvous at Will's Creek, and his excellency General Braddock having been pleased to empower me to contract for the hire of the same, I hereby give notice that I shall attend for that purpose at Lancaster from this day to next Wednesday evening, and at York from next Thursday morning till Friday evening, where I shall be ready to agree for wagons and teams, or single horses, on the following terms, viz.: 1. That there shall be paid for each wagon, with four good horses and a driver, fifteen shillings per diem; and for each able horse with a pack-saddle or other saddle and furniture, two shillings per diem; and for each able horse without a saddle, eighteen pence per diem. 2. That the pay commence from the time of their joining the forces at Will's Creek, which must be on or before the 20th of May ensuing, and that a reasonable allowance be paid over and above for the time necessary for their travelling to Will's Creek and home again after their discharge. 3. Each wagon and team, and every saddle or pack horse, is to be valued by indifferent persons chosen between me and the owner; and in case of the loss of any wagon, team, or other horse in the service, the price according to such valuation is to be allowed and paid. 4. Seven days' pay is to be advanced and paid in hand by me to the owner of each wagon and team or horse, at the time of contracting, if required, and the remainder to be paid by General Braddock, or by the paymaster of the army, at the time of their discharge, or from time to time, as it shall be demanded. 5. No drivers of wagons, or persons taking care of the hired horses, are on any account to be called upon to do the duty of soldiers, or be otherwise employed than in conducting or taking care of their carriages or horses. 6. All oats, Indian corn, or other forage that wagons or horses bring to the camp, more than is necessary for the subsistence of the horses, is to be taken for the use of the army, and a reasonable price paid for the same.

"Note.—My son, William Franklin, is empowered to enter into like contracts with any person in Cumberland County.

B. FRANKLIN."

"*To the Inhabitants of the Counties of Lancaster, York, and Cumberland*

"FRIENDS AND COUNTRYMEN—Being occasionally at the camp at Frederick a few days since, I found the general and officers extremely exasperated on account of their not being supplied with horses and carriages, which had been expected from this province, as most able to furnish them; but, through the dissensions between our governor and Assembly, money had not been provided, nor any steps taken for that purpose.

"It was proposed to send an armed force immediately into these counties, to seize as many of the best carriages and horses as should be wanted, and compel as many persons into the service as would be necessary to drive and take care of them.

"I apprehend that the progress of British soldiers through these counties on such an occasion, especially considering the temper they are in, and their resentment against us, would be attended with many and great inconveniencies to the inhabitants, and therefore more willingly took the trouble of trying first what might be done by fair and equitable means. The people of these back counties have lately complained to the Assembly that a sufficient currency was wanting; you have an opportunity of receiving and dividing among you a very considerable sum; for, if the service of this expedition should continue, as it is more than probable it will, for one hundred and twenty days, the hire of these wagons and horses will amount to upward of thirty thousand pounds, which will be paid you in silver and gold of the king's money.

"The service will be light and easy, for the army will scarce march above twelve miles per day, and the wagons and baggage horses, as they carry those things that are absolutely necessary to the welfare of the army, must march with the army, and no faster; and are, for the army's sake, always placed where they can be most secure, whether in a march or in a camp.

"If you are really, as I believe you are, good and loyal subjects to his majesty, you may now do a most acceptable service, and make it easy to yourselves; for three or four of such as can not separately spare from the business of their plantations a wagon and four horses and a driver, may do it together, one furnishing the wagon, another one or two horses, and another the driver, and divide the pay proportionately between you; but if you do not this service to your king and country voluntarily, when such good pay and reasonable terms are offered to you, your loyalty will be strongly suspected. The king's business must be done; so many brave troops, come so far for your defence, must not stand idle through your backwardness to do what may be reasonably expected from you; wagons and horses must be had; violent measures will probably be used, and you will be left to seek a recompense where you can find it, and your case, perhaps, be little pitied or regarded.

"I have no particular interest in this affair, as, except the satisfaction of endeavoring to do good, I shall have only my labor for my pains. If this method of obtaining the wagons and horses is not likely to succeed, I am obliged to send word to the general in fourteen days; and I suppose Sir John St. Clair, the hussar, with a body of soldiers, will immediately enter the province for the purpose, which I shall be sorry to hear, because I am very sincerely and truly your friend and well-wisher, "B. FRANKLIN."

I received of the general about eight hundred pounds, to be disbursed in advance-money to the wagon owners, etc.; but that sum being insufficient, I advanced upward of two hundred pounds more, and in two weeks the one hundred and fifty wagons, with two hundred and fifty-nine carrying horses, were on their march for the camp. The advertisement promised payment according to the valuation, in case any wagon or horse should be lost. The owners, however, alleging they did not know General Braddock, or what dependence might be had on his promise, insisted on my bond for the performance, which I accordingly gave them.

While I was at the camp, supping one evening with the officers of Colonel Dunbar's regiment, he represented to me his concern for the subalterns, who, he said, were generally not in affluence, and could ill afford, in this dear country, to lay in the stores that might be necessary in so long a march, through a wilderness, where nothing was to be purchased. I commiserated their case, and resolved to endeavor procuring them some relief. I said nothing, however, to him of my intention, but wrote the next morning to the committee of the Assembly, who had the disposition of some public money, warmly recommending the case of these officers to their consideration, and proposing that a present should be sent them of necessaries and refreshments. My son, who had some experience of a camp life, and of its wants, drew up a list for me, which I enclosed in my letter. The committee approved, and used such diligence that, conducted by my son, the stores arrived at the camp as soon as the wagons. They consisted of twenty parcels, each containing—

6 lbs. loaf sugar.
6 lbs. good Muscovado ditto.
1 lb. good green tea.
1 lb. good bohea ditto.
6 lbs. good ground coffee.
6 lbs. chocolate.
1-2 lb. pepper.
1 Gloucester cheese.
1 keg containing 20 lbs good butter.
2 doz. old Madeira wine.
2 gallons Jamaica spirits.
1 bottle flour of mustard.

1-2 cwt. best white biscuit.
1 quart best white wine vinegar.
2 well-cured hams.
1-2 dozen dried tongues.
6 lbs. rice.
6 lbs. raisins.

These twenty parcels, well packed, were placed on as many horses, each parcel, with the horse, being intended as a present for one officer. They were very thankfully received, and the kindness acknowledged by letters to me from the colonels of both regiments, in the most grateful terms. The general, too, was highly satisfied with my conduct in procuring him the wagons, etc., and readily paid my account of disbursements, thanking me repeatedly, and requesting my further assistance in sending provisions after him. I undertook this also, and was busily employed in it till we heard of his defeat, advancing for the service of my own money upward of one thousand pounds sterling, of which I sent him an account. It came to his hands, luckily for me, a few days before the battle, and he returned me immediately an order on the paymaster for the round sum of one thousand pounds, leaving the remainder to the next account. I consider this payment as good luck, having never been able to obtain that remainder, of which more hereafter.

This general was, I think, a brave man, and might probably have made a figure as a good officer in some European war. But he had too much self-confidence, too high an opinion of the validity of regular troops, and too mean a one of both Americans and Indians. George Croghan, our Indian interpreter, joined him on his march with one hundred of those people, who might have been of great use to his army as guides, scouts, etc., if he had treated them kindly; but he slighted and neglected them, and they gradually left him.

In conversation with him one day, he was giving me some account of his intended progress. "After taking Fort Duquesne," says he, "I am to proceed to Niagara; and, having taken that, to Frontenac, if the season will allow time; and I suppose it will, for Duquesne can hardly detain me above three or four days; and then I see nothing that can obstruct my march to Niagara." Having before resolved in my mind the long line his army must make in their march by a very narrow road, to be cut for them through the woods and bushes, and also what I had read of a former defeat of fifteen hundred French, who invaded the Iroquois country, I had conceived some doubts and some fears for the event of the campaign. But I ventured only to say, "To be sure, sir, if you arrive well before Duquesne, with these fine troops, so well provided with artillery, that place not yet completely fortified, and as we hear with no very strong garrison, can probably make but a short resistance. The only danger I apprehend of obstruction to your march is from ambuscades of Indians, who, by constant practice, are dexterous in laying and executing them; and the slender line, near four miles long, which your army must make, may expose it to

ON THE MARCH

be attacked by surprise in its flanks, and to be cut like a thread into several pieces, which, from their distance, cannot come up in time to support each other."

He smiled at my ignorance, and replied, "These savages may, indeed, be a formidable enemy to your raw American militia, but upon the king's regular and disciplined troops, sir, it is impossible they should make any impression." I was conscious of an impropriety in my disputing with a military man in matters of his profession, and said no more. The enemy, however, did not take the advantage of his army which I apprehended its long line of march exposed it to, but let it advance without interruption till within nine miles of the place; and then, when more in a body (for it had just passed a river, where the front had halted till all were come over), and in a more open part of the woods than any it had passed, attacked its advanced guard by a heavy fire from behind trees and bushes, which was the first intelligence the general had of an enemy's being near him. This guard being disordered, the general hurried the troops up to their assistance, which was done in great confusion, through wagons, baggage, and cattle; and presently the fire came upon their flank: the officers, being on horseback, were more easily distinguished, picked out as marks, and fell very fast; and the soldiers were crowded together in a huddle, having or hearing no orders, and standing to be shot at till two-thirds of them were killed; and then, being seized with a panic, the whole fled with precipitation.

The wagoners took each a horse out of his team and scampered; their example was immediately followed by others; so that all the wagons, provisions, artillery, and stores were left to the enemy. The general, being wounded, was brought off with difficulty; his secretary, Mr. Shirley, was killed by his side; and out of eighty-six officers, sixty-three were killed or wounded, and seven hundred and fourteen men killed out of eleven hundred. These eleven hundred had been picked men from the whole army; the rest had been left behind with Colonel Dunbar, who was to follow with the heavier part of the stores, provisions, and baggage. The flyers, not being pursued, arrived at Dunbar's camp, and the panic they brought with them instantly seized him and all his people; and, though he had now above one thousand men, and the enemy who had beaten Braddock did not at most exceed four hundred Indians and French together, in-

PICKING OFF THE OFFICERS

stead of proceeding, and endeavoring to recover some of the lost honor, he ordered all the stores, ammunition, etc., to be destroyed, that he might have more horses to assist his flight toward the settlements, and less lumber to remove. He was there met with requests from the governors of Virginia, Maryland, and Pennsylvania, that he would post his troops on the frontiers, so as to afford some protection to the inhabitants; but he continued his hasty march through all the country, not thinking himself safe till he arrived at Philadelphia, where the inhabitants could protect him. This whole transaction gave us Americans the first suspicion that our exalted ideas of the prowess of British regulars had not been well founded.

In their first march, too, from their landing till they got beyond the settlements, they had plundered and stripped the inhabitants, totally ruining some poor families, besides insulting, abusing, and confining the people if they remonstrated. This was enough to put us out of conceit of such defenders, if we had really wanted any. How different was the conduct of our French friends in 1781, who, during a march through the most inhabited part of our country from Rhode Island to Virginia, near seven hundred miles, occasioned not the smallest complaint for the loss of a pig, a chicken, or even an apple.

Captain Orme, who was one of the general's aides-de-camp, and, being grievously wounded, was brought off with him, and continued with him to his death, which happened in a few days, told me that he was totally silent all day, and at night only said, "*Who would have thought it?*" That he was silent again the following day, saying only at last, "*We shall better know how to deal with them another time;*" and died in a few minutes after.

The secretary's papers, with all the general's

orders, instructions, and correspondence, falling into the enemy's hands, they selected and translated into French a number of the articles, which they printed, to prove the hostile intentions of the British court before the declaration of war. Among these I saw some letters of the general to the ministry, speaking highly of the great service I had rendered the army, and recommending me to their notice. David Hume, too, who was some years after secretary to Lord Hertford, when minister in France, and afterward to General Conway, when secretary of state, told me he had seen among the papers in that office, letters from Braddock highly recommending me. But the expedition having been unfortunate, my service, it seems, was not thought of much value, for these recommendations were never of any use to me.

As to rewards from himself, I asked only one, which was that he would give orders to his officers not to enlist any more of our bought servants, and that he would discharge such as had been already enlisted. This he readily granted, and several were accordingly returned to their masters, on my application. Dunbar, when the command devolved on him, was not so generous. He being at Philadelphia, on his retreat, or rather flight, I applied to him for the discharge of the servants of three poor farmers of Lancaster county that he had enlisted, reminding him of the late general's orders on that head. He promised me that, if the masters would come to him at Trenton, where he should be in a few days on his march to New York, he would there deliver their men to them. They accordingly were at the expense and trouble of going to Trenton, and there he refused to perform his promise, to their great loss and disappointment.

As soon as the loss of the wagons and horses was generally known, all the owners came upon me for the valuation which I had given bond to pay. Their demands gave me a great deal of trouble, my acquainting them that the money was ready in the paymaster's hands, but that orders for paying it must first be obtained from General Shirley, and my assuring them that I had applied to that general by letter, but he being at a distance, an answer could not soon be received, and they must have patience; all this was not sufficient to satisfy, and some began to sue me. General Shirley at length relieved me from this terrible situation by appointing commissioners to examine the claims, and ordering payment. They amounted to nearly twenty thousand pounds, which to pay would have ruined me.

Before we had the news of this defeat, the two Doctors Bond came to me with a subscription paper for raising money to defray the expense of a grand firework, which it was intended to exhibit at a rejoicing on receipt of the news of our taking Fort Duquesne. I looked grave, and said it would, I thought, be time enough to prepare for the rejoicing when we knew we should have occasion to rejoice. They seemed sur-

BENJAMIN FRANKLIN

prised that I did not immediately comply with their proposal. "Why . . . !" says one of them, "you surely don't suppose that the fort will not be taken?" "I don't know that it will not be taken, but I know that the events of war are subject to great uncertainty." I gave them the reasons of my doubting; the subscription was dropped, and the projectors thereby missed the mortification they would have undergone if the firework had been prepared. Dr. Bond, on some other occasion afterward, said that he did not like Franklin's forebodings.

READING HISTORY

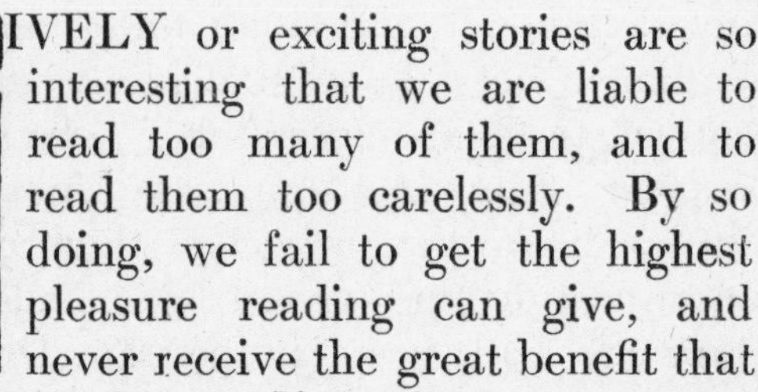

LIVELY or exciting stories are so interesting that we are liable to read too many of them, and to read them too carelessly. By so doing, we fail to get the highest pleasure reading can give, and never receive the great benefit that is ours for the taking. If we let our arms rest idle for a long time, they become weak and useless; if a boy takes no exercise he cannot expect to be a strong man. So, if he reads nothing that makes him exert his mind, he becomes a weakling in intellect and never feels the pure delight that the man has who can read in a masterful way a masterly selection.

As a matter of fact, history when well written is as fascinating as any story that ever was penned, and it has the merit of being true. Sometimes it is a little harder to read than the light things that are so numerously given us by magazines and story books, but no one shuns hard work where it yields pleasure. A boy will play football or tramp all day with a gun over his shoulder, and not think twice about the hard work he is doing. Reading history bears about the same relation to reading mild love stories and overdrawn adventures that football or skating bears to stringing beads.

Not all history is hard to read; in some of it

the interest lies so close to the surface that it grips us with the first glance. Such is the kind we read in the beginning. The adventures of King Arthur, the Cid, Robin Hood, and other half mythical heroes are history in the making—the history that grew up when the world was young, and its great men were something like overgrown boys. That is why we who have boyish hearts like to read about them. Then Robert the Bruce, Cæsar and Alexander are more like the men of to-day and appeal a little more strongly as we get more mature. And finally we have Washington, Lincoln, Lee and Grant as men nearer our own time, whose lives and deeds require our careful thought and our serious study, because they had to contend with the same things and overcome the same obstacles that confront us.

There is really no use in trying to tell just how and in what way history becomes interesting, and nobody cares to read a long article about history. What we older people would wish is merely this: that our young friends should begin to read history and so find out for themselves just how fascinating it is. We can perhaps give a word or two of warning that may save much hard work and many discouragements. Macaulay, Gibbon, Hume and others are great men, and in the tomes they have written are pages and pages of exciting, stimulating narrative; yet one must read so many pages of heavy matter to find the interesting things that it is not worth the time and exertion a young person would need to give. On the other hand, there are writers like Parkman and Prescott who are always readable and entertaining.

The best way to learn to like history is to begin with such readable things as are put into these volumes, and then follow any line of interest that is discovered.

Franklin's description of Braddock's defeat is interesting in itself, and it calls attention to the French and Indian War and to the wonderful career of Franklin himself. These are lines of interest that you may follow out in histories or in works of reference.

THE AMERICAN FLAG

JOSEPH RODMAN DRAKE

When Freedom, from her mountain height,
   Unfurled her standard to the air,
She tore the azure robe of night,
   And set the stars of glory there!
She mingled with its gorgeous dyes
The milky baldric of the skies,
And striped its pure, celestial white
With streakings of the morning light,
Then, from his mansion in the sun,
She called her eagle bearer down,
And gave into his mighty hand
The symbol of her chosen land!

Majestic monarch of the cloud!
   Who rear'st aloft thy regal form,
To hear the tempest-trumpings loud,
And see the lightning lances driven,
   When strive the warriors of the storm,

And rolls the thunder-drum of heaven,—
Child of the Sun! to thee 't is given
To guard the banner of the free,
To hover in the sulphur smoke,
To ward away the battle-stroke,
And bid its blendings shine afar,
Like rainbows on the cloud of war,
The harbingers of victory!

Flag of the brave! thy folds shall fly,
The sign of hope and triumph high!
When speaks the signal-trumpet tone,
And the long line comes gleaming on,
Ere yet the life-blood, warm and wet,
Has dimmed the glistening bayonet,
Each soldier's eye shall brightly turn
To where thy sky-born glories burn,
And, as his springing steps advance,
Catch war and vengeance from the glance.
And when the cannon-mouthings loud
Heave in wild wreaths the battle shroud,
And gory sabres rise and fall
Like shoots of flame on midnight's pall,
Then shall thy meteor glances glow,
And cowering foes shall shrink beneath
Each gallant arm that strikes below
That lovely messenger of death.

Flag of the seas! on ocean wave
Thy stars shall glitter o'er the brave;
When death, careering on the gale,
Sweeps darkly round the bellied sail,
And frighted waves rush wildly back
Before the broadside's reeling rack,

Each dying wanderer of the sea
Shall look at once to heaven and thee,
And smile to see thy splendors fly
In triumph o'er his closing eye.

Flag of the free heart's hope and home,
By angel hands to valor given,
Thy stars have lit the welkin dome,
And all thy hues were born in heaven.
Forever float that standard sheet!
Where breathes the foe but falls before us,
With Freedom's soil beneath our feet,
And Freedom's banner streaming o'er us?

This is a poem that may need a little explanation if every one is to appreciate it.

How fancifully the poet tells of the origin of the flag in the first stanza! The blue field and the stars are taken from the sky, and the white from the milky way which stretches like a broad scarf or baldric across the heavens. The red is from the first red streaks that in the morning flash across the eastern skies to herald the rising sun. The eagle, our national bird who supports the shield in our coat of arms, had by the old legends the power to fly full in the face of the sun, and to shield its eyes from the blaze was gifted with a third eyelid. In the talons of this lordly bird Freedom placed our chosen banner.

The second stanza continues the tribute to the eagle. To this regal bird it is given to fling high among the clouds and smoke of battle our brilliant banner, whose bright colors like the rainbow signify victory and peace—the flag of victory, the bow of promise.

The remainder of the lines are so clear in their meaning and so smooth in their structure that they stir our blood with patriotic fire.

BATTLE HYMN OF THE REPUBLIC

JULIA WARD HOWE

Mine eyes have seen the glory of the coming of
the Lord:
He is trampling out the vintage where the grapes
of wrath are stored;
He hath loosed the fateful lightning of his terrible
swift sword.
His truth is marching on.

I have seen him in the watch-fires of a hundred
circling camps;
They have builded him an altar in the evening
dews and damps;
I have read his righteous sentence by the dim and
flaring lamps.
His day is marching on.

I have read a fiery gospel, writ in burnished rows
of steel:
"As ye deal with my contemners, so with you my
grace shall deal;
Let the Hero, born of woman, crush the serpent
with his heel,
Since God is marching on."

He has sounded forth the trumpet that shall
never call retreat;
He is sifting out the hearts of men before his
judgment-seat:
O, be swift, my soul, to answer him! be jubilant,
my feet!
Our God is marching on.

In the beauty of the lilies Christ was born across
the sea,
With a glory in his bosom that transfigures you
and me;
As he died to make men holy, let us die to make
men free,
While God is marching on.

"'STONEWALL' JACKSON'S WAY"

J. W. PALMER

Note,—Thomas J. Jackson, the great Confederate general, better known as "Stonewall" Jackson, was loved and admired by his men not only for his military ability, but for his personal virtues, and even for his personal peculiarities as well. He was a deeply religious man, and never began a battle without prayer or failed to give public thanks to God for a victory.

While he believed that the people through whose land he was passing, and indeed all non-combatants, should be guarded as far as possible from the evil results of war, he showed no compassion for the enemies sent against him, and pushed the battle against them with all his might. His death in 1863 was a great loss to the Confederate cause.

Come, stack arms, men! Pile on the rails,
Stir up the camp-fire bright;
No matter if the canteen fails,
We'll make a roaring night.
Here Shenandoah brawls along,
There burly Blue Ridge echoes strong,
To swell the brigade's rousing song
Of "'Stonewall' Jackson's way."

We see him now—the old slouched hat
Cocked o'er his eye askew,
The shrewd, dry smile, the speech so pat,
So calm, so blunt, so true.
The "Blue-Light Elder" knows 'em well;
Says he, "That's Banks[1]—he's fond of shell,
Lord save his soul! We'll give him"—well,
That's "'Stonewall' Jackson's way."

Silence! ground arms! kneel all! caps off!
"Old Blue-Light's" going to pray.
Strangle the fool that dares to scoff!
Attention! it's his way.
Appealing from his native sod,
In forma pauperis[2] to God—
"Lay bare thine arm, stretch forth thy rod!
Amen!" That's "'Stonewall's' way."

---

1. Nathaniel Prentiss Banks was a Federal general who was pitted against Jackson in several engagements.

2. *In forma pauperis* is a Latin legal expression, meaning *as a poor man*.

He's in the saddle now—Fall in!
  Steady! the whole brigade!
Hill's[3] at the ford, cut off—we'll win
  His way out, ball and blade!
What matter if our shoes are worn?
What matter if our feet are torn?
"Quick-step! we're with him before dawn!"
  That's "'Stonewall' Jackson's way."

The sun's bright lances rout the mists
  Of morning, and, by George!
Here's Longstreet[4] struggling in the lists,
  Hemmed in an ugly gorge.
Pope[5] and his Yankees, whipped before,—
"Bay'nets and grape!" hear "Stonewall" roar;
"Charge, Stuart![6] Pay off Ashby's[7] score!"
  In "'Stonewall' Jackson's way."

Ah! maiden, wait and watch and yearn
  For news of "Stonewall's" band!
Ah! widow, read with eyes that burn
  That ring upon thy hand.
Ah! wife, sew on, pray on, hope on!
Thy life shall not be all forlorn;
The foe had better ne'er been born
  That gets in "'Stonewall's' way."

3. Ambrose P. Hill was a prominent Confederate general.

4. James Longstreet was one of the most distinguished of the Confederate generals.

5. John Pope, the Federal general, was badly defeated by Jackson and Robert E. Lee in the second battle of Bull Run, August 29 and 30, 1862.

6. James E. B. Stuart, a cavalry leader in the Confederate army, took a prominent part in the second battle of Bull Run, and was with Jackson in other engagements.

7. Turner Ashby, a Confederate general, had greatly aided Jackson by covering the latter's retreat before General Banks. He was killed in a skirmish in June, 1862.

"STONEWALL" JACKSON

BARON MUNCHAUSEN

INTRODUCTION

COLLECTED in a book called *The Travels of Baron Munchausen* is a series of the most extravagant stories imaginable. No one can possibly believe them to be true, and yet when we are reading them they do not appear so absurdly ridiculous as they seem afterward when we think of them. The book is said to have been written by a German named Rudolph Erich Raspe, but we cannot be sure of it, as there are no proofs. It is said, too, that there was a German officer, a Baron Hieronymous Karl Friedrich Munchausen who lived in the early part of the eighteenth century and who told such marvelous stories that he was very popular among his fellow officers and that his stories have been collected in a book.

The book appeared first in 1793, and some have believed that it was written to ridicule the books of travel which had appeared from time to time, some of which contained narratives not much less incredible than some of the Baron's fanciful tales. It is probable, however, that the book is merely a collection of very old stories with many newer ones included among them, and that it was written solely for entertainment.

The Baron always insists upon the strict truthfulness and accuracy of his stories and grows quite indignant when his veracity is questioned. To verify his words he printed the following notice at the beginning of his book:

TO THE PUBLIC:—Having heard, for the first time, that my adventures have been doubted, and looked upon as jokes, I feel bound to come forward, and vindicate my character *for veracity*, by paying three shillings at the Mansion House of this great city for the affidavits hereto appended.

This I have been forced into in regard of my own honor, although I have retired for many years from public and private life; and I hope that this, my last edition, will place me in a proper light with my readers.

AT THE CITY OF LONDON, ENGLAND

We, the undersigned, as true believers in the *profit*, do most solemnly affirm, that all the adventures of our friend Baron Munchausen, in whatever country they may *lie*, are positive and simple facts. *And*, as we have been believed, whose adventures are tenfold more wonderful, *so* do we hope all true believers will give him their full faith and credence.

GULLIVER. +
SINBAD. +
ALADDIN. +

Sworn at the Mansion House 9th November last, in the absence of the Lord Mayor.

JOHN (*the Porter*).

In this volume a few of his most amusing stories are printed—all, perhaps, that it is worth while to read.

I

SOME years before my beard announced approaching manhood, or, in other words, when I was neither man nor boy, but between both, I expressed in repeated conversations a strong desire of seeing the world, from which I was discouraged by my parents, though my father had been no inconsiderable traveler himself, as will appear before I have reached the end of my singular, and, I may add, interesting adventures. A cousin, by my mother's side, took a liking to me, often said I was a fine, forward youth, and was much inclined to gratify my curiosity. His eloquence had more effect than mine, for my father consented to my accompanying him in a voyage to the island of Ceylon, where his uncle had resided as governor many years.

We sailed from Amsterdam with despatches from their High Mightinesses the States of Holland. The only circumstance which happened on our voyage worth relating was the wonderful effects of a storm, which had torn up by the roots a great number of trees of enormous bulk and height, in an island where we lay at anchor to take in wood and water; some of these trees weighed many tons, yet they were carried by the wind so amazingly high that they appeared

THE CUCUMBER-GATHERERS

like the feathers of small birds floating in the air, for they were at least five miles above the earth: however, as soon as the storm subsided they all fell perpendicularly into their respective places, and took root again, except the largest, which happened, when it was blown into the air, to have a man and his wife, a very honest old couple, upon its branches, gathering cucumbers (in this part of the globe that useful vegetable grows upon trees): the weight of this couple, as the tree descended, overbalanced the trunk, and brought it down in a horizontal position: it fell upon the chief man of the island, and killed him on the spot; he had quitted his house in the storm, under an apprehension of its falling upon him, and was returning through his own garden when this fortunate accident happened. The word fortunate here requires some explanation. This chief was a man of a very avaricious and oppressive disposition, and though he had no family, the natives of the island were half starved by his oppressive and infamous impositions.

The very goods which he had thus taken from them were spoiling in his stores, while the poor wretches from whom they were plundered were pining in poverty. Though the destruction of this tyrant was accidental, the people chose the cucumber-gatherers for their governors, as a mark of their gratitude for destroying, though accidentally, their late tyrant.

After we had repaired the damages we sustained in this remarkable storm, and taken leave of the new governor and his lady, we sailed with a fair wind for the object of our voyage.

In about six weeks we arrived at Ceylon, where we were received with great marks of friendship and true politeness. The following singular adventures may not prove unentertaining.

After we had resided at Ceylon about a fortnight I accompanied one of the governor's brothers upon a shooting party. He was a strong, athletic man, and being used to that climate (for he had resided there some years), he bore the violent heat of the sun much better than I could; in our excursion he had made a considerable progress through a thick wood when I was only at the entrance.

Near the banks of a large piece of water, which had engaged my attention, I thought I heard a rustling noise behind; on turning about I was almost petrified (as who would not be?) at the sight of a lion, which was evidently approaching with the intention of satisfying his appetite with my poor carcass, and that without asking my consent. What was to be done in this horrible dilemma? I had not even a moment for reflection; my piece was only charged with swan-shot, and I had no other about me; however, though I could have no idea of killing such an animal with that weak kind of ammunition, yet I had some hopes of frightening him by the report, and perhaps of wounding him also. I immediately let fly, without waiting till he was within reach, and the report did but enrage him, for he now quickened his pace, and seemed to approach me full speed: I attempted to escape, but that only added (if an addition could be made) to my distress; for the moment I turned about, I found a large crocodile, with his mouth extended almost ready to receive me. On my right hand was the piece of water before mentioned, and on my left a deep precipice, said to have, as I have since learned, a

BETWEEN TWO EVILS

receptacle at the bottom for venomous creatures; in short, I gave myself up as lost, for the lion was now upon his hind legs, just in the act of seizing me; I fell involuntarily to the ground with fear, and, as it afterwards appeared, he sprang over me. I lay some time in a situation which no language can describe, expecting to feel his teeth or talons in some part of me every moment. After waiting in this prostrate situation a few seconds I heard a violent but unusual noise, different from any sound that had ever before assailed my ears; nor is it at all to be wondered at, when I inform you from whence it proceeded: after listening for some time I ventured to raise my head and look round, when, to my unspeakable joy, I perceived the lion had, by the eagerness with which he sprung at me, jumped forward as I fell, into the crocodile's mouth! which, as before observed, was wide open; the head of the one stuck in the throat of the other! and they were struggling to extricate themselves! I fortunately recollected my hunting knife, which was by my side; with this instrument I severed the lion's head at one blow, and the body fell at my feet! I then, with the butt end of my fowling piece, rammed the head farther into the throat of the crocodile, and destroyed him by suffocation, for he could neither gorge nor eject it.

Soon after I had thus gained a complete victory over my two powerful adversaries, my companion arrived in search of me; for finding I did not follow him into the wood, he returned, apprehending I had lost my way, or met with some accident.

After mutual congratulations we measured the crocodile, which was just forty feet in length.

As soon as we had related this extraordinary adventure to the governor, he sent a wagon and servants who brought home the two carcasses. The lion's skin was properly preserved with the hair on, after which it was made into tobacco pouches and presented by me, upon our return to Holland, to the burgomasters, who in return requested my acceptance of a thousand ducats.

The skin of the crocodile was stuffed in the

usual manner, and makes a capital article in their public museum at Amsterdam, where the exhibitor relates the whole story to each spectator, with such additions as he thinks proper.

II

I SET off from Rome on a journey to Russia, in the midst of winter, from a just notion that frost and snow must of course mend the roads, which every traveler had described as uncommonly bad through the northern parts of Germany, Poland, Courland, and Livonia. I went on horseback, as the most convenient manner of traveling; I was but lightly clothed, and of this I felt the inconvenience the more I advanced northeast. What must not a poor old man have suffered in that severe weather and climate, whom I saw on a bleak common in Poland, lying on the road, helpless, shivering and hardly having wherewithal to cover his nakedness? I pitied the poor soul: though I felt the severity of the air myself, I threw my mantle over him, and immediately I heard a voice from the heavens blessing me for that piece of charity, saying, "You will be rewarded, my son, for this in time."

I went on: night and darkness overtook me. No village was to be seen. The country was covered with snow, and I was unacquainted with the road.

I BEHELD HIM HANGING

Tired, I alighted and fastened my horse to something like a pointed stump of a tree, which appeared above the snow; for the sake of safety I placed my pistols under my arm, and lay down on the snow, where I slept so soundly that I did not open my eyes till full daylight. It is not easy to conceive my astonishment to find myself in the midst of a village, lying in a churchyard; nor was my horse to be seen, but I heard him soon after neigh somewhere above me. On looking upwards I beheld him hanging by his bridle to the weathercock of the steeple. Matters were now very plain to me: the village had been covered with snow over night; a sudden change of weather had taken place; I had sunk down to the churchyard whilst asleep, gently, and in the same proportion as the snow had melted away; and what in the dark I had taken to be a stump of a little tree appearing above the snow, to which I had tied my horse, proved to have been the cross or weathercock of the steeple!

Without long consideration, I took one of my pistols, shot the bridle in two, brought down the horse, and proceeded on my journey.

III

FOR several months (as it was some time before I could obtain a commission in the army) I was perfectly at liberty to sport away my time and money in the most gentlemanlike manner. You may easily imagine that I spent much of both out of town with such gallant fellows as knew how to make the most of an open forest country. The very recollection of those amusements gives me fresh spirits, and creates a warm wish for a repetition of them. One morning I saw, through the windows of my bedroom, that a large pond not far off was covered with wild ducks. In an instant I took my gun from the corner, ran downstairs, and out of the house in such a hurry that I imprudently struck my face against the doorpost. Fire flew out of my eyes, but it did not prevent my intention; I soon came within shot, when, leveling my piece, I observed to my sorrow, that even the flint had sprung from the cock by the violence of the shock I had just received. There was no time to be lost. I presently remembered the effect it had on my eyes, therefore opened the pan, leveled my piece against the wild fowls, and my fist against one of my eyes. A hearty blow drew sparks again; the shot went off, and I killed fifty brace of ducks, twenty widgeons, and three couple of teals.

IV

I DARE say you have heard of the hunter and sportsman's saint and protector, Saint Hubert, and of the noble stag which appeared to him in the forest, with the holy cross between his antlers. I have paid my homage to that saint every year in good fellowship, and seen this stag a thousand times either painted in churches, or embroidered in the stars of his knights; so that, upon the honor and conscience of a good sportsman, I hardly know whether there may not have been formerly, or whether there are not such crossed stags even at this present day. But let me rather tell what I have seen myself. Having one day spent all my shot, I found myself unexpectedly in presence of a stately stag, looking at me as unconcernedly as

WITH A CHERRY TREE BETWEEN HIS ANTLERS

if he had known of my empty pouches. I charged immediately with powder, and upon it a good handful of cherry-stones, for I had sucked the fruit as far as the hurry would permit. Thus I let fly at him, and hit him just on the middle of the forehead between his antlers; it stunned him—he staggered—yet he made off. A year or two after, being with a party in the same forest, I beheld a noble stag with a fine full-grown cherry tree above ten feet high between his antlers. I immediately recollected my former adventure, looked upon him as my property, and brought him to the ground by one shot, which at once gave me the haunch and cherry sauce; for the tree was covered with the richest fruit, the like I had never tasted before. Who knows but some passionate holy sportsman, or sporting abbot or bishop may have shot, planted and fixed the cross between the antlers of Saint Hubert's stag, in a manner similar to this?

V

I REMEMBER with pleasure and tenderness a superb Lithuanian horse, which no money could have bought. He became mine by an accident, which gave me an opportunity of showing my horsemanship to a great advantage. I was at Count Przobossky's noble country seat in Lithuania, and remained with the ladies at tea in the drawing-room, while the gentlemen were down in the yard to see a young horse of blood which had just arrived from the stud. We suddenly heard a noise of distress; I hastened downstairs, and found the horse so unruly that nobody durst approach or mount him. The most resolute horsemen stood dismayed and aghast; despondency was expressed in every countenance, when, in one leap, I was on his back, took him by surprise, and worked him quite into gentleness and obedience, with the best display of horsemanship I was master of. Fully to show this to the ladies, and save them unnecessary trouble, I forced him to leap in at one of the open windows of the tea room, walk round several times, pace, trot, and gallop, and at last made him mount the tea table, there to repeat his lessons in a pretty style of miniature which was exceedingly pleasing to the ladies, for he performed them amazingly well, and did not break either cup or saucer. It placed me so high in their opinion, and so well in that of the noble lord, that, with his usual politeness, he begged I would accept of this young horse, and ride him to conquest and honor in the campaign against the Turks, which was soon to be opened, under the command of Count Munich.

We had very hot work once in the van of the army, when we drove the Turks into Oczakow. My spirited Lithuanian had almost brought me into a scrape: I had an advanced forepost, and saw the enemy coming against me in a cloud of dust, which left me rather uncertain about their actual numbers and real intentions: to wrap myself up in a similar cloud was common prudence, but would not have much advanced my knowledge, or answered the end for which I had been sent out; therefore I let my flankers on both wings spread to the right and left, and make what dust they could, and I myself led on straight upon the enemy, to have a nearer sight of them; in this I was gratified, for they stood and fought, till, for fear of my flankers, they began to move off rather disorderly. This was the moment to fall upon them with spirit; we broke them entirely—made a terrible havoc amongst them, and drove them not only back to a walled town in their rear, but even through it, contrary to our most sanguine expectation.

The swiftness of my Lithuanian enabled me to be foremost in the pursuit; and seeing the enemy fairly flying through the opposite gate, I thought it would be prudent to stop in the market place, to order the men to rendezvous. I stopped, gentlemen; but judge of my astonishment when in this market place I saw not one of my hussars about me! Are they scouring the other streets? or what is become of them? They could not be far off, and must, at all events, soon join me. In that expectation I walked my panting Lithuanian to a spring in this market place, and let him drink. He drank uncommonly, with an eagerness not to be satisfied, but natural enough; for when I looked round for my men, what should I see, gentlemen! the hind part of the poor creature—croup and legs—were missing, as if he had been cut in two, and the water ran out as it came in, without refreshing or doing him any good! How it could have happened was quite a mystery to me, till I returned with him to the town gate. There I saw that when I rushed in pell-mell with the flying enemy, they had dropped the portcullis (a heavy falling door, with sharp spikes at the bottom, let down suddenly to prevent the entrance of an enemy into a fortified town) unperceived by me, which had totally cut off his hind part, that still lay quivering on the outside of the gate. It would have been an irreparable loss, had not our farrier contrived to bring both parts together while hot. He sewed them up with sprigs and young shoots of laurels that were at hand; the wound healed, and, what could not have happened but to so glorious a horse, the sprigs took root in his body, grew up, and formed a bower over me; so that afterwards I could go upon many other expeditions in the shade of my own and my horse's laurels.

VI

SUCCESS was not always with me. I had the misfortune to be overpowered by numbers, to be made prisoner of war; and, what is worse, but always usual among the Turks, to be sold for a slave. In that state of humiliation my daily task was not very hard and laborious, but rather singular and irksome. It was to drive the Sultan's bees every morning to their pasture grounds, to attend them all the day long, and against night to drive them back to their hives. One evening I missed a bee, and soon observed that two bears had fallen upon her to tear her to pieces for the honey she carried. I had nothing like an offensive weapon in my hands but the silver hatchet, which is the badge of the Sultan's gardeners and farmers. I threw it at the robbers, with an intention to frighten them away, and set the poor bee at liberty; but, by an unlucky turn of my arm, it flew upwards, and continued rising till it reached the moon. How should I recover it? how fetch it down again? I recollected that

Turkey-beans grow very quick, and run up to an astonishing height. I planted one immediately; it grew, and actually fastened itself to one of the moon's horns. I had no more to do now but to climb up by it into the moon, where I safely arrived, and had a troublesome piece of business before I could find my silver hatchet, in a place where everything has the brightness of silver; at last, however, I found it in a heap of chaff and chopped straw. I was now for returning: but, alas! the heat of the sun had dried up my bean; it was totally useless for my descent; so I fell to work and twisted me a rope of that chopped straw, as long and as well as I could make it. This I fastened to one of the moon's horns, and slid down to the end of it. Here I held myself fast with the left hand, and with the hatchet in my right, I cut the long, now useless end of the upper part, which, when tied to the lower end, brought me a good deal lower: this repeated splicing and tying of the rope did not improve its quality, or bring me down to the Sultan's farm. I was four or five miles from the earth at least when it broke; I fell to the ground with such amazing violence that I found myself stunned, and in a hole nine fathoms deep at least, made by the weight of my body falling from so great a height: I recovered, but knew not how to get out again; however, I dug slopes or steps with my finger-nails, and easily accomplished it.

Peace was soon after concluded with the Turks, and gaining my liberty I left Saint

Petersburg at the time of that singular revolution, when the emperor in his cradle, his mother, the Duke of Brunswick, her father, Field-Marshal Munich, and many others were sent to Siberia. The winter was then so uncommonly severe all over Europe that ever since the sun seems to be frost-bitten. At my return to this place I felt on the road greater inconveniences than those I had experienced on my setting out.

I traveled post, and finding myself in a narrow lane, bade the postilion give a signal with his horn, that other travelers might not meet us in the narrow passage. He blew with all his might; but his endeavors were in vain; he could not make the horn sound, which was unaccountable, and rather unfortunate, for soon after we found ourselves in the presence of another coach coming the other way: there was no proceeding; however, I got out of my carriage, and being pretty strong, placed it, wheels and all, upon my head: I then jumped over a hedge about nine feet high (which, considering the weight of the coach, was rather difficult) into a field, and came out again by another jump into the road beyond the other carriage: I then went back for the horses, and placing one upon my head, and the other under my left arm, by the same means brought them to my coach, put to, and proceeded to an inn at the end of our stage. I should have told you that the horse under my arm was very spirited, and not above four years old; in making my second spring over the hedge, he expressed great dislike to that violent kind of motion by kicking and snorting; however, I confined his hind legs by putting them into my coat pocket. After we arrived at the inn my postilion and I refreshed ourselves; he hung his horn on a peg near the kitchen fire; I sat on the other side.

Suddenly we heard a *tereng! tereng! teng! teng!* We looked round, and now found the reason why the postilion had not been able to sound his horn; his tunes were frozen up in the horn, and came out now by thawing, plain enough, and much to the credit of the driver; so that the honest fellow entertained us for some time with a variety of tunes, without putting his mouth to the horn—The King of Prussia's March—Over the Hill and over the Dale—with many other favorite tunes; at length the thawing entertainment concluded, as I shall this short account of my Russian travels.

VII

I EMBARKED at Portsmouth, in a first-rate English man-of-war, of one hundred guns, and fourteen hundred men, for North America. Nothing worth relating happened till we arrived within three hundred leagues of the river Saint Lawrence when the ship struck with amazing force against (as we supposed) a rock; however, upon heaving the lead, we could find no bottom, even with three hundred fathom. What made this circumstance the more wonderful, and indeed beyond all comprehension, was, that the violence of the shock was such that we lost our rudder, broke our bowsprit in the middle, and split all our masts from top to bottom, two of which went by the board; a poor fellow, who was aloft, furling the mainsheet, was flung at least three leagues from the ship; but he fortunately saved his life by laying hold of the tail of a large sea-gull, who brought him back, and lodged him on the very spot from whence he was thrown. Another proof of the violence of the shock was the force with which the people between decks were driven against the floors above them; my head particularly was pressed into my stomach, where it continued some months before it recovered its natural situation. Whilst we were all in a state of astonishment at the general and unaccountable confusion in which we were involved, the whole was suddenly explained by the appearance of a large whale, who had been basking, asleep, within sixteen feet of the surface of the water. This animal was so much displeased with the disturbance which our ship had given him, for in our passage we had with our rudder scratched his nose, that he beat in all the gallery and part of the quarter deck with his tail, and almost at the same instant took the main-sheet anchor, which was suspended, as it usually is, from the head, between his teeth, and ran away with the ship, at least sixty leagues, at the rate of twelve leagues an hour, when fortunately the cable broke, and we lost both the whale and the anchor. However, upon our return to Europe, some months after, we found the same whale within a few leagues of the same spot, floating dead upon the water; it measured above half a mile in length. As we could take but a small quantity of such a monstrous animal on board, we got our boats out, and with much difficulty cut off his head, where, to our great joy, we found the anchor, and above forty fathom of the cable concealed on the left side of his mouth, just under his tongue. (Perhaps this was the cause of his death, as that side of his tongue was much swelled, with a great degree of inflammation.) This was the only extraordinary circumstance on this voyage.

VIII

WE ALL remember Captain Phipp's (now Lord Mulgrave) last voyage of discovery to the north. I accompanied the Captain, not as an officer, but a private friend. When we arrived in a high northern latitude I was viewing the objects around me with the telescope, when I thought I saw two large white bears in violent action upon a body of ice considerably above the masts, and about half a league distant. I immediately took my carbine, slung it across my shoulder, and ascended the ice. When I arrived at the top, the unevenness of the surface made my approach to those animals troublesome and hazardous beyond expression: sometimes hideous cavities opposed me, which I was obliged to spring over;

in other parts the surface was as smooth as a mirror, and I was continually falling: as I approached near enough to reach them, I found they were only at play. I immediately began to calculate the value of their skins, for they were each as large as a well-fed ox: unfortunately the very instant I was presenting my carbine my right foot slipped, and I fell upon my back, and the violence of the blow deprived me totally of my senses for nearly half an hour; however, when I recovered, judge of my surprise at finding one of those large animals I have just been describing had turned me upon my face, and was just laying hold of the waistband of my breeches, which were then new and made of leather: he was certainly going to carry me feet foremost, God knows where, when I took this knife (showing a large clasp knife) out of my side pocket, made a chop at one of his hind feet, and cut off three of his toes; he immediately let me drop, and roared most horribly. I took up my carbine, and fired at him as he ran off; he fell directly. The noise of the piece roused several thousands of these white bears, who were asleep upon the ice within half a mile of me; they came immediately to the spot. There was no time to be lost. A most fortunate thought arrived in my pericranium just at that instant. I took off the skin and head of the dead bear in half the time that some people would be in skinning a rabbit, and wrapped myself in it, placing my own head directly under bruin's; the whole herd came round me immediately, and my apprehensions threw me into a most piteous situation to be sure: however, my scheme turned out a most admirable one for my own safety. They all came smelling, and evidently took me for a brother bruin: I wanted nothing but bulk to make an excellent counterfeit: however, I saw several cubs amongst them not much larger than myself. After they had all smelt me, and the body of their deceased companion, whose skin was now become my protector, we seemed very sociable, and I found I could mimic all their actions tolerably well; but at growling, roaring, and hugging, they were quite my masters. I began now to think how I might turn the general confidence which I had created amongst these animals to my advantage.

I had heard an old army surgeon say a wound in the spine was instant death. I now determined to try the experiment, and had again recourse to my knife, with which I struck the largest in the back of the neck, near the shoulders, but under great apprehensions, not doubting but the creature would, if he survived the stab, tear me to pieces. However, I was remarkably fortunate, for he fell dead at my feet without making the least noise. I was now resolved to demolish them every one in the same manner, which I accomplished without the least difficulty; for, although they saw their companions fall, they had no suspicion of either the cause or the effect. When they all lay dead before me, I felt myself a second Samson, having slain my thousands.

To make short of the story, I went back to the

ship, and borrowed three parts of the crew to assist me in skinning them, and carrying the hams on board, which we did in a few hours, and loaded the ship with them. As to the other parts of the animals, they were thrown into the sea, though I doubt not but the whole would eat as well as the legs, were they properly cured.

IX

HAVE already informed you of one trip I have made to the moon in search of my silver hatchet: I afterwards made another in a much pleasanter manner, and stayed in it long enough to take notice of several things, which I will endeavor to describe as accurately as my memory will permit.

I went on a voyage of discovery at the request of a distant relation, who had a strange notion that there were people to be found equal in magnitude to those described by Gulliver in the empire of Brobdingnag. For my part I always treated that account as fabulous; however, to oblige him, for he had made me his heir, I undertook it, and sailed for the South Seas, where we arrived without meeting with anything remarkable, except some flying men and women who were playing at leapfrog, and dancing minuets in the air.

On the eighteenth day, after we had passed the island of Otaheite, a hurricane blew our ship at least one thousand leagues above the surface of the water, and kept it at that height till a fresh gale arising filled the sails in every part, and onwards we traveled at a prodigious rate; thus we proceeded above the clouds for six weeks. At last we discovered a great land in the sky, like a shining island, round and bright, where, coming into a convenient harbor, we went on shore, and soon found it was inhabited. Below us we saw another earth, containing cities, trees, mountains, rivers, seas, etc., which we conjectured was this world, which we had left. Here we saw huge figures riding upon vultures of a prodigious size, and each of them having three heads. To form some idea of the magnitude of these birds, I must inform you that each of their wings is as wide and six times the length of the main-sheet of our vessel, which was about six hundred tons burden. Thus, instead of riding upon horses, as we do in this world, the inhabitants of the moon (for we now found we were in Madam Luna) fly about on these birds. The king, we found, was engaged in a war with the sun, and he offered me a commission, but I declined the honor his majesty intended me. Everything in *this* world is of extraordinary magnitude! a common flea being much larger than one of our sheep: in making war their principal weapons are radishes, which are used as darts: those who are wounded by them die immediately. Their shields are made of mushrooms, and their darts (when radishes are out of season) of the tops of asparagus. Some of the natives of the dog-star are to be seen here; commerce tempts them to ramble; and their faces are like large mastiffs', with their eyes near the lower end or tip of their noses: they have no eyelids, but cover their eyes with the end of their tongues when they go to sleep; they are generally twenty feet high. As to the natives of the moon, none of them are less in stature than thirty-six feet: they are not called the human species, but the cooking animals, for they all dress their food by fire, as we do, but lose no time at their meals, as they open their left side, and place the whole quantity at once in their stomach, then shut it again till the same day in the next month; for they never indulge themselves with food more than twelve times a year, or once a month. All but gluttons and epicures must prefer this method to ours.

There is but one sex either of the cooking or any other animals in the moon; they are all produced from trees of various sizes and foliage; that which produces the cooking animal, or human species, is much more beautiful than any of the others; it has large, straight boughs and flesh-colored leaves, and the fruit it produces are nuts or pods, with hard shells, at least two yards long; when they become ripe, which is known from their changing color, they are gathered with great care, and laid by as long as they think proper; when they choose to animate the seed of these nuts, they throw them into a large cauldron of boiling water, which opens the shells in a few hours, and out jumps the creature.

Nature forms their minds for different pursuits before they come into the world; from one shell comes forth a warrior, from another a philosopher, from a third a divine, from a fourth a lawyer, from a fifth a farmer, from a sixth a clown, etc., etc., and all of them immediately begin to perfect themselves by practicing what they before knew only in theory.

When they grow old they do not die, but turn into air and dissolve like smoke! As for their drink, they need none. They have but one finger upon each hand, with which they perform everything in as perfect a manner as we do who have four besides the thumb. Their heads are placed under their right arm, and when they are going to travel or about any violent exercise, they generally leave them at home, for they can consult them at any distance; this is a very common practice; and when those of rank or quality among the Lunarians have an inclination to see what's going forward among the common people, they stay at home, *i. e.*, the body stays at home and sends the head only, which is suffered to be present *incog.*, and return at pleasure with an account of what has passed.

Their eyes they can take in and out of their places when they please, and can see as well with them in their hand as in their head! and if by any accident they lose or damage one, they can borrow or purchase another, and see as clearly with it as their own. Dealers in eyes are on that account very numerous in most parts of the moon, and in this article alone all the inhabitants are whimsical: sometimes green and sometimes yellow eyes are the fashion. I know these things appear strange; but if the shadow of a doubt can remain on any person's mind, I say, let him take a voyage there himself, and then he will know I am a traveler of veracity.

X

DURING the early part of his present Majesty's reign I had some business with a distant relation who then lived on the Isle of Thanet; it was a family dispute, and not likely to be finished soon. I made it a practice during my residence there, the weather being fine, to walk out every morning. After a few of these excursions, I observed an object upon a great eminence about three miles distant: I extended my walk to it, and found the ruins of an ancient temple: I approached it with admiration and astonishment; the traces of grandeur and magnificence which yet remained were evident proofs of its former splendor: here I could not help lamenting the ravages and devastations of time, of which that once noble structure exhibited such a melancholy proof. I walked round it several times, meditating on the fleeting and transitory nature of all terrestrial things; on the eastern end were the remains of a lofty tower, near forty feet high, overgrown with ivy, the top apparently flat; I surveyed it on every side very minutely, thinking that if I could gain its summit I should enjoy the most delightful prospect of the circumjacent country. Animated with this hope, I resolved, if possible, to gain the summit, which I at length effected by means of the ivy, though not without great difficulty and danger; the top I found covered with this evergreen, except a large chasm in the middle. After I had surveyed with pleasing wonder the beauties of art and nature that conspired to enrich the scene, curiosity prompted me to sound the opening in the middle, in order to ascertain its depth, as I entertained a suspicion that it might probably communicate with some unexplored subterranean cavern in the hill; but having no line, I was at a loss how to proceed. After revolving the matter in my thoughts for some time, I resolved to drop a stone down and listen to the echo; having found one that answered my purpose, I placed myself over the hole, with one foot on each side, and stooping down to listen, I dropped the stone, which I had no sooner done than I heard a rustling below, and suddenly a monstrous eagle put up its head right opposite my face, and rising up with irresistible force, carried me away, seated on its shoulders: I instantly grasped it around the neck, which was large enough to fill my arms, and its wings, when extended, were ten yards from one extremity to the other. As it rose with a regular ascent, my seat was perfectly easy, and I enjoyed the prospect below with inexpressible pleasure. It hovered over Margate for some time, was seen by several people, and many shots were fired at it; one ball hit the heel of my shoe, but did me no injury. It then directed its course to Dover Cliff, where it alighted, and I thought

THE EAGLE CARRIED ME AWAY

of dismounting, but was prevented by a sudden discharge of musketry from a party of marines that were exercising on the beach; the balls flew about my head, and rattled on the feathers of the eagle like hailstones, yet I could not perceive it had received any injury. It instantly reascended and flew over the sea towards Calais, but so very high that the Channel seemed to be no broader than the Thames at London Bridge. In a quarter of an hour I found myself over a thick wood in France, when the eagle descended very rapidly, which caused me to slip down to the back part of its head; but as it alighted on a large tree, and raised its head, I recovered my seat as before, but saw no possibility of disengaging myself without the danger of being killed by the fall; so I determined to sit fast, thinking it would carry me to the Alps, or some other high mountain, where I could dismount without any danger. After resting a few minutes it took wing, flew several times round the wood, and screamed loud enough to be heard across the English Channel. In a few minutes one of the same species arose out of the wood, and flew directly towards us; it surveyed me with evident marks of displeasure, and came very near me. After flying several times round, they both directed their course to the southwest. I soon observed that the one I rode upon could not keep pace with the other, but inclined towards the earth, on account of my weight; its companion perceiving this, turned round and placed itself in such a position that the other could rest its head on its rump; in this manner they proceeded till noon, when I saw the rock of Gibraltar very distinctly. The day being clear, notwithstanding my degree of elevation, the earth's surface appeared just like a map, where land, sea, lakes, rivers, mountains, and the like were perfectly distinguishable; and having some knowledge of geography, I was at no loss to determine what part of the globe I was in.

While I was contemplating this wonderful

prospect a dreadful howling suddenly began all around me, and in a moment I was invested by thousands of small black, deformed, frightful-looking creatures, who pressed me on all sides in such a manner that I could neither move hand nor foot: but I had not been in their possession more than ten minutes when I heard the most delightful music that can possibly be imagined, which was suddenly changed into a noise the most awful and tremendous, to which the report of a cannon, or the loudest claps of thunder could bear no more proportion than the gentle zephyrs of the evening to the most dreadful hurricane; but the shortness of its duration prevented all those fatal effects which a prolongation of it would certainly have been attended with.

The music commenced, and I saw a great number of the most beautiful little creatures seize the other party, and throw them with great violence into something like a snuffbox, which they shut down, and one threw it away with incredible velocity; then turning to me, he said they whom he had secured were a party of devils, who had wandered from their proper habitation; and that the vehicle in which they were inclosed would fly with unabating rapidity for ten thousand years, when it would burst of its own accord, and the devils would recover their liberty and faculties, as at the present moment. He had no sooner finished this relation than the music ceased, and they all disappeared, leaving me in a state of mind bordering on the confines of despair.

When I had recomposed myself a little, I looked before me with inexpressible pleasure, and observed that the eagles were preparing to light on the peak of Teneriffe: they descended to the top of a rock, but seeing no possible means of escape if I dismounted, I determined to remain where I was. The eagles sat down seemingly fatigued, when the heat of the sun soon caused them both to fall asleep, nor did I long resist its fascinating power. In the cool of the evening, when the sun had retired below the horizon, I was roused from sleep by the eagle moving under me; and having stretched myself along its back, I sat up, and reassumed my traveling position, when they both took wing, and having placed themselves as before, directed their course to South America. The moon shining bright during the whole night, I had a fine view of all the islands in those seas.

About the break of day we reached the great continent of America, that part called Terra-Firma, and descended on the top of a very high mountain. At this time, the moon, far distant in the west, and obscured by dark clouds, but just afforded light sufficient for me to discover a kind of shrubbery all around bearing fruit something like cabbages, which the eagles began to feed on very eagerly. I endeavored to discover my situation, but fogs and passing clouds involved me in the thickest darkness, and what rendered the scene still more shocking was the tremendous howling of wild beasts, some of which appeared to be very near: however, I determined to keep my seat, imagining that the eagle would carry me away if any of them should make a hostile attempt. When daylight began to appear I thought of examining the fruit which I had seen the eagles eat, and as some was hanging which I could easily come at, I took out my knife and cut a slice; but how great was my surprise to see that it had all the appearance of roast beef regularly mixed, both fat and lean! I tasted it, and found it well-flavored and delicious, then cut several large slices, and put in my pocket, where I found a crust of bread which I had brought from Margate; took it out, and found three musket-balls that had been lodged in it on Dover cliff. I extracted them, and cutting a few slices more, made a hearty meal of bread and cold beef fruit. I then cut down two of the largest that grew near me, and tying them together with one of my garters, hung them over the eagle's neck for another occasion, filling my pockets at the same time. While I was settling these affairs, I observed a large fruit like an inflated bladder which I wished to try an experiment upon: and when I struck my knife into one of them, a fine pure liquor like Holland gin rushed out, which the eagles observing, eagerly drank up from the ground. I cut down the bladder as fast as I could, and saved about half a pint in the bottom of it, which I tasted, and could not distinguish it from the best mountain wine. I drank it all, and found myself greatly refreshed. By this time the eagles began to stagger against the shrubs. I endeavored to keep my seat, but was soon thrown to some distance among the bushes. In attempting to rise, I put my hand upon a large hedgehog, which happened to lie among the grass upon its back: it instantly closed round my hand, so that I found it impossible to shake it off. I struck it several times against the ground without effect; but while I was thus employed I heard a rustling among the shrubbery, and looking up, I saw a huge animal within three yards of me; I could make no defence, but held out both my hands, when it rushed upon me and seized that on which the hedgehog was fixed. My hand being soon released, I ran to some distance, where I saw the creature suddenly drop down and expire with the hedgehog in its throat. When the danger was past, I went to view the eagles, and found them lying on the grass fast asleep, being intoxicated with the liquor they had drunk. Indeed, I found myself considerably elevated by it, and seeing everything quiet, I began to search for some more, which I soon found; and having cut down two large bladders, about a gallon each, I tied them together, and hung them over the neck of the other eagle, and the two smaller ones I tied with a cord round my own waist. Having secured a good stock of provisions, and perceiving the eagles begin to recover, I again took my seat. In half an hour they arose majestically from the place, without taking the least notice of their encumbrance. Each reassumed its former station; and directing their course to the northward, they crossed the Gulf of Mexico, entered North America, and steered directly for the Polar regions, which gave me the finest opportunity of viewing this vast continent that can possibly be imagined.

Before we entered the frigid zone the cold began to affect me; but piercing one of my bladders I took a draught, and found that it could make no impression on me afterwards. Passing over Hudson's Bay, I saw several of the company's ships lying at anchor, and many tribes of Indians marching with their furs to market.

By this time I was so reconciled to my seat, and become such an expert rider, that I could sit up and look around me; but in general I lay along the eagle's neck, grasping it in my arms, with my hands immersed in its feathers, in order to keep them warm.

In these cold climates I observed that the eagles flew with greater rapidity, in order, I suppose, to keep their blood in circulation. In passing Baffin's Bay I saw several large Greenlandmen to the eastward, and many surprising mountains of ice in those seas.

While I was surveying these wonders of nature it occurred to me that this was a good opportunity to discover the northwest passage, if any such thing existed, and not only obtain the reward offered by government, but the honor of a discovery pregnant with so many advantages to every European nation. But while my thoughts were absorbed in this pleasing reverie I was alarmed by the first eagle striking its head against a solid transparent substance, and in a moment that which I rode experienced the same fate, and both fell down seemingly dead.

Here our lives must inevitably have terminated, had not a sense of danger and the singularity of my situation inspired me with a degree of skill and dexterity which enabled us to fall near two miles perpendicular with as little inconvenience as if we had been let down with a rope; for no sooner did I perceive the eagles strike against a frozen cloud, which is very common near the poles, than (they being close together) I laid myself along the back of the foremost and took hold of its wings to keep them extended, at the same time stretching out my legs behind to support the wings of the other. This had the desired effect, and we descended very safe on a mountain of ice, which I supposed to be about three miles above the level of the sea.

I dismounted, unloaded the eagles, opened one of the bladders, and administered some of the liquor to each of them, without once considering that the horrors of destruction seemed to have conspired against me. The roaring of waves, crashing of ice, and the howling of bears, conspired to form a scene the most awful and tremendous; but, notwithstanding this, my concern for the recovery of the eagles was so great that I was insensible of the danger to which I was exposed. Having rendered them every assistance in my power, I stood over them in painful anxiety, fully sensible that it was only by means of them that I could possibly be delivered from these abodes of despair.

But suddenly a monstrous bear began to roar behind me, with a voice like thunder. I turned round, and seeing the creature just ready to devour me, having the bladder of liquor in my hands, through fear I squeezed it so hard that it burst, and the liquor, flying in the eyes of the animal, totally deprived it of sight. It instantly turned from me, ran away in a state of distraction, and soon fell over a precipice of ice into the sea, where I saw it no more.

The danger being over, I again turned my attention to the eagles, whom I found in a fair way of recovery, and suspecting that they were faint for want of victuals, I took one of the beef fruit, cut it into small slices, and presented them with it, which they devoured with avidity.

Having given them plenty to eat and drink, and disposed of the remainder of my provisions, I took possession of my seat as before. After composing myself and adjusting everything in the best manner, I began to eat and drink very heartily; and through the effects of the mountain, as I called it, was very cheerful, and began to sing a few verses of a song which I had learned when I was a boy: but the noise soon alarmed the eagles, who had been asleep, through the quantity of liquor which they had drunk, and they arose seemingly much terrified. Happily for me, however, when I was feeding them I had accidentally turned their heads towards the southeast, which course they pursued with a rapid motion. In a few hours I saw the Western Isles, and soon after had the inexpressible pleasure of seeing Old England. I took no notice of the seas or islands over which I passed.

The eagles descended gradually as they drew near the shore, intending, as I supposed, to alight on one of the Welsh mountains; but when they came to the distance of about sixty yards, two guns were fired at them, loaded with balls, one of which penetrated a bladder of liquor that hung to my waist; the other entered the breast of the foremost eagle, who fell to the ground, while that which I rode, having received no injury, flew away with amazing swiftness.

This circumstance alarmed me exceedingly, and I began to think it was impossible for me to escape with my life; but recovering a little, I once more looked down upon the earth, when, to my inexpressible joy, I saw Margate at a little distance, and the eagle descending on the old tower whence it had carried me on the morning of the day before. It no sooner came down than I threw myself off, happy to find that I was once more restored to the world. The eagle flew away in a few minutes, and I sat down to compose my fluttering spirits, which I did in a few hours.

I soon paid a visit to my friends, and related these adventures. Amazement stood in every countenance; their congratulations on my returning in safety were repeated with an unaffected degree of pleasure, and we passed the evening as we are doing now, every person present paying the highest compliments to my COURAGE and VERACITY.

THE FIDDLING PARSON

ADAPTED FROM THE AUTOBIOGRAPHY OF DAVY CROCKETT

LITTLE Rock lay on my way to Texas, and as I left it several companions accompanied me a short distance from the village. We were talking briskly together as we drew near the Washita River, and imagined ourselves the only travelers in that vicinity. In a lull in the conversation we were somewhat startled by the sound of music. We checked our horses and listened, while the music continued.

"What can all that mean?" asked I.

"Blast my old shoes if I know," said one of the party.

We listened again and heard *Hail Columbia! Happy Land!* played in first-rate style.

"That's fine," said I.

"Fine as silk, Colonel, and a leetle finer," said another; "but hark! the tune is changed."

We listened again, and the musician struck up in a brisk and lively manner, *Over the Water to Charlie.*

"That's mighty mysterious," said one of my friends.

"Can't cipher it out nohow," said another.

"A notch beyant my measure," said a third.

"Then let's see what it is," said I, and off we dashed at a rapid gait.

As we approached the river, we saw to the right of the road a new clearing on a hill, from which several men were running down toward the river like wild Indians. There appeared no time to be lost, so we all cut ahead for the crossing. All this time the music kept growing stronger and stronger, every note distinctly saying, *Over the Water to Charlie.*

When we reached the crossing, we were astonished to see a man seated in a sulky in the middle of the river and playing for his life on a fiddle. The horse was up to his middle in water, and it seemed as if the flimsy vehicle was ready to be swept away by the current. Still the fiddler fiddled on composedly as if his life had been insured. We thought he was mad, and shouted to him. He heard us and stopped the music.

"You have missed the crossing," shouted one of the men.

"I know I have," replied the fiddler.

"If you go ten feet farther you will be drowned."

"I know I shall."

"Turn back," cried the man.

"I can't," said the fiddler.

"Then how the deuce will you get out?"

"I'm sure I don't know; come and help me."

The men from the clearing, who understood the river, took our horses, rode up to the sulky, and after some difficulty succeeded in bringing the traveler safe to shore. Then we recognized him as the worthy parson, who had played for us at a puppet show in Little Rock.

THE PARSON FIDDLED

"You have had a narrow escape," said we.

"I found that out an hour ago," he said. "I have been fiddling to the fishes all the time, and played everything I can play without notes."

"What made you think of fiddling in the time of such peril?" he was asked.

"I have found in my progress through life,"

said he, "that there is nothing so well calculated to draw people together as the sound of a fiddle. I might bawl for help till I was hoarse, and no one would stir a peg, but as soon as people hear the scraping of a fiddle, they will quit all other business and come to the spot in flocks."

We laughed heartily at the knowledge the parson showed of human nature; and he was right.

WE PLAN A RIVER TRIP[1]

THERE were four of us—George, and William Samuel Harris, and myself, and Montmorency. We were sitting in my room, smoking and talking about how bad we were—bad from a medical point of view I mean, of course.

We were all feeling seedy, and we were getting quite nervous about it. Harris said he felt such extraordinary fits of giddiness come over him at times, that he hardly knew what he was doing; and then George said that *he* had fits of giddiness, too, and hardly knew what he was doing. With me, it was my liver that was out of order. I knew it was my liver that was out of order, because I had just been reading a patent liver-pill circular, in which were detailed the various symptoms by which a man could tell when his liver was out of order. I had them all.

It is a most extraordinary thing, but I never read a patent medicine advertisement without being impelled to the conclusion that I am suffering from the particular disease therein dealt with, in its most virulent form. The diagnosis seems in every case to correspond exactly with all the sensations that I have ever felt.

I remember going to the British Museum one

1. This selection, with *On Comic Songs*, which follows, is taken from *Three Men in a Boat*, by Jerome K. Jerome. The complete title of the book is *Three Men in a Boat* (*To say nothing of the Dog*).

day to read up the treatment for some slight ailment of which I had a touch—hay fever, I fancy it was. I got down the book, and read all I came to read; and then, in an unthinking moment, I idly turned the leaves, and began indolently to study diseases generally. I forget which was the first distemper I plunged into—some fearful, devastating scourge, I know—and, before I had glanced half down the list of "premonitory symptoms," it was borne in upon me that I had fairly got it.

I sat for a while, frozen with horror; and then, in the listlessness of despair, I again turned over the pages. I came to typhoid fever—read the symptoms—discovered that I had typhoid fever, must have had it for months without knowing it—wondered what else I had got; turned up Saint Vitus's Dance—found, as I had expected, that I had that, too—began to get interested in my case, and determined to sift it to the bottom, and so started alphabetically—read up ague, and learned that I was sickening for it, and that the acute stage would commence in about another fortnight. Bright's disease, I was relieved to find, I had only in a modified form, and, so far as that was concerned, I might live for years. Cholera I had, with severe complications; and diphtheria I seemed to have been born with. I plodded conscientiously through the twenty-six letters, and the only malady I could conclude I had not got was housemaid's knee.

I felt rather hurt about this at first; it seemed somehow to be a sort of slight. Why hadn't I

WHY HADN'T I GOT HOUSEMAID'S KNEE?

got housemaid's knee? Why this invidious reservation? After a while, however, less grasping feelings prevailed. I reflected that I had every other known malady in the pharmacology, and grew less selfish, and determined to do without housemaid's knee. Gout, in its most malignant stage, it would appear, had seized me without my being aware of it; and zymosis I had evidently been suffering with from boyhood. There were no more diseases after zymosis, so I concluded there was nothing else the matter with me.

I sat and pondered. I thought what an interesting case I must be from a medical point of view, what an acquisition I should be to a class! Students would have no need to "walk the hospitals," if they had me. I was a hospital in myself. All they need do would be to walk round me, and, after that, take their diplomas.

Then I wondered how long I had to live. I tried to examine myself. I felt my pulse. I could not at first feel any pulse at all. Then, all of a sudden, it seemed to start off. I pulled out my watch and timed it. I made a hundred and forty-seven to the minute. I tried to feel my heart. I could not feel my heart. It had stopped beating. I have since been induced to come to the opinion that it must have been there all the time, and must have been beating, but I cannot account for it. I patted myself all over my front, from what I call my waist up to my head, and I went a bit round each side, and a little way up the back. But I could not feel or hear anything. I tried to look at my tongue. I stuck it out as far as ever it would go, and I shut one eye, and tried to examine it with the other. I could only see the tip, and the only thing that I could gain from that was to feel more certain than before that I had scarlet fever.

I had walked into that reading-room a happy, healthy man. I crawled out a decrepit wreck.

I went to my medical man. He was an old chum of mine, and feels my pulse, and looks at my tongue, and talks about the weather, all for nothing, when I fancy I'm ill; so I thought I would do him a good turn by going to him now. "What a doctor wants," I said, "is practice. He shall have me. He will get more practice out of me than out of seventeen hundred of your ordinary, commonplace patients, with only one or two diseases each." So I went straight up and saw him, and he said:

"Well, what's the matter with you?"

I said:

"I will not take up your time, dear boy, with telling you what is the matter with me. Life is brief, and you might pass away before I had finished. But I will tell you what is not the matter with me. I have not got housemaid's knee. Why I have not got housemaid's knee, I cannot tell you; but the fact remains that I have not got it. Everything else, however, I *have* got.

And I told him how I came to discover it all.

Then he opened me and looked down me, and clutched hold of my wrist, and then hit me over the chest when I wasn't expecting it—a cowardly thing to do, I call it—and immediately afterward butted me with the side of his head. After that, he sat down and wrote out a prescription, and folded it up and gave it to me, and I put it in my pocket and went out.

I did not open it. I took it to the nearest

chemist's, and handed it in. The man read it, and then handed it back.

He said he didn't keep it.

I said:

"You are a chemist?"

"I am a chemist. If I were a coöperative store and family hotel combined, I might be able to oblige you. Being only a chemist hampers me."

I read the prescription. It ran:

"1 lb. beefsteak, with
1 pt. bitter beer
every six hours.
1 ten-mile walk every morning.
1 bed at 11 sharp every night.
And don't stuff up your head with things you don't understand."

I followed the directions, with the happy result—speaking for myself—that my life was preserved, and is still going on.

* * * * * * * *

George said:

"Let's go up the river."

He said we should have fresh air, exercise and quiet; the constant change of scene would occupy our minds (including what there was of Harris's); and the hard work would give us an appetite, and make us sleep well.

Harris said he didn't think George ought to do anything that would have a tendency to make him sleepier than he always was, as it might be dangerous. He said he didn't very well understand how George was going to sleep any more than he did now, seeing that there were only twenty-four hours in each day, summer and winter, alike; but thought that if he *did* sleep any more, he might just as well be dead, and so save his board and lodging.

Harris said, however, that the river would suit him to a "T." It suited me to a "T," too, and Harris and I both said it was a good idea of George's; and we said it in a tone that seemed to imply somehow that we were surprised that George should have come out so sensible.

The only one who was not struck with the suggestion was Montmorency. He never did care for the river, did Montmorency.

"It's all very well for you fellows," he says; "you like it, but *I* don't. There's nothing for me to do. Scenery is not in my line, and I don't smoke. If I see a rat, you won't stop; and if I go to sleep, you get fooling about with the boat, and slop me overboard. If you ask me, I call the whole thing bally foolishness."

We were three to one, however, and the motion was carried.

* * * * * * * *

We made a list of the things to be taken, and a pretty lengthy one it was, before we parted that evening. The next day, which was Friday, we got them all together, and met in the evening to pack. We got a big Gladstone for the clothes, and a couple of hampers for the victuals and the cooking utensils. We moved the table up against the window, piled everything in a heap in the middle of the floor, and sat round and looked at it. I said I'd pack.

I rather pride myself on my packing. Packing is one of those many things that I feel I know more about than any other person living. (It surprises me myself, sometimes, how many of these subjects there are.) I impressed the fact upon George and Harris, and told them they had better leave the whole matter entirely to me. They fell into the suggestion with a readiness that had something uncanny about it. George put on a pipe and spread himself over the easy-chair, and Harris cocked his legs on the table and lit a cigar.

This was hardly what I intended. What I meant, of course, was, that I should boss the job, and that Harris and George should potter about under my directions, I pushing them aside every now and then with, "Oh, you——!" "Here, let me do it." "There you are, simple enough!" —really teaching them, as you might say. Their taking it in the way they did irritated me. There is nothing does irritate me more than seeing other people sitting about doing nothing when I'm working.

I lived with a man once who used to make me mad that way. He would loll on the sofa and watch me doing things by the hour together, following me round the room with his eyes, wherever I went. He said it did him real good to look on at me, messing about. He said it made him feel that life was not an idle dream to be gaped and

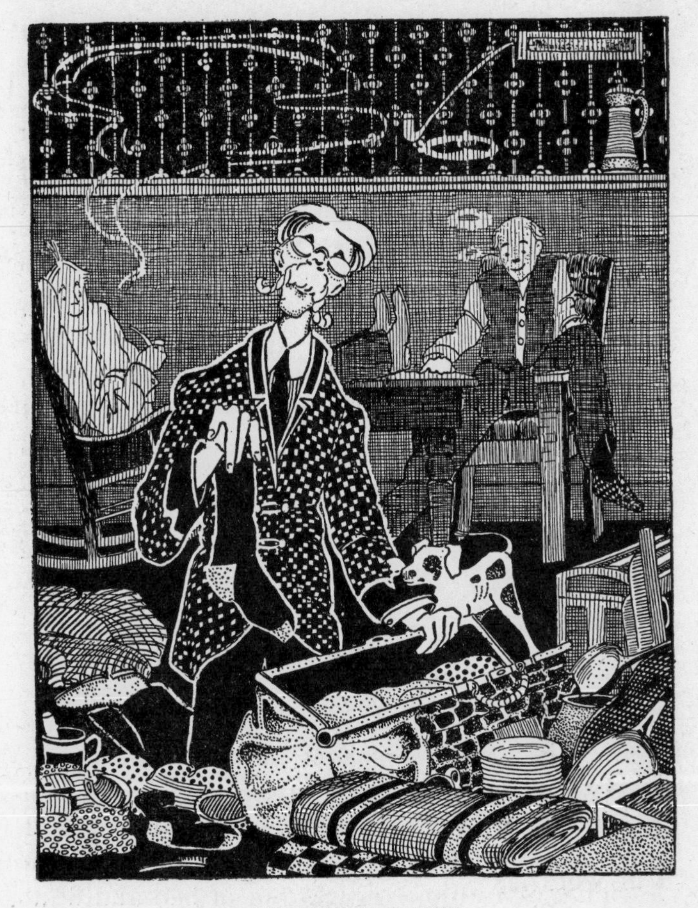

I STARTED THE PACKING

yawned through, but a noble task, full of duty and stern work. He said he often wondered now how he could have gone on before he met me, never having anybody to look at while they worked.

Now, I'm not like that. I can't sit still and

see another man slaving and working. I want to get up and superintend, and walk round with my hands in my pockets, and tell what to do. It is my energetic nature. I can't help it.

However, I did not say anything, but started the packing. It seemed a longer job than I had thought it was going to be, but I got the bag finished at last, and I sat on it and strapped it."

"Ain't you going to put the boots in?" said Harris.

And I looked round and found I had forgotten them. That's just like Harris. He couldn't have said a word until I'd got the bag shut and strapped, of course. And George laughed—one of those irritating, senseless, chuckle-headed, crack-jawed laughs of his. They do make me so wild.

I opened the bag and packed the boots in; and then, just as I was going to close it, a horrible idea occurred to me. Had I packed my toothbrush? I don't know how it is, but I never do know whether I've packed my toothbrush.

My toothbrush is a thing that haunts me when I'm traveling, and makes my life a misery. I dream that I haven't packed it, and wake up in a cold perspiration, and get out of bed and hunt for it. And, in the morning, I pack it before I have used it, and have to unpack again to get it, and it is always the last thing I turn out of the bag; and then I repack and forget it, and have to rush upstairs for it at the last moment and carry it to the railway station, wrapped up in my pocket handkerchief.

Of course I had to turn every mortal thing out now, and, of course, I could not find it. I rummaged the things up into much the same state that they must have been in before the world was created, and when chaos reigned. Of course, I found George's and Harris's eighteen times over, but I couldn't find my own. I put the things back one by one, and held everything up and shook it. Then I found it inside a boot. I repacked once more.

When I had finished, George asked if the soap was in. I said I didn't care a hang whether the soap was in or whether it wasn't; and I slammed the bag to and strapped it, and found that I had packed my tobacco pouch in it and had to re-open it. It got shut up finally at 10:05 p. m., and then there remained the hampers to do. Harris said that we should be wanting to start in less than twelve hours' time, and thought that he and George had better do the rest; and I agreed and sat down, and they had a go.

They began in a light-hearted spirit, evidently intending to show me how to do it. I made no comment. I only waited. When George is hanged, Harris will be the worst packer in this world; and I looked at the piles of plates and cups, and kettles, and bottles and jars, and pies, and stoves, and cakes, and tomatoes, etc., and felt that the thing would soon become exciting.

It did. They started with breaking a cup. That was the first thing they did. They did that just to show you what they *could* do, and to get you interested.

Then Harris packed the strawberry jam on top of a tomato and squashed it, and they had to pick out the tomato with a teaspoon.

And then it was George's turn, and he trod on the butter. I didn't say anything, but I came over and sat on the edge of the table and watched them. It irritated them more than anything I could have said. I felt that. It made them nervous and excited, and they stepped on things, and put things behind them, and then couldn't find them when they wanted them; and they packed the pies at the bottom, and put heavy things on top, and smashed the pies in.

They upset salt over everything, and as for the butter! I never saw two men do more with one-and-two pence worth of butter in my whole life than they did. After George had got it off his slipper, they tried to put it in the kettle. It wouldn't go in, and what *was* in wouldn't come out. They did scrape it out at last, and put it down on a chair, and Harris sat on it, and it stuck to him, and they went looking for it all over the room.

"I'll take my oath I put it down on that chair," said George, staring at the empty seat.

"I saw you do it myself, not a minute ago," said Harris.

Then they started round the room again looking for it; and then they met again in the center, and stared at one another.

"Most extraordinary thing I ever heard of," said George.

MONTMORENCY WAS IN IT ALL

"So mysterious!" said Harris.

Then George got around at the back of Harris and saw it.

"Why, here it is all the time," he exclaimed indignantly.

"Where?" cried Harris, spinning round.

"Stand still, can't you!" roared George, flying after him.

And they got it off, and packed it in the teapot.

Montmorency was in it all, of course. Montmorency's ambition in life is to get in the way and be sworn at. If he can squirm in anywhere where he particularly is not wanted, and be a perfect nuisance, and make people mad, and have things thrown at his head, then he feels his day has not been wasted.

He came and sat down on things, just when they were wanted to be packed; and he labored under the fixed belief that, whenever Harris or George reached out a hand for anything, it was his cold, damp nose that they wanted. He put his leg into the jam, and he worried the teaspoons, and he pretended that the lemons were rats, and got into the hamper and killed three of them before Harris could land him with the frying-pan.

Harris said I encouraged him. I didn't encourage him. A dog like that doesn't want any encouragement. It's the natural, original sin that is born in him that makes him do things like that.

The packing was done at 12:50; and Harris sat on the big hamper, and said he hoped nothing would be found broken. George said that if anything was broken it *was* broken, which reflection seemed to comfort him. He also said he was ready for bed. We were all ready for bed.

ON COMIC SONGS

JEROME K. JEROME

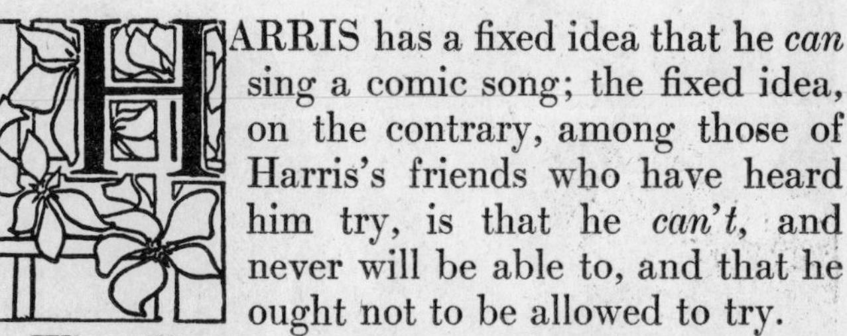

HARRIS has a fixed idea that he *can* sing a comic song; the fixed idea, on the contrary, among those of Harris's friends who have heard him try, is that he *can't*, and never will be able to, and that he ought not to be allowed to try.

When Harris is at a party and is asked to sing, he replies: "Well, I can only sing a *comic* song, you know;" and he says it in a tone that implies that his singing of *that*, however, is a thing that you ought to hear once, and then die.

"Oh, that *is* nice," says the hostess. "Do sing one, Mr. Harris;" and Harris gets up and makes for the piano, with the beaming cheeriness of a generous-minded man who is just about to give somebody something.

"Now, silence, please, everybody," says the hostess, turning round; "Mr. Harris is going to sing a comic song!"

"Oh, how jolly!" they murmur; and they hurry in from the conservatory, and come up from the stairs, and go and fetch each other from all over the house, and crowd into the drawing-room, and sit round, all smirking in anticipation.

Then Harris begins.

Well, you don't look for much of a voice in a comic song. You don't expect correct phrasing

"OH, THAT IS NICE!"

or vocalization. You don't mind if a man does find out, when in the middle of a note, that he is too high, and comes down with a jerk. You don't bother about time. You don't mind a man being two bars in front of the accompaniment, and easing up in the middle of a line to argue it out with the pianist, and then starting the verse afresh. But you do expect the words.

You don't expect a man never to remember more than the first three lines of the first verse, and to keep on repeating these until it is time to begin the chorus. You don't expect a man to break off in the middle of a line, and snigger, and say, it's very funny, but he's blest if he can think of the rest of it, and then try and make it up for himself, and, afterward, suddenly recollect it, when he has got to an entirely different part of the song, and break off, without a word of warning, to go back and let you have it then and there. You don't—well, I will just give you an idea of Harris's comic singing, and then you can judge of it for yourself.

HARRIS (*standing up in front of piano and addressing the expectant mob*): "I'm afraid it's a very old thing, you know. I expect you all know it, you know. But it's the only thing I know. It's the Judge's song out of *Pinafore*—no, I don't mean *Pinafore*—I mean—you know what I mean—the other thing, you know. You must all join in the chorus, you know."

[*Murmurs of delight and anxiety to join in the chorus. Brilliant performance of prelude to the Judge's song in "Trial by Jury" by nervous pianist. Moment arrives for Harris to join in. Harris takes no notice of it. Nervous pianist commences prelude over again, and Harris, commencing singing at the same time, dashes off the first two lines of the First*

Lord's song out of "Pinafore." Nervous pianist tries to push on with prelude, gives it up, and tries to follow Harris with accompaniment to Judge's song out of "Trial by Jury," finds that doesn't answer, and tries to recollect what he is doing, and where he is, feels his mind giving way, and stops short.]

HARRIS (*with kindly encouragement*): "It's all right. You're doing very well, indeed—go on."

NERVOUS PIANIST: "I'm afraid there's a mistake somewhere. What are you singing?"

HARRIS (*promptly*): "Why, the Judge's song out of *Trial by Jury*. Don't you know it?"

SOME FRIEND OF HARRIS'S (*from the back of the room*): "No, you're not, you chucklehead, you're singing the Admiral's song from *Pinafore*."

[*Long argument between Harris and Harris's friend as to what Harris is really singing. Friend finally suggests that it doesn't matter what Harris is singing so long as Harris gets on and sings it, and Harris, with an evident sense of injustice rankling inside him, requests pianist to begin again. Pianist, thereupon, starts prelude to the Admiral's song, and Harris, seizing what he considers to be a favorable opening in the music, begins:*

HARRIS:

"'When I was young and called to the Bar.'"

[*General roar of laughter, taken by Harris as a compliment. Pianist, thinking of his wife and family, gives up the unequal contest and retires: his place being taken by a stronger-nerved man.*]

THE NEW PIANIST (*cheerily*): "Now then, old man, you start off, and I'll follow. We won't bother about any prelude."

HARRIS (*upon whom the explanation of matters has slowly dawned—laughing*): "By Jove! I beg your pardon. Of course—I've been mixing up the two songs. It was Jenkins confused me, you know. Now then."

[*Singing; his voice appearing to come from the cellar, and suggesting the first low warnings of an approaching earthquake.*]

"'When I was young I served a term
As office-boy to an attorney's firm.'"

(*Aside to pianist*): "It is too low, old man; we'll have that over again, if you don't mind."

[*Sings first two lines over again, in a high falsetto this time. Great surprise on the part of the audience. Nervous old lady begins to cry, and has to be led out.*]

HARRIS (*continuing*):

"'I swept the windows and I swept the door,
And I——'"

No—no, I cleaned the windows of the big front door. And I polished up the floor—no, dash it—I beg your pardon—funny thing, I can't think of that line. And I—and I—oh, well, we'll get on the chorus and chance it (*sings*):

"'And I diddle-diddle-diddle-diddle-diddle-diddle-de,
Till now I am the ruler of the Queen's navee.'

Now then chorus—it's the last two lines repeated, you know."

General Chorus:

"'And he diddle-diddle-diddle-diddle-diddle-did-dle-dee'd,
Till now he is the ruler of the Queen's navee.'"

And Harris never sees what an ass he is making of himself, and how he is annoying a lot of people who never did him any harm. He honestly imagines that he has given them a treat, and says he will sing another comic song after supper.

Speaking of comic songs and parties, reminds me of a rather curious incident at which I once assisted; which, as it throws much light upon the inner mental working of human nature in general, ought, I think, to be recorded in these pages.

We were a fashionable and highly cultured party. We had on our best clothes, and we talked pretty, and were very happy—all except two young fellows, students, just returned from Germany, commonplace young men, who seemed restless and uncomfortable, as if they found the proceedings slow. The truth was, we were too clever for them. Our brilliant but polished conversation, and our high-class tastes, were beyond them. They were out of place among us. They never ought to have been there at all. Everybody agreed upon that, later on.

We discussed philosophy and ethics. We flirted with graceful dignity. We were even humorous—in a high-class way.

Somebody recited a French poem after supper, and we said it was beautiful; and then a lady sang a sentimental ballad in Spanish and it made one or two of us weep—it was so pathetic.

And then those two young men got up, and asked us if we had ever heard Herr Slossenn Boschen (who had just arrived, and was then down in the supper room) sing his great German comic song.

None of us had heard it, that we could remember.

The young men said it was the funniest song that had ever been written, and that, if we liked, they would get Herr Slossenn Boschen, whom they knew very well, to sing it. They said it was so funny that, when Herr Slossenn Boschen had sung it once before the German Emperor, he (the German Emperor) had had to be carried off to bed.

They said nobody could sing it like Herr Slossenn Boschen; he was so intensely serious all through it that you might fancy he was reciting a tragedy, and that, of course, made it all the funnier. They said he never once suggested by his tone or manner that he was singing anything funny—that would spoil it. It was his air of seriousness, almost of pathos, that made it so irresistibly amusing.

We said we yearned to hear it, that we wanted a good laugh; and they went downstairs, and fetched Herr Slossenn Boschen.

He appeared to be quite pleased to sing it,

for he came up at once, and sat down to the piano without another word.

"Oh, it will amuse you. You will laugh," whispered the two young men, as they passed through the room and took up an unobtrusive position behind the Professor's back.

Herr Slossenn Boschen accompanied himself. The prelude did not suggest a comic song exactly. It was a weird, soulful air. It quite made one's flesh creep; but we murmured to one another that it was the German method, and prepared to enjoy it.

I don't understand German myself. I learned it at school, but forgot every word of it two years after I had left, and have felt much better ever since. Still, I did not want the people there to guess my ignorance; so I hit upon what I thought to be rather a good idea. I kept my eye on the two young students, and followed them. When they tittered, I tittered; when they roared, I roared; and I also threw in a little snigger all by myself now and then, as if I had seen a bit of humor that had escaped the others. I considered this particularly artful on my part.

I noticed, as the song progressed, that a good many other people seemed to have their eyes fixed on the two young men, as well as myself. These other people also tittered when the young men tittered, and roared when the young men roared; and, as the two young men tittered and roared and exploded with laughter pretty continuously all through the song, it went exceedingly well.

THE GERMAN PROFESSOR DID NOT SEEM HAPPY

And yet that German professor did not seem happy. At first, when we began to laugh, the expression of his face was one of intense surprise, as if laughter were the very last thing he had expected to be greeted with. We thought this very funny: we said his earnest manner was half the humor. The slightest hint on his part that he knew how funny he was would have completely ruined it all. As we continued to laugh, his surprise gave way to an air of annoyance and indignation, and he scowled fiercely round upon us all (except the two young men, who, being behind him, could not be seen). That sent us into convulsions. We told each other it would be the death of us, this thing. The words alone, we said, were enough to send us into fits, but added to his mock seriousness—oh, it was too much!

In the last verse, he surpassed himself. He glowered round upon us with a look of such concentrated ferocity that, but for our being forewarned as to the German method of comic singing, we should have been nervous; and he threw such a wailing note of agony into the weird music that, if we had not known it was a funny song, we might have wept.

He finished amid a perfect shriek of laughter. We said it was the funniest thing we had ever heard in all our lives. We said how strange it was that, in the face of things like these, there should be a popular notion that the Germans hadn't any sense of humor. And we asked the Professor why he didn't translate the song into English, so that the common people could understand it, and hear what a real comic song was like.

Then Herr Slossenn Boschen got up, and went on awful. He swore at us in German (which I should judge to be a singularly effective language for that purpose), and he danced, and shook his fists, and called us all the English he knew. He said he had never been so insulted in all his life.

It appeared that the song was not a comic song at all. It was about a young girl who lived in the Hartz Mountains, and who had given up her life to save her lover's soul; and he died, and met her spirit in the air; and then, in the last verse, he jilted her spirit, and went on with another spirit—I'm not quite sure of the details, but it was something very sad, I know. Herr Boschen said he had sung it once before the German Emperor, and he (the German Emperor) had sobbed like a little child. He (Herr Boschen) said it was generally acknowledged to be one of the most tragic and pathetic songs in the German language.

It was a trying situation for us—very trying. There seemed to be no answer. We looked around for the two young men who had done this thing, but they had left the house in an unostentatious manner immediately after the end of the song.

That was the end of that party. I never saw a party break up so quietly, and with so little fuss. We never said good-night even to one another. We came downstairs one at a time, walking softly, and keeping the shady side. We asked the servant for our hats and coats in whispers, and opened the door, and slipped out, and got round the corner quickly, avoiding each other as much as possible.

I have never taken much interest in German songs since then.

THE INCHCAPE ROCK

ROBERT SOUTHEY

NOTE,—The Inchcape Rock, or Bell Rock, is a dangerous reef in the North Sea, east of the Firth of Tay, in Scotland, and twelve miles from all land. The story of the forethought of the abbot of Aberbrothok in placing the bell on the buoy as a warning to sailors is an ancient one, and one old writer thus gives the tradition made use of by Southey in this poem:

"In old times upon the said rocke there was a bell fixed upon a timber, which rang continually, being moved by the sea, giving notice to saylers of the danger. The bell was put there and maintained by the abbot of Aberbrothok, but being taken down by a sea-pirate, a yeare thereafter he perished upon the same rocke, with ship and goodes, in the righteous judgement of God."

A lighthouse, built with the greatest difficulty, has stood on the rock since 1810.

No stir in the air, no stir in the sea,—
The ship was still as she might be;
Her sails from heaven received no motion;
Her keel was steady in the ocean.

Without either sign or sound of their shock,
The waves flowed over the Inchcape Rock;
So little they rose, so little they fell,
They did not move the Inchcape bell.

The holy abbot of Aberbrothok
Had floated that bell on the Inchcape Rock;
On the waves of the storm it floated and swung,
And louder and louder its warning rung.

When the rock was hid by the tempest's swell,
The mariners heard the warning bell;
And then they knew the perilous rock,
And blessed the priest of Aberbrothok.

The sun in heaven shone so gay,—
All things were joyful on that day;
The sea-birds screamed as they sported round,
And there was pleasure in their sound.

The float of the Inchcape bell was seen,
A darker speck on the ocean green;
Sir Ralph, the rover, walked his deck,
And he fixed his eye on the darker speck.

He felt the cheering power of spring,—
It made him whistle, it made him sing;
His heart was mirthful to excess;
But the rover's mirth was wickedness.

His eye was on the bell and float:
Quoth he, "My men, pull out the boat;
And row me to the Inchcape Rock,
And I'll plague the priest of Aberbrothok."

The boat is lowered, the boatmen row,
And to the Inchcape Rock they go;
Sir Ralph bent over from the boat,
And cut the warning bell from the float.

RALPH, THE ROVER, WALKED HIS DECK

Down sank the bell with a gurgling sound;
The bubbles rose, and burst around.
Quoth Sir Ralph, "The next who comes to the rock
Will not bless the priest of Aberbrothok."

Sir Ralph, the rover, sailed away,—
He scoured the seas for many a day;

And now, grown rich with plundered store,
He steers his course to Scotland's shore.

So thick a haze o'erspreads the sky
They could not see the sun on high;
The wind hath blown a gale all day;
At evening it hath died away.

On the deck the rover takes his stand;
So dark it is they see no land.
Quoth Sir Ralph, "It will be lighter soon,
For there is the dawn of the rising moon."

"Canst hear," said one, "the breakers roar?
For yonder, methinks, should be the shore.
Now where we are I cannot tell,
But I wish we could hear the Inchcape bell."

They hear no sound; the swell is strong,
Though the wind hath fallen, they drift along;
Till the vessel strikes with a shivering shock,—
O Christ! it is the Inchcape Rock!

Sir Ralph, the rover, tore his hair;
He beat himself in wild despair.
The waves rush in on every side;
The ship is sinking beneath the tide.

But ever in his dying fear
One dreadful sound he seemed to hear,—
A sound as if with the Inchcape bell
The evil spirit was ringing his knell.

TOM BROWN AT RUGBY[1]

THOMAS HUGHES

TOM AND ARTHUR

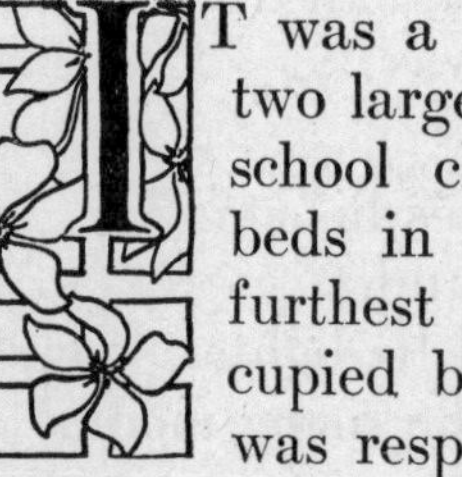

IT was a huge, high, airy room, with two large windows looking on to the school close.[2] There were twelve beds in the room, the one in the furthest corner by the fireplace occupied by the sixth-form[3] boy who was responsible for the discipline of the room, and the rest by boys in the lower-fifth and other junior forms, all fags[4] (for the fifth-

1. *Tom Brown's School Days,* a description of life at the great English public school of Rugby, is one of the best-known and best-liked books ever written for boys. The author, Thomas Hughes, was himself a Rugby boy, and many of the incidents of the story are drawn from his own experience. One of the most interesting things about the book is the picture it gives of Thomas Arnold, head-master of Rugby from 1828 to 1842. The influence for good of this famous scholar and educator, called affectionately "the doctor," can scarcely be overestimated.

He held that fully as much attention should be paid to the development of manly character in the boys as to mental training, and that the prime object of a school was not to turn out scholars, but to turn out men. This Doctor Arnold was the father of Matthew Arnold, the poet.

2. Tom Brown, an old Rugby boy, has come back after his vacation, full of plans for the good times which he expects to have with his chum East and other cronies. He is, however, called into the housekeeper's room and introduced to a shy, frail boy, whom he is asked to receive as his roommate and to look out for in the early days of his life at Rugby. Although greatly disappointed, Tom sees no way to refuse the request, and at the beginning of the selection here given we find him with young Arthur in the boys' dormitory.

3. The word *form* is used in English schools instead of *class.*

4. In English schools the name *fag* is applied to a boy who does, under compulsion, menial work for a boy of a higher form. The fagging system used to be greatly abused, the boys of the higher classes treating

form boys, as has been said, slept in rooms by themselves). Being fags, the eldest of them was not more than about sixteen years old, and all were bound to be up and in bed by ten; the sixth-form boys came to bed from ten to a quarter-past (at which time the old verger came round to put the candles out), except when they sat up to read.

Within a few minutes, therefore, of their entry, all the other boys who slept in Number 4, had come up. The little fellows went quietly to their own beds, and began undressing and talking to each other in whispers; while the elder, among whom was Tom, sat chatting about on one another's beds, with their jackets and waistcoats off. Poor little Arthur was overwhelmed with the novelty of his position. The idea of sleeping in the room with strange boys had clearly never crossed his mind before, and was as painful as it was strange to him. He could hardly bear to take his jacket off; however, presently, with an effort, off it came, and then he paused and looked at Tom, who was sitting at the bottom of his bed talking and laughing.

"Please, Brown," he whispered, "may I wash my face and hands?"

"Of course, if you like," said Tom, staring; "that's your washhand-stand, under the window, second from your bed. You'll have to go down for more water in the morning if you use it all." And on he went with his talk, while Arthur stole

their fags with the greatest cruelty; but the bad points of the custom have been largely done away with.

timidly from between the beds out to his wash-hand-stand, and began his ablutions, thereby drawing for a moment on himself the attention of the room.

On went the talk and laughter. Arthur finished his washing and undressing, and put on his nightgown. He then looked round more nervously than ever. Two or three of the little boys were already in bed, sitting up with their chins on their knees. The light burned clear, the noise went on. It was a trying moment for the poor little lonely boy; however, this time he didn't ask Tom what he might or might not do, but dropped on his knees by his bedside, as he had done every day from his childhood, to open his heart to Him who heareth the cry and beareth the sorrows of the tender child, and the strong man in agony.

Tom was sitting at the bottom of his bed unlacing his boots, so that his back was toward Arthur, and he didn't see what had happened, and looked up in wonder at the sudden silence. Then two or three boys laughed and sneered, and a big brutal fellow, who was standing in the middle of the room, picked up a slipper, and shied it at the kneeling boy, calling him a sniveling young shaver. Then Tom saw the whole, and the next moment the boot he had just pulled off flew straight at the head of the bully, who had just time to throw up his arm and catch it on his elbow.

"Confound you, Brown, what's that for?" roared he, stamping with pain.

"Never mind what I mean," said Tom, stepping on to the floor, every drop of blood in his body tingling; "if any fellow wants the other boot, he knows how to get it."

What would have been the result is doubtful, for at this moment the sixth-form boy came

THE BULLY CAUGHT IT ON HIS ELBOW

in, and not another word could be said. Tom and the rest rushed into bed and finished unrobing there, and the old verger, as punctual as the clock, had put out the candle in another minute, and toddled on to the next room, shutting the door with his usual "Good night, genl'm'n."

There were many boys in the room by whom that little scene was taken to heart before they slept. But sleep seemed to have deserted the pillow of poor Tom. For some time his excitement, and the flood of memories which chased one another through his brain, kept him from thinking or resolving. His head throbbed, his heart leaped, and he could hardly keep himself from springing out of bed and rushing about the room. Then the thought of his own mother came across him, and the promise he had made at her knee, years ago, never to forget to kneel by his bedside, and give himself up to his Father, before he laid his head on the pillow, from which it might never rise; and he lay down gently and cried as if his heart would break. He was only fourteen years old.

It was no light act of courage in those days, my dear boys, for a little felllow to say his prayers publicly even at Rugby. A few years later, when Arnold's manly piety had begun to leaven the school, the tables turned; before he died, in the school-house at least, and I believe in the other houses, the rule was the other way. But poor Tom had come to school in other times. The first few nights after he came he did not kneel down because of the noise, but sat up in bed till the candle was out, and then stole out and said his prayers in fear, lest some one should find him out. So did many another poor little fellow. Then he began to think that he might just as well say his prayers in bed, and then that it didn't matter whether he was kneeling, or sitting, or lying down. And so it had come to pass with Tom as with all who will not confess their Lord before men: and for the last year he had probably not said his prayers in earnest a dozen times.

Poor Tom! the first and bitterest feeling which was like to break his heart was the sense of his own cowardice. The vice of all others which he loathed was brought in and burned in on his own soul. He had lied to his mother, to his conscience, to his God. How could he bear it? And then the poor little weak boy, whom he had pitied and almost scorned for his weakness, had done that which he, braggart as he was, dared not do. The first dawn of comfort came to him in swearing to himself that he would stand by that boy through thick and thin, and cheer him, and help him, and bear his burdens, for the good deed done that night. Then he resolved to write home next day and tell his mother all, and what a coward her son had been. And then peace came to him as he resolved, lastly, to bear his testimony next morning. The morning would be harder than the night to begin with, but he felt that he could not afford to let one chance slip. Several times he faltered, for the devil showed him, first, all his old friends calling him "Saint" and "Squaretoes," and a dozen hard names, and whispered to him that his motives would be misunderstood, and he would only be left alone with the new boy; whereas it was his duty to keep all means of influence, that he might do good to the largest number. And then came the more subtle temptation, "Shall I not be showing myself braver than others by doing this? Have I any right to begin it now? Ought I not rather to pray in my own study, letting other boys know that I do so, and trying to lead them to it, while in public at least I should go on as I have done?" However, his good angel was too strong that night, and he turned on his side and slept, tired of trying to reason, but resolved to follow the impulse which had been so strong, and in which he had found peace.

Next morning he was up and washed and dressed, all but his jacket and waistcoat, just as the ten minutes' bell began to ring, and then in the face of the whole room knelt down to pray. Not five words could he say—the bell mocked him; he was listening for every whisper in the room—what were they all thinking of him? He was ashamed to go on kneeling, ashamed to rise from his knees. At last, as it were from his inmost heart, a still small voice seemed to breathe forth the words of the publican, "God be merciful to me a sinner!" He repeated them over and over, clinging to them as for his life, and rose from his knees comforted and humbled, and ready to face the whole world. It was not needed: two other boys besides Arthur had already followed his example, and he went down to the great school with a glimmering of another lesson in his heart—the lesson that he who has conquered his own coward spirit has conquered the whole outward world; and that other one which the old prophet learned in the cave of Mount Horeb, when he hid his face, and the still small voice asked, "What doest thou here, Elijah?" that however we may fancy ourselves alone on the side of good, the King and Lord of men is nowhere without His witnesses; for in every society, however seemingly corrupt and godless, there are those who have not bowed the knee to Baal.

He found too how greatly he had exaggerated the effect to be produced by his act. For a few nights there was a sneer or a laugh when he knelt down, but this passed off soon and one by one all the other boys but three or four followed the lead. I fear that this was in some measure owing to the fact, that Tom could probably have thrashed any boy in the room except the præpostor;[5] at any rate, every boy knew that he would try upon very slight provocation, and didn't choose to run the risk of a hard fight because Tom Brown had taken a fancy to say his prayers.

THE FIGHT

THERE is a certain sort of fellow—we who are used to studying boys all know him well enough—of whom you can predicate with almost positive certainty, after he has been a month at school, that he is sure to have a fight, and with almost equal certainty that he will have but one. Tom Brown was one of these; and as it is our well-weighed intention to give a full, true, and

5. A præpostor is a monitor, a scholar appointed to oversee other scholars.

correct account of Tom's only single combat with a school-fellow, let those young persons whose stomachs are not strong, or who think a good set-to with the weapons which God has given to us all, an uncivilized, unchristian, or ungentlemanly, affair, just skip this chapter at once, for it won't be to their taste.

It was not at all usual in those days for two school-house boys to have a fight. Of course there were exceptions, when some cross-grained, hard-headed fellow came up, who would never be happy unless he was quarreling with his nearest neighbors, or when there was some class-dispute between the fifth-form and the fags, for instance, which required blood-letting; and a champion was picked out on each side tacitly, who settled the matter by a good, hearty mill. But for the most part the constant use of those surest keepers of the peace, the boxing-gloves, kept the school-house boys from fighting one another. Two or three nights in every week the gloves were brought out, either in the hall or fifth-form room; and every boy who was ever likely to fight at all, knew all his neighbors' prowess perfectly well, and could tell to a nicety what chance he would have in a stand-up fight with any other boy in the house. But of course no such experience could be gotten as regarded boys in other houses; and as most of the other houses were more or less jealous of the school-house, collisions were frequent.

After all, what would life be without fighting, I should like to know? From the cradle to the grave, fighting, rightly understood, is the business, the real, highest, honestest business of every son of man. Every one who is worth his salt has his enemies, who must be beaten, be they evil thoughts and habits in himself, or spiritual wickedness in high places, or Russians, or border-ruffians, or Bill, Tom, or Harry, who will not let him live his life in quiet till he has thrashed them.

It is no good for Quakers, or any other body of men to uplift their voices against fighting. Human nature is too strong for them, and they don't follow their own precepts. Every soul of them is doing his own piece of fighting, somehow and somewhere. The world might be a better world without fighting, for anything I know, but it wouldn't be our world; and therefore I am dead against crying peace when there is no peace, and isn't meant to be. I am as sorry as any man to see folk fighting the wrong people and the wrong things, but I'd a deal sooner see them doing that, than that they should have no fight in them. So having recorded, and being about to record, my hero's fights of all sorts, with all sorts of enemies, I shall now proceed to give an account of his passage-at-arms with the only one of his school-fellows whom he ever had to encounter in this manner.

It was drawing toward the close of Arthur's first half-year, and the May evenings were lengthening out. Locking-up was not till eight o'clock, and everybody was beginning to talk about what he would do in the holidays. The shell,[6] in which form all our *dramatis personæ* now are, were reading among other things the last book of "Homer's Iliad," and had worked through it as far as the speeches of the women over Hector's body. It is a whole school-day, and four or five of the school-house boys (among whom are Arthur, Tom and East) are preparing third lesson together. They have finished the regulation forty lines, and are for the most part getting very tired, notwithstanding the exquisite pathos of Helen's lamentation. And now several long four-syllabled words come together, and the boy with the dictionary strikes work.

"I am not going to look out any more words," says he; "we've done the quantity. Ten to one we shan't get so far. Let's go out into the close."

"Come along, boys," cries East, always ready to leave the grind, as he called it; "our old coach is laid up, you know, and we shall have one of the new masters, who's sure to go slow and let us down easy."

So an adjournment to the close was carried *nem. con.*,[7] little Arthur not daring to lift up his voice; but, being deeply interested in what they were reading, he stayed quietly behind, and learned on for his own pleasure.

As East had said, the regular master of the form was unwell, and they were to be heard by one of the new masters, quite a young man, who

6. *Shell* is the name applied, in some public schools, to a sort of intermediate class.

7. *Nemine contradicente* is a Latin expression meaning *no one speaking in opposition.*

had only just left the university. Certainly it would be hard lines, if, by dawdling as much as possible in coming in and taking their places, entering into long-winded explanations of what was the usual course of the regular master of the form, and others of the stock contrivances of boys for wasting time in school, they could not spin out the lesson so that he should not work them through more than the forty lines; as to which quantity there was a perpetual fight going on between the master and his form, the latter insisting, and enforcing by passive resistance, that it was the prescribed quantity of Homer for a shell lesson, the former that there was no fixed quantity, but that they must always be ready to go on to fifty or sixty lines if there were time within the hour. However, notwithstanding all their efforts, the new master got on horribly quick; he seemed to have the bad taste to be really interested in the lesson, and to be trying to work them up into something like appreciation of it, giving them good spirited English words, instead of the wretched bald stuff into which they rendered poor old Homer; and construing over each piece himself to them, after each boy, to show them how it should be done.

Now the clock strikes the three quarters; there is only a quarter of an hour more; but the forty lines are all but done. So the boys, one after another, who are called up, stick more and more, and make balder and ever more bald work of it. The poor young master is pretty near beat by this time, and feels ready to knock his head against the wall, or his fingers against somebody else's head. So he gives up altogether the lower and middle parts of the form, and looks round in despair at the boys on the top bench to see if there is one out of whom he can strike a spark or two, and who will be too chivalrous to murder the most beautiful utterances of the most beautiful woman of the old world. His eye rests on Arthur, and he calls him up to finish construing Helen's speech. Whereupon all the other boys draw long breaths, and begin to stare about and take it easy. They are all safe; Arthur is the head of the form, and sure to be able to construe, and that will tide on safely till the hour strikes.

Arthur proceeds to read out the passage in Greek before construing it, as the custom is. Tom, who isn't paying much attention, is suddenly caught by the falter in his voice as he reads the two lines:

> ἀλλὰ σὺ τόν γ' ἐπέεσσι μαραιφάμενος κατέρυκες,
> Σῇ τ' ἀγανοφροσύνῃ καὶ σοῖς ἀγανοῖς ἐπέεσσιν.[8]

He looks up at Arthur. "Why, bless us," thinks he, "what can be the matter with the young 'un? He's never going to get floored. He's sure to have learned to the end." Next moment he is reassured by the spirited tone in which Arthur begins construing, and betakes himself to drawing dogs' heads in his notebook, while the

8. Pope's free rendering of these lines is as follows:

> If some proud brother eyed me with disdain,
> Or scornful sister with her sweeping train,
> Thy gentle accents softened all my pain.

master, evidently enjoying the change, turns his back on the middle bench and stands before Arthur, beating a sort of time with his hand and foot and saying "Yes, yes," "very well," as Arthur goes on.

But as he nears the fatal two lines, Tom catches that falter and again looks up. He sees that there is something the matter—Arthur can hardly get on at all. What can it be?

Suddenly at this point Arthur breaks down altogether, and fairly bursts out crying, and dashes the cuff of his jacket across his eyes, blushing up to the roots of his hair, and feeling as if he should like to go down suddenly through the floor. The whole form are taken aback; most of them stare stupidly at him, while those who are gifted with presence of mind find their places and look steadily at their books, in hopes of not catching the master's eye and getting called up in Arthur's place.

The master looks puzzled for a moment, and then seeing, as the fact is, that the boy is really affected to tears by the most touching thing in Homer, perhaps in all profane poetry put together, steps up to him and lays his hand kindly on his shoulder, saying, "Never mind, my little man, you've construed very well. Stop a minute, there's no hurry."

Now, as luck would have it, there sat next above Tom that day, in the middle bench of the form, a big boy, by name Williams, generally supposed to be the cock of the shell, therefore, of all the school below the fifths. The small boys, who are great speculators on the prowess of their elders, used to hold forth to one another about Williams' great strength, and to discuss whether East or Brown would take a licking from him. He was called Slogger Williams, from the force with which it was supposed he could hit. In the main, he was a rough, good-natured fellow enough, but very much alive to his own dignity. He reckoned himself the king of the form, and kept up his position with a strong hand, especially in the matter of forcing boys not to construe more than the legitimate forty lines. He had already grunted and grumbled to himself when Arthur went on reading beyond the forty lines. But now that he had broken down just in the middle of all the long words, the slogger's wrath was fairly roused.

"Sneaking little brute," muttered he, regardless of prudence, "clapping on the waterworks just in the hardest place; see if I don't punch his head after fourth lesson."

"Whose?" said Tom, to whom the remark seemed to be addressed.

"Why, that little sneak, Arthur's," replied Williams.

"No, you shan't," said Tom.

"Hullo!" exclaimed Williams, looking at Tom with great surprise for a moment, and then giving him a sudden dig in the ribs with his elbow, which sent Tom's books flying on the floor, and called the attention of the master, who turned suddenly round, and seeing the state of things, said:

"Williams, go down three places, and then go on."

The slogger found his legs very slowly, and proceeded to go below Tom and two other boys with great disgust, and then turning round and facing the master, said, "I haven't learned any more, sir; our lesson is only forty lines."

"Is that so?" said the master, appealing generally to the top bench. No answer.

"Who is the head boy of the form?" said he, waxing wroth.

"Arthur, sir," answered three or four boys, indicating our friend.

"Oh, your name's Arthur. Well now, what is the length of your regular lesson?"

Arthur hesitated a moment, and then said, "We call it only forty lines, sir."

"How do you mean, you call it?"

"Well, sir, Mr. Graham says we ain't to stop there, when there's time to construe more."

"I understand," said the master. "Williams, go down three more places, and write me out the lesson in Greek and English. And now, Arthur, finish construing."

"Oh! would I be in Arthur's shoes after fourth lesson?" said the little boys to one another; but Arthur finished Helen's speech without any further catastrophe, and the clock struck four, which ended third lesson.

Another hour was occupied in preparing and saying fourth lesson, during which Williams was bottling up his wrath; and when five struck, and the lessons for the day were over, he prepared to take summary vengeance on the innocent cause of his misfortune.

Tom was detained in school a few minutes after the rest, and on coming out into the quadrangle, the first thing he saw was a small ring of boys, applauding Williams, who was holding Arthur by the collar.

"There, you young sneak," said he, giving Arthur a cuff on the head with his other hand, "what made you say that—"

"Hullo!" said Tom, shouldering into the crowd, "you drop that, Williams; you shan't touch him."

"Who'll stop me?" said the slogger, raising his hand again.

"I," said Tom; and suiting the action to the word, struck the arm which held Arthur's arm so sharply, that the slogger dropped it with a start, and turned the full current of his wrath on Tom.

"Will you fight?"

"Yes, of course."

"Huzza, there's going to be a fight between Slogger Williams and Tom Brown!"

The news ran like wild-fire about, and many boys who were on their way to tea at their several houses turned back, and sought the back of the chapel, where the fights come off.

"Just run and tell East to come and back me," said Tom to a small school-house boy, who was off like a rocket to Harrowell's, just stopping for a moment to poke his head into the school-house hall, where the lower boys were already at tea, and sing out, "Fight! Tom Brown and Slogger Williams."

Up start half the boys at once, leaving bread, eggs, butter, sprats, and all the rest to take care of themselves. The greater part of the remainder follow in a minute, after swallowing their tea, carrying their food in their hands to

"A FIGHT!"

consume as they go. Three or four only remain, who steal the butter of the more impetuous, and make to themselves an unctuous feast.

In another minute East and Martin tear through the quadrangle carrying a sponge, and arrive at the scene of action just as the combatants are beginning to strip.

Tom felt he had got his work cut out for him, as he stripped off his jacket, waistcoat, and braces. East tied his handkerchief round his waist, and rolled up his shirt-sleeves for him: "Now, old boy, don't you open your mouth to say a word, or try to help yourself a bit, we'll do all that; you keep all your breath and strength for the slogger." Martin meanwhile folded the clothes, and put them under the chapel rails; and now Tom, with East to handle him and Martin to give him a knee, steps out on the turf, and is ready for all that may come: and here is the slogger too, all stripped, and thirsting for the fray.

It doesn't look a fair match at first glance: Williams is nearly two inches taller, and probably a long year older than his opponent, and he is very strongly made about the arms and shoulders; "peels well," as the little knot of big fifth-form boys, the amateurs, say; who stand outside the ring of little boys, looking complacently on, but taking no active part in the proceedings. But down below he is not so good by any means; no spring from the loins, and feebleish, not to say shipwrecky, about the knees. Tom, on the contrary, though not half so strong in the arms, is good all over, straight, hard, and springy from neck to ankle, better perhaps in his legs than anywhere. Besides, you can see by the clear white of his eye and fresh bright look of his skin, that he is in tip-top training, able to do all he knows; while the slogger looks rather sodden, as if he didn't take much exercise and ate too much tuck.[9] The time-keeper is chosen, a large ring

9. *Tuck* is a slang name for pastry or sweetmeats.

made, and the two stand up opposite one another for a moment, giving us time just to make our little observations.

"If Tom'll only condescend to fight with his head and heels," as East mutters to Martin, "we shall do."

But seemingly he won't, for there he goes in, making play with both hands. Hard all, is the

TOM SITS ON MARTIN'S KNEE

word; the two stand to one another like men; rally follows rally in quick succession, each fighting as if he thought to finish the whole thing out of hand. "Can't last at this rate," say the knowing ones, while the partisans of each make the air ring with their shouts and counter-shouts, of encouragement, approval and defiance.

"Take it easy, take it easy—keep away, let him come after you," implores East, as he wipes Tom's face after the first round with a wet sponge, while he sits back on Martin's knee, supported by the Madman's long arms, which tremble a little from excitement.

"Time's up," calls the time-keeper.

"There he goes again, hang it all!" growls East as his man is at it again as hard as ever. A very severe round follows, in which Tom gets out and out the worst of it, and is at last hit clean off his legs, and deposited on the grass by a right-hander from the slogger.

Loud shouts rise from the boys of slogger's house, and the school-house are silent and vicious, ready to pick quarrels anywhere.

"Two to one in half-crowns on the big 'un," says Rattle, one of the amateurs, a tall fellow, in thunder-and-lightning waistcoat, and puffy, good-natured face.

"Done!" says Groove, another amateur of quieter look, taking out his note-book to enter it—for our friend Rattle sometimes forgets these little things.

Meantime East is freshening up Tom with the sponges for the next round, and has set two other boys to rub his hands.

"Tom, old boy," whispers he, "this may be fun for you, but it's death to me. He'll hit all the fight out of you in another five minutes, and then I shall go and drown myself in the island ditch. Feint him—use your legs! draw him about! he'll lose his wind then in no time, and you can go into him. Hit at his body too, we'll take care of his frontispiece by and by."

Tom felt the wisdom of the counsel, and saw already that he couldn't go in and finish the slogger off at mere hammer and tongs, so changed his tactics completely in the third round. He now fights cautious, getting away from and parrying the slogger's lunging hits, instead of trying to counter, and leading his enemy a dance all round the ring after him. "He's funking; go in, Williams," "Catch him up," "Finish him off," scream the small boys of the slogger party.

"Just what we want," thinks East, chuckling to himself, as he sees Williams, excited by these shouts and thinking the game in his own hands, blowing himself in his exertions to get to close quarters again, while Tom is keeping away with perfect ease.

They quarter over the ground again and again, Tom always on the defensive.

The slogger pulls up at last for a moment, fairly blown.

"Now then, Tom," sings out East dancing with delight. Tom goes in in a twinkling, and hits two heavy body blows, and gets away again before the slogger can catch his wind; which when he does he rushes with blind fury at Tom, and being skillfully parried and avoided, overreaches himself and falls on his face, amid terrific cheers from the school-house boys.

"Double your two to one?" says Groove to Rattle, note-book in hand.

"Stop a bit," says that hero, looking uncomfortably at Williams, who is puffing away on his second's knee, winded enough, but little the worse in any other way.

After another round the slogger too seems to see that he can't go in and win right off, and has met his match or thereabouts. So he too begins to use his head and tries to make Tom lose patience and come in before his time. And so the fight sways on, now one, and now the other, getting a trifling pull.

Tom's face begins to look very one-sided—there are little queer bumps on his forehead, and his mouth is bleeding; but East keeps the wet sponge going so scientifically, that he comes up looking as fresh and bright as ever. Williams is only slightly marked in the face, but by the nervous movement of his elbows you can see that Tom's body blows are telling. In fact, half the vice of the slogger's hitting is neutralized, for he daren't lunge out freely for fear of exposing his sides. It is too interesting by this time for much shouting, and the whole ring is very quiet.

"All right, Tommy," whispers East; "hold on's the horse that's to win. We've got the last. Keep your head, old boy."

But where is Arthur all this time? Words cannot paint the poor little fellow's distress. He couldn't muster courage to come up to the ring, but wandered up and down from the great fives'-court to the corner of the chapel rails, now trying to make up his mind to throw himself between them, and try to stop them; then thinking of running in and telling Mary, the

THE SLOGGER OVERREACHES HIMSELF.

matron, who he knew would instantly report it to the doctor. The stories he had heard of men being killed in prize-fights rose up horribly before him.

Once only, when the shouts of "Well done, Brown!" "Huzza for the school-house!" rose higher than ever, he ventured up to the ring, thinking the victory was won. Catching sight of Tom's face in the state I have described, all fear of consequences vanishing out of his mind, he rushed straight off to the matron's room, beseeching her to get the fight stopped, or he should die.

But it's time for us to get back to the close. What is this fierce tumult and confusion? The ring is broken, and high and angry words are being bandied about; "It's all fair,"—"It isn't"—"No hugging;" the fight is stopped. The combatants, however, sit there quietly, tended by their seconds, while their adherents wrangle in the middle. East can't help shouting challenges to two or three of the other side, though he never leaves Tom for a moment, and plies the sponges as fast as ever.

The fact is, that at the end of the last round, Tom seeing a good opening, had closed with his opponent, and after a moment's struggle had thrown him heavily, by the help of the fall he had learned from his village rival in the vale of White Horse. Williams hadn't the ghost of a chance with Tom at wrestling; and the conviction broke at once on the slogger faction, that if this were allowed their man must be licked. There was a strong feeling in the school against catching hold and throwing, though it was generally ruled all fair within certain limits; so the ring was broken and the fight stopped.

The school-house are overruled—the fight is on again, but there is to be no throwing; and East in high wrath threatens to take his man away after next round (which he don't mean to do, by the way), when suddenly young Brooke comes through the small gate at the end of the chapel. The school-house faction rush to him. "Oh, hurra! now we shall get fair play."

"Please, Brooke, come up, they won't let Tom Brown throw him."

"Throw whom?" says Brooke, coming up to the ring. "Oh! Williams, I see. Nonsense! of course he may throw him if he catches him fairly above the waist."

Now, young Brooke, you're in the sixth, you know, and you ought to stop all fights. He looks hard at both boys. "Anything wrong?" says he to East, nodding at Tom.

"Not a bit."

"Not beat at all?"

"Bless you, no! heaps of fight in him. Ain't there, Tom?"

Tom looks at Brooke and grins.

"How's he?" nodding at Williams.

"So, so; rather done, I think, since his last fall. He won't stand above two more."

"Time's up!" the boys rise again and face one another. Brooke can't find it in his heart to stop them just yet, so the round goes on, the slogger waiting for Tom, and reserving all his strength to hit him out should he come in for the wrestling dodge again, for he feels that that must be stopped, or his sponge will soon go up in the air.

And now another newcomer appears on the field, to-wit, the under-porter, with his long brush and great wooden receptacle for dust under his arm. He has been sweeping out the schools.

"You'd better stop, gentlemen," he says; "the doctor knows that Brown's fighting—he'll be out in a minute."

"You go to Bath, Bill," is all that that excellent servitor gets by his advice. And being a man of his hands, and a stanch upholder of the school-house, can't help stopping to look on for a bit, and see Tom Brown, their pet craftsman, fight a round.

It is grim earnest now, and no mistake. Both boys feel this, and summon every power of head, hand, and eye to their aid. A piece of luck on either side, a foot slipping, a blow getting well home, or another fall, may decide it. Tom works slowly round for an opening; he has all the legs, and can choose his own time: the slogger waits for the attack, and hopes to finish it by some heavy right-handed blow. As they quarter slowly over the ground, the evening sun comes out from behind a cloud and falls full on Williams' face. Tom starts in; the heavy right hand is delivered, but only grazes his head. A short rally at close quarters, and they close: in another moment the slogger is thrown again heavily for the third time.

"I'll give you three to two on the little one in half-crowns," said Groove to Rattle.

"No, thank 'ee," answers the other, diving his hands further into his coat-tails.

Just at this stage of the proceedings, the door of the turret which leads to the doctor's library suddenly opens, and he steps into the close, and makes straight for the ring, in which Brown and the slogger are both seated on their seconds' knees for the last time.

"The doctor! the doctor!" shouts some small boy who catches sight of him, and the ring melts away in a few seconds, the small boys tearing off, Tom collaring his jacket and waistcoat, and slipping through the little gate by the chapel, and round the corner to Harrowell's with his backers, as lively as need be; Williams and his backers making off not quite so fast across the close; Groove, Rattle and the other bigger fellows trying to combine dignity and prudence in a comical manner, and walking off fast enough, they hope, not to be recognized, and not fast enough to look like running away.

Young Brooke alone remains on the ground by the time the doctor gets there, and touches his hat, not without a slight inward qualm.

"Hah! Brooke. I am surprised to see you here. Don't you know that I expect the sixth to stop fighting?"

Brooke felt much more uncomfortable than he had expected, but he was rather a favorite with the doctor for his openness and plainness of speech; so blurted out, as he walked by the doctor's side, who had already turned back:

"Yes, sir, generally. But I thought you wished us to exercise a discretion in the matter, too—not to interfere too soon."

"But they had been fighting this half-hour and more," said the doctor.

"Yes, sir, but neither was hurt. And they're the sort of boys who'll be all the better friends now, which they wouldn't have been if they had been stopped any earlier—before it was so equal."

"Who was fighting with Brown?" said the doctor.

"Williams, sir, of Thompson's. He is bigger than Brown, and had the best of it at first, but not when you came up, sir. There's a good deal of jealousy between our house and Thompson's, and there would have been more fights if this hadn't been let go on, or if either of them had had much the worst of it."

"Well but, Brooke," said the doctor, "doesn't this look a little as if you exercised your discretion by only stopping a fight when the school-house boy is getting the worst of it?"

Brooke, it must be confessed, felt rather graveled.

"Remember," added the doctor, as he stopped at the turret-door, "this fight is not to go on—you'll see to that. And I expect you to stop all fights in future at once."

"Very well, sir," said young Brooke, touching his hat, and not sorry to see the turret-door close behind the doctor's back.

Meantime Tom and the stanchest of his adherents had reached Harrowell's, and Sally was bustling about to get them a late tea, while Stumps had been sent off to Tew, the butcher, to get a piece of raw beef for Tom's eye, which was to be healed off-hand, so that he might show well in the morning. He was not a bit the worse except a slight difficulty in his vision, a singing in his ears, and a sprained thumb, which he kept in a cold-water bandage, while he drank lots of tea, and listened to the babel of voices talking and speculating of nothing but the fight, and how Williams would have given in after another fall (which he didn't in the least believe), and how on earth the doctor could have gotten to know of it—such bad luck! He couldn't help thinking to himself that he was glad he hadn't won; he liked it better as it was, and felt very friendly to the slogger. And then poor little Arthur crept in and sat down quietly near him, and kept looking at him and the raw beef with such plaintive looks, that Tom at last burst out laughing.

"Don't make such eyes, young'un," said he, "there's nothing the matter."

"Oh, but Tom, are you much hurt? I can't bear thinking it was all for me."

"Not a bit of it, don't flatter yourself. We were sure to have had it out sooner or later."

"Well, but you won't go on, will you? You'll promise me you won't go on."

"Can't tell about that—all depends on the houses. We're in the hands of our countrymen, you know. Must fight for the school-house flag, if so be."

And now, boys all, three words before we quit the subject. I have put in this chapter on fighting of malice prepense, partly because I want to give you a true picture of what every-day school life was in my time, and not a kid-glove and go-to-meeting-coat picture; and partly because of the cant and twaddle that's talked of boxing and fighting with fists now-a-days. Even Thackeray has given in to it; and only a few weeks ago there was some rampant stuff in the *Times* on the subject, in an article on field sports.

Boys will quarrel, and when they quarrel will sometimes fight. Fighting with fists is the natural and English way for English boys to settle their quarrels. What substitute for it is there, or ever was there, among any nation under the sun? What would you like to see take its place?

Learn to box, then, as you learn to play cricket and football. Not one of you will be the worse, but very much the better for learning to box well. Should you never have to use it in earnest, there's no exercise in the world so good for the temper, and for the muscles of the back and legs.

As to fighting, keep out of it if you can, by all means. When the time comes, if it ever should, that you have to say "Yes" or "No" to a challenge to fight, say "No" if you can—only take care you make it clear to yourselves why you say

"No." It's a proof of the highest courage, if done from true Christian motives. It's quite right and justifiable, if done from a simple aversion to physical pain and danger. But don't say "No" because you fear a licking, and say or think it's because you fear God, for that's neither Christian nor honest. And if you do fight, fight it out; and don't give in while you can stand and see.

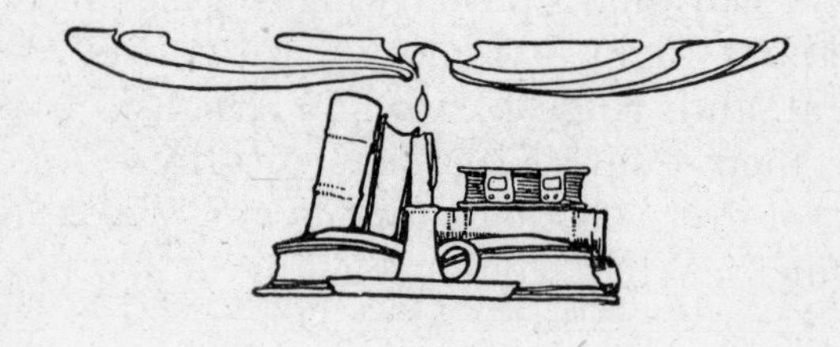

HORATIUS

LORD MACAULAY

NOTE,—This spirited poem by Lord Macaulay is founded on one of the most popular Roman legends. While the story is based on facts, we can by no means be certain that all of the details are historical.

According to Roman legendary history, the Tarquins, Lucius Tarquinius Priscus and Lucius Tarquinius Superbus, were among the early kings of Rome. The reign of the former was glorious, but that of the latter was most unjust and tyrannical. Finally the unscrupulousness of the king and his son reached such a point that it became unendurable to the people, who in 509 B. C. rose in rebellion and drove the entire family from Rome. Tarquinius Superbus appealed to Lars Porsena, the powerful king of Clusium, for aid, and the story of the expedition against Rome is told in this poem.

Lars Porsena of Clusium[1]
  By the Nine Gods[2] he swore
That the great house of Tarquin
  Should suffer wrong no more.
By the Nine Gods he swore it,

1. Clusium was a powerful town in Etruria.

2. According to the religion of the Etruscans there were nine great gods. An oath by them was considered the most binding oath that a man could take.

And named a trysting day,
And bade his messengers ride forth
East and west and south and north,
To summon his array.

East and west and south and north
The messengers ride fast,
And tower and town and cottage
Have heard the trumpet's blast.
Shame on the false Etruscan
Who lingers in his home,
When Porsena of Clusium
Is on the march for Rome.

The horsemen and the footmen
Are pouring in amain
From many a stately market-place;
From many a fruitful plain.
From many a lonely hamlet,
Which, hid by beech and pine,
Like an eagle's nest, hangs on the crest
Of purple Apennine;

* * * * * *

There be thirty chosen prophets,
The wisest of the land,
Who alway by Lars Porsena
Both morn and evening stand:
Evening and morn the Thirty
Have turned the verses o'er,
Traced from the right on linen white[3]
By mighty seers of yore.

3. This line shows us that the writing of the Etruscans was done backwards, as we should consider it; that is, they wrote from right to left instead of from left to right.

And with one voice the Thirty
  Have their glad answer given:
"Go forth, go forth, Lars Porsena;
  Go forth, beloved of Heaven:
Go, and return in glory
  To Clusium's royal dome;
And hang round Nurscia's[4] altars
  The golden shields of Rome."

And now hath every city
  Sent up her tale[5] of men:
The foot are fourscore thousand,
  The horse are thousands ten.
Before the gates of Sutrium[6]
  Is met the great array.
A proud man was Lars Porsena
  Upon the trysting day.

For all the Etruscan armies
  Were ranged beneath his eye,
And many a banished Roman,
  And many a stout ally;
And with a mighty following
  To join the muster came
The Tusculan Mamilius,
  Prince of the Latian[7] name.

4. Nurscia was a city of the Sabines.

5. *Tale* here means *number*.

6. Sutrium was an Etruscan town twenty-nine miles from Rome.

7. The Latins were an Italian race who, even before the dawn of history, dwelt on the plains south of the Tiber. Rome was supposed to be a colony of Alba Longa, the chief Latin city, but the Latin peoples were in the fourth century brought into complete subjection to Rome.

But by the yellow Tiber
  Was tumult and affright:
From all the spacious champaign[8]
  To Rome men took their flight.
A mile around the city,
  The throng stopped up the ways;
A fearful sight it was to see
  Through two long nights and days.

For aged folks on crutches,
  And women great with child,
And mothers sobbing over babes
  That clung to them and smiled,
And sick men borne in litters
  High on the necks of slaves,
And troops of sunburnt husbandmen
  With reaping-hooks and staves,

And droves of mules and asses
  Laden with skins of wine,
And endless flocks of goats and sheep,
  And endless herds of kine,
And endless trains of wagons
  That creaked beneath the weight
Of corn-sacks and of household goods,
  Choked every roaring gate.

Now, from the rock Tarpeian[9]
  Could the wan burghers spy
The line of blazing villages
  Red in the midnight sky.

8. *Champaign*, or *campagna*, means any open, level tract of country. The name is specifically applied to the extensive plains about Rome.

9. A part of the Capitoline, one of the seven hills on which Rome is built, was called the Tarpeian Rock, after Tarpeia, daughter of an

The Fathers of the City,[10]
They sat all night and day,
For every hour some horseman came
With tidings of dismay.

To eastward and to westward
Have spread the Tuscan bands;
Nor house nor fence nor dovecote
In Crustumerium stands.
Verbenna down to Ostia[11]
Hath wasted all the plain;
Astur hath stormed Janiculum,[12]
And the stout guards are slain.

Iwis,[13] in all the Senate,
There was no heart so bold,
But sore it ached, and fast it beat,
When that ill news was told.
Forthwith up rose the Consul,[14]
Uprose the Fathers all;
In haste they girded up their gowns,
And hied them to the wall.

early governor of the citadel on the Capitoline. According to the popular legend, when the Sabines came against Rome, Tarpeia promised to open the gate of the fortress to them if they would give her what they wore on their left arms. It was their jewelry which she coveted, but she was punished for her greed and treachery, for when the soldiers had entered the fortress they hurled their shields upon her, crushing her to death.

10. *Fathers of the City* was the name given to the members of the Roman Senate.

11. Ostia was the port of Rome, situated at the mouth of the Tiber.

12. Janiculum is a hill on the west bank of the Tiber at Rome. It was strongly fortified, and commanded the approach to Rome.

13. *Iwis* is an obsolete word meaning *truly*.

14. When the kings were banished from Rome the people vowed that never again should one man hold the supreme power. Two chief rulers were therefore chosen, and were given the name of *consuls*.

They held a council standing
  Before the River-Gate;
Short time was there, ye well may guess,
  For musing or debate.
Out spake the Consul roundly:
  "The bridge must straight go down;
For since Janiculum is lost,
  Naught else can save the town."

Just then a scout came flying,
  All wild with haste and fear;
"To arms! to arms! Sir Consul:
  Lars Porsena is here."
On the low hills to westward
  The Consul fixed his eye,
And saw the swarthy storm of dust
  Rise fast along the sky.

And nearer fast and nearer
  Doth the red whirlwind come;
And louder still and still more loud,
From underneath that rolling cloud,
Is heard the trumpet's war-note proud,
  The trampling, and the hum.
And plainly and more plainly
  Now through the gloom appears,
Far to left and far to right,
In broken gleams of dark-blue light,
The long array of helmets bright,
  The long array of spears.

And plainly, and more plainly
  Above that glimmering line,

NEARER FAST AND NEARER

Now might ye see the banners
   Of twelve fair cities shine;
But the banner of proud Clusium
   Was highest of them all,
The terror of the Umbrian,
   The terror of the Gaul.

Fast by the royal standard,
O'erlooking all the war,
Lars Porsena of Clusium
Sat in his ivory car.
By the right wheel rode Mamilius,
Prince of the Latian name,
And by the left false Sextus,[15]
That wrought the deed of shame.

But when the face of Sextus
Was seen among the foes,
A yell that rent the firmament
From all the town arose.
On the house-tops was no woman
But spat toward him and hissed,
No child but screamed out curses,
And shook its little fist.

But the Consul's brow was sad,
And the Consul's speech was low,
And darkly looked he at the wall,
And darkly at the foe.
"Their van will be upon us
Before the bridge goes down;
And if they once may win the bridge,
What hope to save the town?"

Then out spake brave Horatius,
The Captain of the Gate:
"To every man upon this earth
Death cometh soon or late.

15. Sextus was the son of the last king of Rome. It was a shameful deed of his which finally roused the people against the Tarquin family.

And how can man die better
  Than facing fearful odds,
For the ashes of his fathers,
  And the temples of his gods,

"And for the tender mother
  Who dandled him to rest,
And for the wife who nurses
  His baby at her breast,
And for the holy maidens
  Who feed the eternal flame,[16]
To save them from false Sextus
  That wrought the deed of shame?

"Hew down the bridge, Sir Consul,
  With all the speed ye may;
I, with two more to help me,
  Will hold the foe in play.
In yon strait path a thousand
  May well be stopped by three.
Now who will stand on either hand,
  And keep the bridge with me?"

Then out spake Spurius Lartius;
  A Ramnian proud was he:
"Lo, I will stand at thy right hand,
  And keep the bridge with thee."
And out spake strong Herminius;
  Of Titian blood was he:
"I will abide on thy left side,
  And keep the bridge with thee."

16. In the temple of the goddess Vesta a sacred flame was kept burning constantly, and it was thought that the consequences to the city would be most dire if the fire were allowed to go out. The Vestal virgins, priestesses who tended the flame, were held in the highest honor.

"Horatius," quoth the Consul,
  "As thou sayest, so let it be."
And straight against that great array
  Forth went the dauntless Three.
For Romans in Rome's quarrel
  Spared neither land nor gold,
Nor son nor wife, nor limb nor life,
  In the brave days of old.

Then none was for a party;
  Then all were for the state;
Then the great man helped the poor,
  And the poor man loved the great:
Then lands were fairly portioned;
  Then spoils were fairly sold:
The Romans were like brothers
  In the brave days of old.

Now while the Three were tightening
  Their harness on their backs,
The Consul was the foremost man
  To take in hand an axe:
And Fathers mixed with Commons[17]
  Seized hatchet, bar, and crow,
And smote upon the planks above,
  And loosed the props below.

Meanwhile the Tuscan army,
  Right glorious to behold,
Came flashing back the noonday light,
Rank behind rank, like surges bright
  Of a broad sea of gold.

17. The Roman people were divided into two classes, the patricians, to whom belonged all the privileges of citizenship, and the plebeians, who were not allowed to hold office or even to own property. Macaulay gives the English name *Commons* to the plebeians.

THE THREE STOOD CALM AND SILENT

Four hundred trumpets sounded
  A peal of warlike glee,
As that great host, with measured tread,
And spears advanced, and ensigns spread,
Rolled slowly towards the bridge's head,
  Where stood the dauntless Three.

The Three stood calm and silent,
And looked upon the foes,
And a great shout of laughter
From all the vanguard rose;
And forth three chiefs came spurring
Before that deep array;
To earth they sprang, their swords they drew,
And lifted high their shields, and flew
To win the narrow way;

Aunus from green Tifernum,[18]
Lord of the Hill of Vines;
And Seius, whose eight hundred slaves
Sicken in Ilva's mines;
And Picus, long to Clusium
Vassal in peace and war,
Who led to fight his Umbrian powers
From that gray crag where, girt with towers,
The fortress of Nequinum lowers
O'er the pale waves of Nar.

Stout Lartius hurled down Aunus
Into the stream beneath:
Herminius struck at Seius,
And clove him to the teeth:
At Picus brave Horatius
Darted one fiery thrust;
And the proud Umbrian's gilded arms
Clashed in the bloody dust.

18. A discussion as to who these chiefs were, or as to where the places mentioned were located, would be profitless. The notes attempt to give only such information as will aid in understanding the story.

Then Ocnus of Falerii
  Rushed on the Roman Three:
And Lausulus of Urgo,
  The rover of the sea;
And Aruns of Volsinium,
  Who slew the great wild boar,
The great wild boar that had his den
Amidst the reeds of Cosa's fen,
And wasted fields, and slaughtered men,
  Along Albinia's shore.

Herminius smote down Aruns:
  Lartius laid Ocnus low:
Right to the heart of Lausulus
  Horatius sent a blow.
"Lie there," he cried, "fell pirate!
  No more, aghast and pale,
From Ostia's walls the crowd shall mark
The track of thy destroying bark.
No more Campania's[19] hinds[20] shall fly
To woods and caverns when they spy
  Thy thrice accursèd sail."

But now no sound of laughter
  Was heard among the foes.
A wild and wrathful clamor
  From all the vanguard rose.
Six spears' lengths from the entrance
  Halted that deep array,
And for a space no man came forth
  To win the narrow way.

19. *Campania* is another name for the campagna.
20. *Hinds* here means *peasants*.

But hark! the cry is Astur:
  And lo! the ranks divide;
And the great Lord of Luna
  Comes with his stately stride.
Upon his ample shoulders
Clangs loud the fourfold shield,
And in his hand he shakes the brand
  Which none but he can wield.

He smiled on those bold Romans
  A smile serene and high;
He eyed the flinching Tuscans,
  And scorn was in his eye.
Quoth he, "The she-wolf's litter[21]
  Stand savagely at bay:
But will ye dare to follow,
  If Astur clears the way?"

Then, whirling up his broadsword
  With both hands to the height,
He rushed against Horatius,
  And smote with all his might.
With shield and blade Horatius
  Right deftly turned the blow.
The blow, though turned, came yet too nigh;
It missed his helm, but gashed his thigh:
The Tuscans raised a joyful cry
  To see the red blood flow.

He reeled, and on Herminius
  He leaned one breathing-space;
Then, like a wild-cat mad with wounds,
  Sprang right at Astur's face.

21. Romulus, the founder of Rome, and Remus, his brother, were,

Through teeth, and skull, and helmet,
  So fierce a thrust he sped,
The good sword stood a handbreadth out
  Behind the Tuscan's head.

And the great Lord of Luna
  Fell at that deadly stroke,
As falls on Mount Alvernus
  A thunder-smitten oak.
Far o'er the crashing forest
  The giant arms lie spread;
And the pale augurs, muttering low,
  Gaze on the blasted head.

On Astur's throat Horatius
  Right firmly pressed his heel,
And thrice and four times tugged amain,
  Ere he wrenched out the steel.
"And see," he cried, "the welcome,
  Fair guests, that waits you here!
What noble Lucumo comes next
  To taste our Roman cheer?"

But at his haughty challenge
  A sullen murmur ran,
Mingled of wrath and shame and dread,
  Along that glittering van.
There lacked not men of prowess,
  Nor men of lordly race;
For all Etruria's noblest
  Were round the fatal place.

---

according to the legend, rescued and brought up by a she-wolf, after they had been cast into the Tiber to die.

But all Etruria's noblest
  Felt their hearts sink to see
On the earth the bloody corpses,
  In the path the dauntless Three:
And, from the ghastly entrance
  Where those bold Romans stood,
All shrank, like boys who unaware,
Ranging the woods to start a hare,
Come to the mouth of the dark lair
Where, growling low, a fierce old bear
  Lies amidst bones and blood.

Was none who would be foremost
  To lead such dire attack:
But those behind cried "Forward!"
  And those before cried "Back!"
And backward now and forward
  Wavers the deep array;
And on the tossing sea of steel,
To and fro the standards reel;
And the victorious trumpet-peal
  Dies fitfully away.

Yet one man for one moment
  Stood out before the crowd;
Well known was he to all the Three
  And they gave him greeting loud,
"Now welcome, welcome, Sextus!
  Now welcome to thy home!
Why dost thou stay, and turn away?
  Here lies the road to Rome."

Thrice looked he at the city;
  Thrice looked he at the dead;

And thrice came on in fury,
  And thrice turned back in dread;
And, white with fear and hatred,
  Scowled at the narrow way
Where, wallowing in a pool of blood,
  The bravest Tuscans lay.

But meanwhile axe and lever
  Have manfully been plied;
And now the bridge hangs tottering
  Above the boiling tide.
"Come back, come back, Horatius!"
  Loud cried the Fathers all.
"Back, Lartius! back, Herminius!
  Back, ere the ruin fall!"

Back darted Spurius Lartius;
  Herminius darted back:
And, as they passed, beneath their feet
  They felt the timbers crack.
But when they turned their faces,
  And on the farther shore
Saw brave Horatius stand alone,
  They would have crossed once more.

But with a crash like thunder
  Fell every loosened beam,
And, like a dam, the mighty wreck
  Lay right athwart the stream;
And a long shout of triumph
  Rose from the walls of Rome,
As to the highest turret-tops
  Was splashed the yellow foam.

And, like a horse unbroken
  When first he feels the rein,
The furious river struggled hard,
  And tossed his tawny mane,
And burst the curb, and bounded,
  Rejoicing to be free,
And whirling down, in fierce career,
Battlement, and plank, and pier,
  Rushed headlong to the sea.

Alone stood brave Horatius,
  But constant still in mind;
Thrice thirty thousand foes before,
  And the broad flood behind.
"Down with him!" cried false Sextus,
  With a smile on his pale face.
"Now yield thee," cried Lars Porsena,
  "Now yield thee to our grace."

Round turned he, as not deigning
  Those craven ranks to see;
Naught spake he to Lars Porsena,
  To Sextus naught spake he;
But he saw on Palatinus[22]
  The white porch of his home;
And he spake to the noble river
  That rolls by the towers of Rome.

"O Tiber! father Tiber![23]
  To whom the Romans pray,
A Roman's life, a Roman's arms,
  Take thou in charge this day!"

22. The Palatine is one of the seven hills of Rome.
23. The Romans personified the Tiber River, and even offered prayers to it.

So he spake, and speaking sheathed
  The good sword by his side,
And with his harness on his back
  Plunged headlong in the tide.

No sound of joy or sorrow
  Was heard from either bank;
But friends and foes in dumb surprise,
With parted lips and straining eyes,
  Stood gazing where he sank;
And when above the surges
  They saw his crest appear,
All Rome sent forth a rapturous cry,
And even the ranks of Tuscany
  Could scarce forbear to cheer.

But fiercely ran the current,
  Swollen high by months of rain:
And fast his blood was flowing,
  And he was sore in pain,
And heavy with his armor,
  And spent with changing blows:
And oft they thought him sinking,
  But still again he rose.

Never, I ween, did swimmer,
  In such an evil case,
Struggle through such a raging flood
  Safe to the landing-place:
But his limbs were borne up bravely
  By the brave heart within,
And our good father Tiber
  Bore bravely up his chin.

"Curse on him!" quoth false Sextus;
"Will not the villain drown?
But for this stay, ere close of day
We should have sacked the town!"
"Heaven help him!" quoth Lars Porsena,
"And bring him safe to shore;
For such a gallant feat of arms
Was never seen before."

And now he feels the bottom;
Now on dry earth he stands;
Now round him throng the Fathers
To press his gory hands;
And now, with shouts and clapping,
And noise of weeping loud,
He enters through the River-Gate,
Borne by the joyous crowd.

They gave him of the corn-land,
That was of public right,
As much as two strong oxen
Could plow from morn till night;
And they made a molten image,
And set it up on high,
And there it stands unto this day
To witness if I lie.

It stands in the Comitium,[24]
Plain for all folk to see;
Horatius in his harness,
Halting upon one knee:

24. The comitium was the old Roman polling-place, a square situated between the Forum and the Senate House.

ROUND HIM THRONG THE FATHERS

And underneath is written,
  In letters all of gold,
How valiantly he kept the bridge
  In the brave days of old.

And still his name sounds stirring
  Unto the men of Rome,

As the trumpet-blast that cries to them
  To charge the Volscian[25] home;
And wives still pray to Juno[26]
  For boys with hearts as bold
As his who kept the bridge so well
  In the brave days of old.

And in the nights of winter,
  When the cold north-winds blow,
And the long howling of the wolves
  Is heard amidst the snow;
When round the lonely cottage
  Roars loud the tempest's din,
And the good logs of Algidus
  Roar louder yet within:

When the oldest cask is opened,
  And the largest lamp is lit;
When the chestnuts glow in the embers,
  And the kid turns on the spit;
When young and old in circle
  Around the firebrands close;
And the girls are weaving baskets,
  And the lads are shaping bows;

When the goodman mends his armor,
  And trims his helmet's plume;
When the goodwife's shuttle merrily
  Goes flashing through the loom,—

---

25. The Volscians were among the most determined of the Italian enemies of Rome.

26. Juno was the goddess who was thought of as presiding over marriage and the birth of children.

With weeping and with laughter
  Still is the story told,
How well Horatius kept the bridge
  In the brave days of old.[27]

27. You can tell from these last three stanzas that Macaulay is writing his poem, not as an Englishman of the nineteenth century, but as if he were a Roman in the days when Rome, though powerful, had not yet become the luxurious city which it afterward was. That is, he thought of himself as writing in the days of the Republic, not in the days of the Empire.

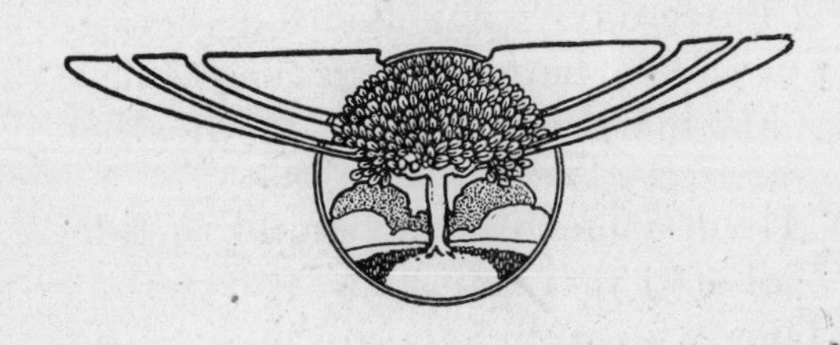

LORD ULLIN'S DAUGHTER

THOMAS CAMPBELL

A chieftain, to the Highlands bound,
  Cries, "Boatman, do not tarry!
And I'll give thee a silver pound,
  To row us o'er the ferry."

"Now who be ye, would cross Lochgyle,
  This dark and stormy water?"
"O, I'm the chief of Ulva's isle,
  And this Lord Ullin's daughter.

"And fast before her father's men
  Three days we've fled together,
For should he find us in the glen,
  My blood would stain the heather.

"His horsemen hard behind us ride;
  Should they our steps discover,
Then who will cheer my bonny bride
  When they have slain her lover?"

Out spoke the hardy Highland wight,
  "I'll go, my chief—I'm ready;
It is not for your silver bright,
  But for your winsome lady:

"And by my word! the bonny bird
  In danger shall not tarry;
So though the waves are raging white,
  I'll row you o'er the ferry."

"BOATMAN, DO NOT TARRY!"

By this the storm grew loud apace,
  The water-wraith was shrieking;
And in the scowl of heaven each face
  Grew dark as they were speaking.

But still as wilder blew the wind,
  And as the night grew drearer,

Adown the glen rode armèd men,
  Their trampling sounded nearer.

"O haste thee, haste!" the lady cries,
  "Though tempests round us gather;
I'll meet the raging of the skies,
  But not an angry father."

The boat had left a stormy land,
  A stormy sea before her,—
When, oh! too strong for human hand,
  The tempest gather'd o'er her.

And still they row'd amidst the roar
  Of waters fast prevailing:
Lord Ullin reach'd that fatal shore,
  His wrath was changed to wailing.

For sore dismay'd, through storm and shade,
  His child he did discover:—
One lovely hand she stretch'd for aid,
  And one was round her lover.

"Come back! come back!" he cried in grief,
  "Across this stormy water:
And I'll forgive your Highland chief,
  My daughter!—oh my daughter!"

'Twas vain: the loud waves lashed the shore,
  Return or aid preventing;
The waters wild went o'er his child,
  And he was left lamenting.

SIR WALTER SCOTT

SIR WALTER SCOTT

GRACE E. SELLON

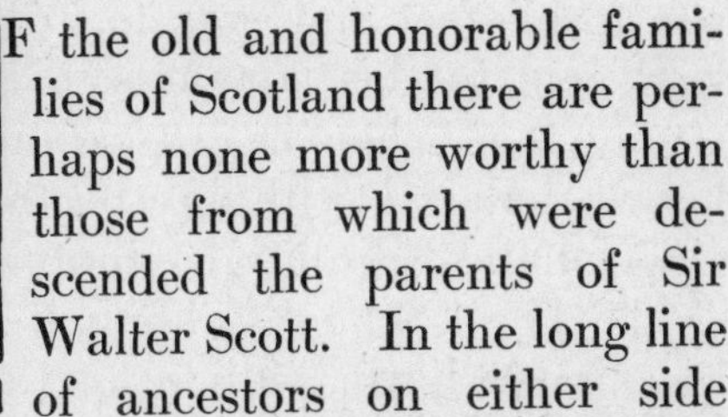

F the old and honorable families of Scotland there are perhaps none more worthy than those from which were descended the parents of Sir Walter Scott. In the long line of ancestors on either side were fearless knights and bold chiefs of the Scottish Border whose adventures became a delightful heritage to the little boy born into the Edinburgh family of Scott in 1771. Perhaps his natural liking for strange and exciting events would have made him even more eager than other children to be told fairy stories and tales of real heroes of his own land. But even had this not been so, the way in which he was forced to spend his early childhood was such that entertainment of this kind was about all that he could enjoy. He was not two years old when, after a brief illness, he lost the use of one of his legs and thus became unable to run about as before, or even to stand. Soon afterward he was sent to his grandfather's farm at Sandy-Knowe, where it was thought that the country life would help him. There he spent his days in listening to lively stories of Scotsmen who had lived in the brave and rollicking fashion of Robin Hood, in being read to by his aunt or in lying out among the rocks, cared for by his grandfather's old shepherd. When thus out of doors he found so much of interest about him that he could not lie still and would try so hard to move himself about that at length he became able to rise to his feet and even to walk and run.

Except for his lameness, he grew so well and strong that when he was about eight years old he was placed with his brothers in the upper class of the Edinburgh grammar school, known as the High School. Though he had had some lessons in Latin with a private tutor, he was behind his class in this subject, and being a high-spirited and sensitive boy, he felt rather keenly this disadvantage. Perhaps the fact that he could not be one of the leaders of his class made him careless; at any rate, he could never be depended upon to prepare his lesson, and at no time did he make a consistently good record. However, he found not a little comfort for his failure as a student in his popularity as a story-teller and kind-hearted comrade. Among the boys of his own rank in the school he won great admiration for his never-ending supply of exciting narratives and his willingness to give help upon lessons that he would otherwise have left undone.

At the end of three years his class was promoted, and he found the new teacher much more to his liking. Indeed, his ability to appreciate the meaning and beauty of the Latin works studied became recognized: he began to make translations in verse that won praise, and, with a new feeling of distinction, he was thus urged on to earnest efforts. After leaving this school, he continued his excellent progress in the study of Latin for a short time under a teacher in the village of Kelso, where he had gone to visit an aunt.

Meanwhile his hours out of school were spent in ways most pleasing to his lively imagination. His lameness did not debar him from the most active sports, nor even from the vigorous encounters in which, either with a single opponent or with company set against company, the Scotch schoolboys defended their reputation as hard fighters. One of these skirmishes that made a lasting impression upon Walter Scott he himself tells us of, and his biographer, Lockhart, has quoted it in describing the hardy boyhood days of the great writer. It frequently happened that bands of children from different parts of Edinburgh would wage war with each other, fighting with stones and clubs and other like weapons. Perhaps the city authorities thought that these miniature battles afforded good training: at least the police seem not to have interfered. The boys in the neighborhood where Walter lived had formed a company that had been given a beautiful standard by a young noblewoman. This company fought every week with a band composed of boys of the poorer classes. The leader of the latter was a fine-looking young fellow who bore himself as bravely as any chieftain. In the midst of a hotly fought contest, this boy had all but captured the enemy's proudly erected standard when he was struck severely to the ground with a cruelly heavy weapon. The dismayed companies fled in all directions, and the lad was taken to the hospital. In a few days, however, he recovered; and then it was that through a friendly baker Walter Scott and his brothers were able to get word to their mistreated opponent and to offer a sum of money in token of their regret. But Green-breeks, as the young leader had been dubbed, refused to accept this, and said besides that they might be sure of his not telling what he knew of the affair in which he had been hurt, for he felt it a disgrace to be a talebearer. This generous conduct so impressed young Scott and his companions that always afterward the fighting was fair.

It must have been with not a little difficulty that this warlike spirit was subdued and made obedient to the strict rules observed in the Presbyterian home on Sunday. To a boy whose mind was filled with stirring deeds of adventure and all sorts of vivid legends and romances, the long, gloomy services seemed a tiresome burden. Monday, however, brought new opportunities for reading favorite poets and works of history and travel, and many were the spare moments through the week that were spent thus. The marvelous characters and incidents in Spenser's *Faerie Queene* were a never-ending source of enjoyment, and later Percy's *Reliques of Ancient English Poetry* was discovered by the young reader with a gladness that made him forget everything else in the world. "I remember well," he has written, "the spot where I read these volumes for the first time. It was beneath a huge platanus tree, in the ruins of what had been intended for an old-fashioned arbor in the garden I have mentioned. The summer day sped onward so fast that, notwithstanding the sharp appetite of thirteen, I forgot the hour of dinner, was sought for with anxiety, and was found still entranced in my intellectual banquet. To read and to remember was in this instance the same thing, and henceforth I overwhelmed my schoolfellows, and all who would hearken to me, with tragical recitations from the ballads of Bishop Percy. The first time, too, I could scrape a few shillings together, which were not common occurrences with me, I bought unto myself a copy of these beloved volumes; nor do I believe I ever read a book half so frequently, or with half the enthusiasm."

After his return from Kelso, Walter was sent to college, but with no better results than in the early years at the High School. The Latin teacher was so mild in his requirements that it was easy to neglect the lessons, and in beginning the study of Greek the boy was again at a disadvantage, for nearly all his classmates, unlike himself, knew a little of the language. He was scarcely more successful in a private course in mathematics, but did well in his classes in moral philosophy. History and civil and municipal law completed his list of studies. So meager did this education seem that in later years Scott wrote in a brief autobiography, "If, however, it should ever fall to the lot of youth to peruse these pages—let such a reader remember that it is with the deepest regret that I recollect in my manhood the opportunities of learning which I neglected in my youth: that through every part of my literary career I have felt pinched and hampered by my own ignorance: and that I would at this moment give half the reputation I have had the good fortune to acquire, if by doing so I could rest the remaining part upon a sound foundation of learning and science."

It had been decided that Walter should follow his father's profession, that of the law, and accordingly he entered his father's office, to serve a five years' apprenticeship. Though it may seem surprising, in view of his former indolence, it is true that he gave himself to his work with great industry. At the same time, however, he continued to read stories of adventure and history and other similar works with as much zest as ever, and entered into an agreement with a friend whereby each was to entertain the other with original romances. The monotony of office duties was also relieved by many trips about the country, in which the keenest delight was felt in natural beauties and in the historical associations of old ruins and battlefields and other places of like interest. Then, too, there were literary societies that advanced the young law-apprentice both intellectually and socially. Thus the years with his father passed. Then, as he was to prepare himself for admission to the bar, he entered law classes in the University of

Edinburgh, with the result that in 1792 he was admitted into the Faculty of Advocates.

The first years of his practice, though not without profit, might have seemed dull and irksome to the young lawyer, had not his summers been spent in journeys about Scotland in which he came into possession of a wealth of popular legends and ballads. It was during one of these excursions, made in 1797, that he met the attractive young French woman, Charlotte Carpenter, who a few months later became his wife. A previous and unfortunate love affair had considerably sobered Scott's ardent nature, but his friendship and marriage with Miss Carpenter brought him much of the happiness of which he had believed himself to have been deprived.

The young couple spent their winters in Edinburgh and their summers at the suburb Lasswade. During the resting time passed in the country cottage, Scott found enjoyment in composing poems based upon some of the legends and superstitions with which he had become familiar in his jaunts among ruined castles and scenes in the Highlands. Some of these verses, shown in an offhand manner to James Ballantyne, who was the head of a printing establishment in Kelso, met with such favorable recognition that Scott was encouraged to lay bare to his friend a plan that had been forming in his mind for publishing a great collection of Scotch ballads. As a result Scott entered upon the work of editing the ballads that he had been so industriously gathering for several summers, and by 1803 had published the three volumes of his *Minstrelsy of the Scottish Border.* So successful was this venture that shortly afterward he began the *Lay of the Last Minstrel,* a lengthy poem in which his keen interest in the thrilling history of the Scottish Border found full expression. This poem, published in 1805, was heartily welcomed, and opened to its author the career for which he was best fitted.

The popularity of the *Lay,* together with the fact that the young poet had won no honors as an advocate, doubtless accounts for his retiring from the bar in 1806. He had been made sheriff of Selkirkshire in 1799, and to the income thus received was added that of a clerk of the Court of Sessions, an office to which he was appointed in 1806. More than this, he had in the preceding year become a partner in the Ballantyne printing establishment, which had moved to Edinburgh, and his growing fame as a writer seemed to promise that his association with this firm would bring considerable profit.

With a good income thus assured, Scott was able within the following four years to produce besides minor works, two other great poems, *Marmion, a Tale of Flodden Field,* and *The Lady of the Lake.* These rank with the most stirring and richly colored narrative poems in our language. So vivid, indeed, are the pictures of Scottish scenery found in *The Lady of the Lake* that, according to a writer who was living when it was published, "The whole country rang with the praises of the poet—crowds set off to view the scenery of Loch Katrine, till then comparatively unknown; and as the book came out just before the season for excursions, every house and inn in that neighborhood was crammed with a constant succession of visitors."

This lively and pleasing story, with its graceful verse form, has become such a favorite for children's reading, that it seems very amusing to be told of the answer given by one of Scott's little daughters to a family friend who had asked her how she liked the poem: "Oh, I have not read it; papa says there's nothing so bad for young people as reading bad poetry." The biographer Lockhart recounts also a little incident in which young Walter Scott, returning from school with the marks of battle showing plainly on his face, was asked why he had been fighting, and replied, looking down in shame, that he had been called a *lassie*. Never having heard of even the title of his father's poem, the boy had fiercely resented being named, by some of his playmates, *The Lady of the Lake*.

In order to fulfil his duties as sheriff, Scott had in 1804 leased the estate of Ashestiel, and in this wild and beautiful stretch of country on the Tweed River had spent his summers. When his lease expired in 1811, he bought a farm of one hundred acres extending along the same river, and in the following year removed with his family to the cottage on this new property. This was the simple beginning of the magnificent Abbotsford home. Year after year changes were made, and land was added to the estate until by the close of 1824 a great castle had been erected. The building and furnishing of this mansion were of the keenest interest to its owner, an interest that was expressed probably with most delight in the two wonderful armories containing weapons borne by many heroes of history, and in the library with its carved oak ceiling, its bookcases filled with from fifteen to twenty thousand volumes, among which are some of unusual value, and its handsome portrait of the eldest of Scott's sons.

The building of this splendid dwelling place shows Scott to have been exceptionally prosperous as a writer. Yet his way was by no means always smooth. In 1808 he had formed with the Ballantynes a publishing house that, as a result of poor management, failed completely in 1813. Scott bore the trouble with admirable coolness, and by means of good management averted further disaster and made arrangements for the continued publication of his works.

After this event it must have seemed more necessary than ever before that his popularity as a writer should be made secure. Then, too, when Byron's fame as a poet continued to rise, and his own power to please the readers of his verse declined somewhat, he appears to have felt much as he had when a boy at school, that unless he could be a leader he did not care to strive for a lower degree of honor. "Byron hits the mark where I don't even pretend to fledge my arrow," he remarked on one occasion.

By this time he had found through the marked

ABBOTSFORD

success of his novel *Waverley*, published in 1814, that a new and promising field lay before him. He decided then to give up poetry and devote himself especially to writing romances, in which his love of the picturesque and thrilling in history and of the noble and chivalrous in human character could find the widest range of expression. With marvelous industry he added one after another to the long series of his famous Waverley Novels. Perhaps the height of his power was reached in 1819 in the production of *Ivanhoe*, though *Waverley*, *Guy Mannering* and *The Heart of Midlothian*, previously written, as well as *Kenilworth* and *Quentin Durward*, published later, must also be given first rank. In the intervals of his work on these novels, Scott also wrote reviews and essays and miscellaneous articles. He became recognized as the most gifted prose writer of his age, and his works, it is said, became "the daily food, not only of his countrymen, but of all educated Europe." He was sought after with eager homage by the wealthy and notable, and was given the title of baronet, yet remained as simple and sincere at heart as in the early days of his career.

With the sales of his books amounting to $50,000 or more a year, it is not strange that he should have felt his fortune assured. But again, and this time with the most serious results, he was deceived by the mismanagement of others. The printing firm of James Ballantyne and Company, in which he had remained a partner, became bankrupt in 1826. Had it not been for a high sense of honor, he would have withdrawn with the others of the firm; but the sense of his great debt pressed upon him so sorely that he agreed to pay all that he owed, at whatever cost to himself. For the remaining six years of his life he worked as hard as failing health would allow, and the strain of his labor told on him severely.

At length he consented to a trip to southern Europe, but the change did not bring back his health. Not long after his return to Abbotsford, in 1832, he called his son-in-law to his bedside early one morning, and speaking in calm tones, said: "Lockhart, I may have but a minute to speak to you. My dear, be a good man—be virtuous—be religious—be a good man. Nothing else will give you any comfort when you come to lie here." After a few words more he asked God's blessing on all in the household and then fell into a quiet sleep from which he did not awake on earth.

Had Scott lived but a few years longer he would undoubtedly have paid off all his voluntarily assumed obligations. As it was, all his debts were liquidated in 1847 by the sale of copyrights.

Many years have passed since the death of Sir Walter Scott, and to the young readers of to-day the time in which he lived may seem far away and indistinct. But every boy and girl can share with him the pleasure that he felt, all his life, in stories of battle on sea and land, in love tales of knights and ladies, in mysterious superstitions and in everything else that spurs one on at the liveliest speed through the pages of a book. These interests and delights of his boyhood he never outgrew. They kept him always young at heart and gave to his works a freshness and brightness that few writers have been able to retain throughout their lives.

When he became *laird* of Abbotsford, the same sunny nature and kindly feeling for others that had drawn about him many comrades in his schoolboy days, attracted to him crowds of visitors who, though they intruded on his time, were received with generous courtesy. His tall, strongly built figure was often the center of admiring groups of guests who explored with him the wonders and beauties of Abbotsford, listening meanwhile to his humorous stories. At such times, with his clear, wide-open blue eyes, and his pleasant smile lighting his somewhat heavy features, he would have been called a handsome man. Of all who came to the home at Abbotsford, none were more gladly received than the children of the tenants who lived in the little homes on the estate. Each year, on the last morning in December, it was customary for them to pay a visit of respect to the *laird*, and though they may not have known it, he found more pleasure in this simple ceremony than in all the others of the Christmas season.

To these gentler qualities of his nature was joined not a little of the hardihood of the Scotch heroes whose lives he has celebrated. The same "high spirit with which, in younger days," he has written, "I used to enjoy a Tam-o'-Shanter ride through darkness, wind and rain, the boughs groaning and cracking over my head, the good horse free to the road and impatient for home, and feeling the weather as little as I did," was that which bore him bravely through misfortune and gave him the splendid courage with which in his last years he faced the ruin of his fortune. With an influence as strong and wholesome as that of his works as a writer, remains the example of his loyal, industrious life.

THE TOURNAMENT

SIR WALTER SCOTT

NOTE,—Scott's *Ivanhoe,* from which this account of *The Tournament* is taken, belongs to the class of books known as historical novels. Such a book does not necessarily have as the center of its plot an historical incident, nor does it necessarily have an historical character as hero or heroine; it does, however, introduce historic scenes or historic people, or both. In *Ivanhoe,* the events of which take place in England in the twelfth century, during the reign of Richard I, both the king and his brother John appear, though they are by no means the chief characters. The great movements known as the Crusades, while they are frequently mentioned and give a sort of an atmosphere to the book, do not influence the plot directly.

Ivanhoe does much more, however, than introduce us casually to Richard and John; it gives us a striking picture of customs and manners in the twelfth century. The story is not made to halt for long descriptions, but the events themselves and their settings are so brought before us that we have much clearer pictures of them than hours of reading in histories and encyclopedias could give us. This account of a tournament, for instance, while it lets us see all the gorgeousness that was a part of such pageants, does not fail to give us also the cruel, brutal side.

THE poor as well as the rich, the vulgar as well as the noble, in the event of a tournament, which was the grand spectacle of that age, felt as much interested as the half-starved citizen of Madrid, who has not a real left to buy provisions for his family, feels in the issue of a bull-feast. Neither duty nor infirmity could keep youth or age from such exhibitions. The passage of arms, as it was called, which was to take place at Ashby, in the county of Leicester, as champions of the first renown were to take the field in the presence of Prince John himself, who was expected to grace the lists, had attracted universal attention, and an immense confluence of persons of all ranks hastened upon the appointed morning to the place of combat.

The scene was singularly romantic. On the verge of a wood, which approached to within a mile of the town of Ashby, was an extensive meadow of the finest and most beautiful green turf, surrounded on one side by the forest, and fringed on the other by straggling oak trees, some of which had grown to an immense size. The ground, as if fashioned on purpose for the martial display which was intended, sloped gradually down on all sides to a level bottom, which was enclosed for the lists with strong palisades, forming a space of a quarter of a mile in length, and about half as broad. The form of the enclosure was an oblong square, save that the corners were considerably rounded off, in order to afford more convenience for the spectators. The openings for the entry of the combatants were at the northern and southern extremities of the lists, accessible by strong wooden gates, each wide enough to admit two horsemen riding abreast. At each of these portals were stationed two heralds, attended by six trumpets, as many pursuivants,[1] and a strong body of men-at-arms, for maintaining order, and ascertaining the quality of the knights who proposed to engage in this martial game.

On a platform beyond the southern entrance, formed by a natural elevation of the ground, were pitched five magnificent pavilions, adorned with pennons of russet and black, the chosen colors of the five knights challengers. The cords of the tents were of the same color. Before each pavilion was suspended the shield of the knight by whom it was occupied, and beside it stood his squire, quaintly disguised as a salvage[2] or silvan man, or in some other fantastic dress, according to the taste of his master and the character he was pleased to assume during the game. The central pavilion, as the place of honor, had been assigned to Brian de Bois-Guilbert, whose renown in all games of chivalry, no less than his connection with the knights who had undertaken this passage of arms, had occasioned him to be eagerly received into the company of challengers, and even adopted as their chief and leader, though he had so recently joined them. On one side of his tent were

1. A pursuivant was an attendant on a herald.
2. *Salvage* is an old form of the word *savage*.

pitched those of Reginald Front-de-Bœuf and Richard (Philip) de Malvoisin, and on the other was the pavilion of Hugh de Grantmesnil, a noble baron in the vicinity, whose ancestor had been Lord High Steward of England in the time of the Conqueror and his son William Rufus. Ralph de Vipont, a knight of Saint John of Jerusalem, who had some ancient possessions at a place called Heather, near Ashby-de-la-Zouche, occupied the fifth pavilion. From the entrance into the lists a gently sloping passage, ten yards in breadth, led up to the platform on which the tents were pitched. It was strongly secured by a palisade on each side, as was the esplanade in front of the pavilions, and the whole was guarded by men-at-arms.

The northern access to the lists terminated in a similar entrance of thirty feet in breadth, at the extremity of which was a large enclosed space for such knights as might be disposed to enter the lists with the challengers, behind which were placed tents containing refreshments of every kind for their accommodation, with armorers, farriers, and other attendants, in readiness to give their services wherever they might be necessary.

The exterior of the lists was in part occupied by temporary galleries, spread with tapestries and carpets, and accommodated with cushions for the convenience of those ladies and nobles who were expected to attend the tournament. A narrow space between these galleries and the lists gave accommodation for yeomanry and

THE PROMISCUOUS MULTITUDE

spectators of a better degree than the mere vulgar, and might be compared to the pit of a theatre. The promiscuous multitude arranged themselves upon large banks of turf prepared for the purpose, which, aided by the natural elevation of the ground, enabled them to overlook the galleries, and obtain a fair view into the lists. Besides the accommodation which these stations afforded, many hundreds had perched themselves on the branches of the trees which surrounded the meadow; and even the steeple of a country church, at some distance, was crowded with spectators.

It only remains to notice respecting the general arrangement, that one gallery in the very centre of the eastern side of the lists, and consequently exactly opposite to the spot where the shock of the combat was to take place, was raised higher than the others, more richly decorated, and graced by a sort of throne and canopy, on which the royal arms were emblazoned. Squires, pages, and yeomen in rich liveries waited around this place of honor, which was designed for Prince John and his attendants. Opposite to this royal gallery was another, elevated to the same height, on the western side of the lists; and more gayly, if less sumptuously, decorated than that destined for the Prince himself. A train of pages and of young maidens, the most beautiful who could be selected, gayly dressed in fancy habits of green and pink, surrounded a throne decorated in the same colors. Among pennons and flags bearing wounded hearts, burning hearts, bleeding hearts, bows and quivers, and all the commonplace emblems of the triumphs of Cupid, a blazoned inscription informed the spectators that this seat of honor was designed for *La Royne de la Beaute et des Amours.* But who was to represent the Queen of Beauty and of Love on the present occasion no one was prepared to guess.

Meanwhile, spectators of every description

thronged forward to occupy their respective stations, and not without many quarrels concerning those which they were entitled to hold. Some of these were settled by the men-at-arms with brief ceremony; the shafts of their battle-axes and pummels of their swords being readily employed as arguments to convince the more refractory. Others, which involved the rival claims of more elevated persons, were determined by the heralds, or by the two marshals of the field, William de Wyvil and Stephen de Martival, who, armed at all points, rode up and down the lists to enforce and preserve good order among the spectators.

Gradually the galleries became filled with knights and nobles, in their robes of peace, whose long and rich-tinted mantles were contrasted with the gayer and more splendid habits of the ladies, who, in a greater proportion than even the men themselves, thronged to witness a sport which one would have thought too bloody and dangerous to afford their sex much pleasure. The lower and interior space was soon filled by substantial yeomen and burghers, and such of the lesser gentry as, from modesty poverty, or dubious title, durst not assume any higher place.

Suddenly the attention of every one was called to the entrance of Prince John, who at that moment entered the lists, attended by a numerous and gay train, consisting partly of laymen, partly of churchmen, as light in their dress, and as gay in their demeanor, as their companions. Among the latter was the Prior of Jorvaulx, in the most gallant trim which a dignitary of the church could venture to exhibit. Fur and gold were not spared in his garments; and the points of his boots turned up so very far as to be attached not to his knees merely, but to his very girdle, and effectually prevented him from putting his foot into the stirrup. This, how-

THE ENTRANCE OF PRINCE JOHN

ever, was a slight inconvenience to the gallant Abbot, who, perhaps even rejoicing in the opportunity to display his accomplished horsemanship before so many spectators, especially of the fair sex, dispensed with the use of these supports to a timid rider. The rest of Prince John's retinue consisted of the favorite leaders of his mercenary troops, some marauding barons and profligate attendants upon the court, with several Knights Templars and Knights of Saint John.

Attended by this gallant equipage, himself well mounted, and splendidly dressed in crimson and in gold, bearing upon his hand a falcon, and having his head covered by a rich fur bonnet, adorned with a circle of precious stones, from which his long curled hair escaped and overspread his shoulders, Prince John, upon a gray and high-mettled palfrey, caracoled within the lists at the head of his jovial party, laughing loud with his train, and eyeing with all the boldness of royal criticism the beauties who adorned the lofty galleries.

In the midst of Prince John's cavalcade, he suddenly stopped, and, appealing to the Prior of Jorvaulx, declared the principal business of the day had been forgotten.

"By my halidom," said he, "we have neglected, Sir Prior, to name the fair Sovereign of Love and of Beauty, by whose white hand the palm is to be distributed. For my part, I am liberal in my ideas, and I care not if I give my vote for the black-eyed Rebecca."

"Holy Virgin," answered the Prior, turning up his eyes in horror, "a Jewess! We should deserve to be stoned out of the lists; and I am not yet old enough to be a martyr. Besides, I swear by my patron saint that she is far inferior to the lovely Saxon, Rowena."

From the tone in which this was spoken, John saw the necessity of acquiescence. "I did but jest," he said; "and you turn upon me like an adder! Name whom you will, in the fiend's name, and please yourselves."

"Nay, nay," said De Bracy, "let the fair sovereign's throne remain unoccupied until the conqueror shall be named, and then let him choose the lady by whom it shall be filled. It will add another grace to his triumph, and teach fair ladies to prize the love of valiant knights, who can exalt them to such distinction."

"If Brian de Bois-Guilbert gain the prize," said the Prior, "I will gage my rosary that I name the Sovereign of Love and Beauty."

"Bois-Guilbert," answered De Bracy, "is a good lance; but there are others around these lists, Sir Prior, who will not fear to encounter him."

"Silence, sirs," said Waldemar, "and let the Prince assume his seat. The knights and spectators are alike impatient, the time advances, and highly fit it is that the sports should commence."

Prince John, though not yet a monarch, had in Waldemar Fitzurse all the inconveniences of a favorite minister, who, in serving his sovereign, must always do so in his own way. The Prince acquiesced, however, although his disposition was precisely of that kind which is apt to be obstinate upon trifles, and, assuming his throne, and being surrounded by his followers, gave signal to the heralds to proclaim the laws of the tournament, which were briefly as follows:

First, the five challengers were to undertake all comers.

Secondly, any knight proposing to combat might, if he pleased, select a special antagonist from among the challengers, by touching his shield. If he did so with the reverse of his lance, the trial of skill was made with what were called the arms of courtesy, that is, with lances at whose extremity a piece of round flat board was fixed, so that no danger was encountered, save from the shock of the horses and riders. But if the shield was touched with the sharp end of the lance, the combat was understood to be at *outrance*,[3] that is, the knights were to fight with sharp weapons, as in actual battle.

Thirdly, when the knights present had accomplished their vow, by each of them breaking five lances, the Prince was to declare the victor in the first day's tourney, who should receive as prize a war-horse of exquisite beauty and matchless strength; and in addition to this reward of valor, it was now declared, he should have the peculiar honor of naming the Queen of Love and Beauty, by whom the prize should be given on the ensuing day.

Fourthly, it was announced that, on the second day, there should be a general tournament, in which all the knights present, who were desirous to win praise, might take part; and being divided into two bands, of equal numbers, might fight it out manfully until the signal was given by Prince John to cease the combat. The elected Queen of Love and Beauty was then to crown the knight, whom the Prince should adjudge to have borne himself best in this second day, with a coronet composed of thin gold plate, cut into

3. *Outrance* is an old word meaning *the last extremity*.

the shape of a laurel crown. On this second day the knightly games ceased. But on that which was to follow, feats of archery, of bull-baiting, and other popular amusements were to be practiced, for the more immediate amusement of the populace. In this manner did Prince John endeavor to lay the foundation of a popularity which he was perpetually throwing down by some inconsiderate act of wanton aggression upon the feelings and prejudices of the people.

The lists now presented a most splendid spectacle. The sloping galleries were crowded with all that was noble, great, wealthy, and beautiful in the northern and midland parts of England; and the contrast of the various dresses of these dignified spectators rendered the view as gay as it was rich, while the interior and lower space, filled with the substantial burgesses and yeomen of merry England, formed, in their more plain attire, a dark fringe, or border, around this circle of brilliant embroidery, relieving, and at the same time setting off, its splendor.

The heralds finished their proclamation with their usual cry of "Largesse,[4] largesse, gallant knights!" and gold and silver pieces were showered on them from the galleries, it being a high point of chivalry to exhibit liberality toward those whom the age accounted at once the secretaries and historians of honor. The bounty of the spectators was acknowledged by the customary shouts of "Love of ladies—Death of champions—Honor to the generous—Glory to the

4. A largesse is a gift or donation.

brave!" To which the more humble spectators added their acclamations, and a numerous band of trumpeters the flourish of their martial instruments. When these sounds had ceased, the heralds withdrew from the lists in gay and glittering procession, and none remained within them save the marshals of the field, who, armed cap-à-pie, sat on horseback, motionless as statues, at the opposite ends of the lists. Meantime, the inclosed space at the northern extremity of the lists, large as it was, was now completely crowded with knights desirous to prove their skill against the challengers, and, when viewed from the galleries, presented the appearance of a sea of waving plumage, intermixed with glistening helmets and tall lances, to the extremities of which were, in many cases, attached small pennons of about a span's breadth, which, fluttering in the air as the breeze caught them, joined with the restless motion of the feathers to add liveliness to the scene.

At length the barriers were opened, and five knights, chosen by lot, advanced slowly into the area; a single champion riding in front, and the other four following in pairs. All were splendidly armed, and my Saxon authority (in the Wardour Manuscript) records at great length their devices, their colors, and the embroidery of their horse trappings. It is unnecessary to be particular on these subjects.

Their escutcheons have long mouldered from the walls of their castles. Their castles themselves are but green mounds and shattered ruins:

the place that once knew them, knows them no more—nay, many a race since theirs has died out and been forgotten in the very land which they occupied with all the authority of feudal proprietors and feudal lords. What, then, would it avail the reader to know their names, or the evanescent symbols of their martial rank?

Now, however, no whit anticipating the oblivion which awaited their names and feats, the champions advanced through the lists, restraining their fiery steeds, and compelling them to move slowly, while, at the same time, they exhibited their paces, together with the grace and dexterity of the riders. As the procession entered the lists, the sound of a wild barbaric music was heard from behind the tents of the challengers, where the performers were concealed. It was of Eastern origin, having been brought from the Holy Land; and the mixture of the cymbals and bells seemed to bid welcome at once, and defiance, to the knights as they advanced. With the eyes of an immense concourse of spectators fixed upon them, the five knights advanced up the platform upon which the tents of the challengers stood, and there separating themselves, each touched slightly, and with the reverse of his lance, the shield of the antagonist to whom he wished to oppose himself. The lower order of spectators in general—nay, many of the higher class, and it is even said several of the ladies—were rather disappointed at the champions choosing the arms of courtesy. For the same sort of persons who, in the present day, applaud most highly the deepest tragedies were then interested in a tournament exactly in proportion to the danger incurred by the champions engaged.

Having intimated their more pacific purpose, the champions retreated to the extremity of the lists, where they remained drawn up in a line; while the challengers, sallying each from his pavilion, mounted their horses, and, headed by Brian de Bois-Guilbert, descended from the platform and opposed themselves individually to the knights who had touched their respective shields.

At the flourish of clarions and trumpets, they started out against each other at full gallop; and such was the superior dexterity or good fortune of the challengers, that those opposed to Bois-Guilbert, Malvoisin, and Front-de-Bœuf rolled on the ground. The antagonist of Grantmesnil, instead of bearing his lance-point fair against the crest or the shield of his enemy, swerved so much from the direct line as to break the weapon athwart the person of his opponent—a circumstance which was accounted more disgraceful than that of being actually unhorsed, because the latter might happen from accident, whereas the former evinced awkwardness and want of management of the weapon and of the horse. The fifth knight alone maintained the honor of his party, and parted fairly with the Knight of Saint John, both splintering their lances without advantage on either side.

The shouts of the multitude, together with the

acclamations of the heralds and the clangor of the trumpets, announced the triumph of the victors and the defeat of the vanquished. The former retreated to their pavilions, and the latter, gathering themselves up as they could, withdrew from the lists in disgrace and dejection, to agree with their victors concerning the redemption of their arms and their horses, which, according to the laws of the tournament, they had forfeited. The fifth of their number alone tarried in the lists long enough to be greeted by the applauses of the spectators, among whom he retreated, to the aggravation, doubtless, of his companions' mortification.

A second and a third party of knights took the field; and although they had various success, yet, upon the whole, the advantage decidedly remained with the challengers, not one of whom lost his seat or swerved from his charge—misfortunes which befell one or two of their antagonists in each encounter. The spirits, therefore, of those opposed to them seemed to be considerably damped by their continued success. Three knights only appeared on the fourth entry, who, avoiding the shields of Bois-Guilbert and Front-de-Bœuf, contented themselves with touching those of the three other knights who had not altogether manifested the same strength and dexterity. This politic selection did not alter the fortune of the field: the challengers were still successful. One of their antagonists was overthrown; and both the others failed in the *attaint*, that is, in striking the helmet and shield of their antagonist firmly and strongly, with the lance held in a direct line, so that the weapon might break unless the champion was overthrown.

After this fourth encounter, there was a considerable pause; nor did it appear that any one was very desirous of renewing the contest. The spectators murmured among themselves; for, among the challengers, Malvoisin and Front-de-Bœuf were unpopular from their characters, and the others, except Grantmesnil, were disliked as strangers and foreigners.

But none heard the general feeling of dissatisfaction so keenly as Cedric the Saxon, who saw, in each advantage gained by the Norman challengers, a repeated triumph over the honor of England. His own education had taught him no skill in the games of chivalry, although, with the arms of his Saxon ancestors, he had manifested himself, on many occasions, a brave and determined soldier. He looked anxiously to Athelstane, who had learned the accomplishments of the age, as if desiring that he should make some personal effort to recover the victory which was passing into the hands of the Templar and his associates. But, though both stout of heart and strong of person, Athelstane had a disposition too inert and unambitious to make the exertions which Cedric seemed to expect from him.

"The day is against England, my lord," said Cedric, in a marked tone; "are you not tempted to take the lance?"

"I shall tilt to-morrow," answered Athelstane,

"in the *melee;* it is not worth while for me to arm myself to-day."

Two things displeased Cedric in this speech. It contained the Norman word *melee* (to express the general conflict), and it evinced some indifference to the honor of the country; but it was spoken by Athelstane, whom he held in such profound respect that he would not trust himself to canvass his motives or his foibles. Moreover, he had no time to make any remark, for Wamba thrust in his word, observing, "It was better, though scarce easier, to be the best man among a hundred than the best man of two."

Athelstane took the observation as a serious compliment; but Cedric, who better understood the Jester's meaning, darted at him a severe and menacing look; and lucky it was for Wamba, perhaps, that the time and place prevented his receiving, notwithstanding his place and service, more sensible marks of his master's resentment.

The pause in the tournament was still uninterrupted, excepting by the voices of the heralds exclaiming—"Love of ladies, splintering of lances! stand forth, gallant knights, fair eyes look upon your deeds!"

The music also of the challengers breathed from time to time wild bursts expressive of triumph or defiance, while the clowns[5] grudged a holiday which seemed to pass away in inactivity; and old knights and nobles lamented in whispers the decay of martial spirit, spoke of the triumphs of their younger days, but agreed that the land

5. *Clowns* here means *peasants.*

did not now supply dames of such transcendent beauty as had animated the jousts of former times. Prince John began to talk to his attendants about making ready the banquet, and the necessity of adjudging the prize to Brian de Bois-Guilbert, who had, with a single spear, overthrown two knights and foiled a third.

At length, as the Saracenic music of the challengers concluded one of those long and high flourishes with which they had broken the silence of the lists, it was answered by a solitary trumpet, which breathed a note of defiance from the northern extremity. All eyes were turned to see the new champion which these sounds announced, and no sooner were the barriers opened than he paced into the lists. As far as could be judged of a man sheathed in armor, the new adventurer did not greatly exceed the middle size, and seemed to be rather slender than strongly made. His suit of armor was formed of steel, richly inlaid with gold, and the device on his shield was a young oak-tree pulled up by the roots, with the Spanish word *Desdichado*, signifying Disinherited. He was mounted on a gallant black horse, and as he passed through the lists he gracefully saluted the Prince and the ladies by lowering his lance. The dexterity with which he managed his steed, and something of youthful grace which he displayed in his manner, won him the favor of the multitude, which some of the lower classes observed by calling out, "Touch Ralph de Vipont's shield—touch the

Hospitaller's shield; he has the least sure seat, he is your cheapest bargain."

The champion, moving onward amid these well-meant hints, ascended the platform by the sloping alley which led to it from the lists, and, to the astonishment of all present, riding straight up to the central pavilion, struck with the sharp end of his spear the shield of Brian de Bois-Guilbert until it rang again. All stood astonished at his presumption, but none more than the redoubted Knight whom he had thus defied to mortal combat, and who, little expecting so rude a challenge, was standing carelessly at the door of the pavilion.

"Have you confessed yourself, brother," said the Templar, "and have you heard mass this morning, that you peril your life so frankly?"

"I am fitter to meet death than thou art," answered the Disinherited Knight; for by this name the stranger had recorded himself in the books of the tourney.

"Then take your place in the lists," said Bois-Guilbert, "and look your last upon the sun; for this night thou shalt sleep in paradise."

"Gramercy for thy courtesy," replied the Disinherited Knight, "and to requite it, I advise thee to take a fresh horse and a new lance, for by my honor you will need both."

Having expressed himself thus confidently, he reined his horse backward down the slope which he had ascended, and compelled him in the same manner to move backward through the lists, till he reached the northern extremity, where he remained stationary, in expectation of his antagonist. This feat of horsemanship again attracted the applause of the multitude.

However incensed at his adversary for the precautions he recommended, Brian de Bois-Guilbert did not neglect his advice; for his honor was too nearly concerned to permit his neglecting any means which might insure victory over his presumptuous opponent. He changed his horse for a proved and fresh one of great strength and spirit. He chose a new and tough spear, lest the wood of the former might have been strained in the previous encounters he had sustained. Lastly he laid aside his shield, which had received some little damage, and received another from his squires. His first had only borne the general device of his order, representing two knights riding upon one horse, an emblem expressive of the original humility and poverty of the Templars, qualities which they had since exchanged for the arrogance and wealth that finally occasioned their suppression. Bois-Guilbert's new shield bore a raven in full flight, holding in its claws a skull, and bearing the motto, *Gare le Corbeau.*[6]

When the two champions stood opposed to each other at the two extremities of the lists, the public expectation was strained to the highest pitch. Few augured the possibility that the encounter could terminate well for the Disinherited Knight; yet his courage and gallantry secured the general good wishes of the spectators.

6. *Gare le Corbeau* means *Beware of the raven.*

The trumpets had no sooner given the signal, than the champions vanished from their posts with the speed of lightning, and closed in the centre of the lists with the shock of a thunderbolt. The lances burst into shivers up to the very grasp, and it seemed at the moment that both knights had fallen, for the shock had made each horse recoil backward upon its haunches. The address of the riders recovered their steeds by use of the bridle and spur; and having glared on each other for an instant with eyes which seemed to flash fire through the bars of their visors, each made a demi-volte,[7] and, retiring to the extremity of the lists, received a fresh lance from the attendants.

A loud shout from the spectators, waving of scarfs and handkerchiefs, and general acclamations, attested the interest taken by the spectators in this encounter—the most equal, as well as the best performed, which had graced the day. But no sooner had the knights resumed their station than the clamor of applause was hushed into a silence so deep and so dead that it seemed the multitude were afraid even to breathe.

A few minutes' pause having been allowed, that the combatants and their horses might recover breath, Prince John with his truncheon signed to the trumpets to sound the onset. The champions a second time sprung from their stations, and closed in the centre of the lists, with the same speed, the same dexterity, the same

7. A demi-volte is a certain movement of a horse, by which he makes a half turn with the fore-feet off the ground.

violence, but not the same equal fortune as before.

In this second encounter, the Templar aimed at the centre of his antagonist's shield, and struck it so fair and forcibly that his spear went to shivers, and the Disinherited Knight reeled in his saddle. On the other hand, that champion had, at the beginning of his career, directed the point of his lance toward Bois-Guilbert's shield, but, changing his aim almost in the moment of encounter, he addressed it to the helmet, a mark more difficult to hit, but which, if attained, rendered the shock more irresistible. Fair and true he hit the Norman on the visor, where his lance's point kept hold of the bars. Yet, even at this disadvantage, the Templar sustained his high reputation; and had not the girths of his saddle burst, he might not have been unhorsed. As it chanced, however, saddle, horse, and man rolled on the ground under a cloud of dust.

To extricate himself from the stirrups and fallen steed was to the Templar scarce the work of a moment; and, stung with madness, both at his disgrace and at the acclamations with which it was hailed by the spectators, he drew his sword and waved it in defiance of his conqueror. The Disinherited Knight sprung from his steed, and also unsheathed his sword. The marshals of the field, however, spurred their horses between them, and reminded them that the laws of the tournament did not, on the present occasion, permit this species of encounter.

"We shall meet again, I trust," said the

THE DISINHERITED KNIGHT UNSHEATHED HIS SWORD

Templar, casting a resentful glance at his antagonist; "and where there are none to separate us."

"If we do not," said the Disinherited Knight, "the fault shall not be mine. On foot or horseback, with spear, with axe, or with sword, I am alike ready to encounter thee."

More and angrier words would have been exchanged, but the marshals, crossing their lances between them, compelled them to separate. The Disinherited Knight returned to his first station, and Bois-Guilbert to his tent, where he remained for the rest of the day in an agony of despair.

Without alighting from his horse, the conqueror called for a bowl of wine, and opening the beaver, or lower part of his helmet, announced that he quaffed it, "To all true English hearts, and to the confusion of foreign tyrants." He then commanded his trumpet to sound a defiance to the challengers, and desired a herald to announce to them that he should make no election, but was willing to encounter them in the order in which they pleased to advance against him.

The gigantic Front-de-Bœuf, armed in sable armor, was the first who took the field. He bore on a white shield a black bull's head,[8] half defaced by the numerous encounters which he had undergone, and bearing the arrogant motto, *Cave, Adsum.*[9] Over this champion the Disinherited Knight obtained a slight but decisive advantage. Both knights broke their lances fairly, but Front-de-Bœuf, who lost a stirrup in the encounter, was adjudged to have the disadvantage.

In the stranger's third encounter, with Sir Philip Malvoisin, he was equally successful; striking that baron so forcibly on the casque that the laces of the helmet broke, and Malvoisin, only saved from falling by being unhelmeted, was declared vanquished like his companions.

In his fourth combat, with De Grantmesnil, the Disinherited Knight showed as much cour-

8. *Front-de-Bœuf* means *bull's head.*
9. *Cave, Adsum* is a Latin expression meaning *Beware, I am here.*

tesy as he had hitherto evinced courage and dexterity. De Grantmesnil's horse, which was young and violent, reared and plunged in the course of the career so as to disturb the rider's aim, and the stranger, declining to take the advantage which this accident afforded him, raised his lance, and passing his antagonist without touching him, wheeled his horse and rode back again to his own end of the lists, offering his antagonist, by a herald, the chance of a second encounter. This De Grantmesnil declined, avowing himself vanquished as much by the courtesy as by the address of his opponent.

Ralph de Vipont summed up the list of the stranger's triumphs, being hurled to the ground with such force that the blood gushed from his nose and his mouth, and he was borne senseless from the lists.

The acclamations of thousands applauded the unanimous award of the Prince and marshals, announcing that day's honors to the Disinherited Knight.

William de Wyvil and Stephen de Martival, the marshals of the field, were the first to offer their congratulations to the victor, praying him, at the same time, to suffer his helmet to be unlaced, or, at least, that he would raise his visor ere they conducted him to receive the prize of the day's tourney from the hands of Prince John. The Disinherited Knight, with all knightly courtesy, declined their request, alleging, that he could not at this time suffer his face to be seen, for reasons which he had assigned to the heralds when he entered the lists. The marshals were perfectly satisfied by this reply; for amid the frequent and capricious vows by which knights were accustomed to bind themselves in the days of chivalry, there were none more common than those by which they engaged to remain incognito for a certain space, or until some particular adventure was achieved. The marshals, therefore, pressed no further into the mystery of the Disinherited Knight, but, announcing to Prince John the conqueror's desire to remain unknown, they requested permission to bring him before his Grace, in order that he might receive the reward of his valor.

John's curiosity was excited by the mystery observed by the stranger; and, being already displeased with the issue of the tournament, in which the challengers whom he favored had been successively defeated by one knight, he answered haughtily to the marshals, "By the light of Our Lady's brow, this same knight hath been disinherited as well of his courtesy as of his lands, since he desires to appear before us without uncovering his face. Wot ye, my lords," he said, turning round to his train, "who this gallant can be that bears himself thus proudly?"

"I cannot guess," answered De Bracy, "nor did I think there had been within the four seas that girth Britain a champion that could bear down these five knights in one day's jousting. By my faith, I shall never forget the force with which he shocked De Vipont. The poor Hospitaller[10] was hurled from his saddle like a stone from a sling."

"Boast not of that," said a Knight of Saint John, who was present; "your Temple champion had no better luck. I saw your brave lance, Bois-Guilbert, roll thrice over, grasping his hands full of sand at every turn."

De Bracy, being attached to the Templars, would have replied, but was prevented by Prince John. "Silence, sirs!" he said; "what unprofitable debate have we here?"

"The victor," said De Wyvil, "still waits the pleasure of your Highness."

"It is our pleasure," answered John, "that he do so wait until we learn whether there is not some one who can at least guess at his name and quality. Should he remain there till nightfall, he has had work enough to keep him warm."

"Your Grace," said Waldemar Fitzurse, "will do less than due honor to the victor if you compel him to wait till we tell your Highness that which we cannot know; at least I can form no guess—unless he be one of the good lances who accompanied King Richard to Palestine, and who are now straggling homeward from the Holy Land."

While he was yet speaking, the marshals brought forward the Disinherited Knight to the foot of a wooden flight of steps, which formed the ascent from the lists to Prince John's throne. With a short and embarrassed eulogy

10. *Hospitallers* was another name for the Knights of Saint John.

upon his valor, the Prince caused to be delivered to him the war-horse assigned as the prize.

But the Disinherited Knight spoke not a word in reply to the compliment of the Prince, which he only acknowledged with a profound obeisance.

The horse was led into the lists by two grooms richly dressed, the animal itself being fully accoutred with the richest war-furniture; which, however, scarcely added to the value of the noble creature in the eyes of those who were judges. Laying one hand upon the pommel of the saddle, the Disinherited Knight vaulted at once upon the back of the steed without making use of the stirrup, and, brandishing aloft his lance, rode twice around the lists, exhibiting the points and paces of the horse with the skill of a perfect horseman.

The appearance of vanity which might otherwise have been attributed to this display was removed by the propriety shown in exhibiting to the best advantage the princely reward with which he had been just honored, and the Knight was again greeted by the acclamations of all present.

In the meanwhile, the bustling Prior of Jorvaulx had reminded Prince John, in a whisper, that the victor must now display his good judgment, instead of his valor, by selecting from among the beauties who graced the galleries a lady who should fill the throne of the Queen of Beauty and of Love, and deliver the prize of the tourney, upon the ensuing day. The Prince accordingly made a sign with his truncheon as the Knight passed him in his second career around the lists. The Knight turned toward the throne, and, sinking his lance until the point was within a foot of the ground, remained motionless, as if expecting John's commands; while all admired the sudden dexterity with which he instantly reduced his fiery steed from a state of violent emotion and high excitation to the stillness of an equestrian statue.

"Sir Disinherited Knight," said Prince John, "since that is the only title by which we can address you, it is now your duty, as well as privilege, to name the fair lady who, as Queen of Honor and of Love, is to preside over next day's festival. If, as a stranger in our land, you should require the aid of other judgment to guide your own, we can only say that Alicia, the daughter of our gallant knight Waldemar Fitzurse, has at our court been long held the first in beauty as in place. Nevertheless, it is your undoubted prerogative to confer on whom you please this crown, by the delivery of which to the lady of your choice the election of to-morrow's Queen will be formal and complete. Raise your lance."

The Knight obeyed; and Prince John placed upon its point a coronet of green satin, having around its edge a circlet of gold, the upper edge of which was relieved by arrow-points and hearts placed interchangeably, like the strawberry leaves and balls upon a ducal crown.

In the broad hint which he dropped respecting the daughter of Waldemar Fitzurse, John had more than one motive, each the offspring of a mind which was a strange mixture of carelessness and presumption with low artifice and cunning. He was desirous of conciliating Alicia's father, Waldemar, of whom he stood in awe, and who had more than once shown himself dissatisfied during the course of the day's proceedings; he had also a wish to establish himself in the good graces of the lady. But besides all these reasons, he was desirous to raise up against the Disinherited Knight, toward whom he already entertained a strong dislike, a powerful enemy in the person of Waldemar Fitzurse, who was likely, he thought, highly to resent the injury done to his daughter in case, as was not unlikely, the victor should make another choice.

And so indeed it proved. For the Disinherited Knight passed the gallery, close to that of the Prince, in which the Lady Alicia was seated in the full pride of triumphant beauty, and pacing forward as slowly as he had hitherto rode swiftly around the lists, he seemed to exercise his right of examining the numerous fair faces which adorned that splendid circle.

It was worth while to see the different conduct of the beauties who underwent this examination, during the time it was proceeding. Some blushed; some assumed an air of pride and dignity; some looked straight forward, and essayed to seem utterly unconscious of what was going on; some drew back in alarm, which was perhaps affected; some endeavored to forbear smiling; and there were two or three who laughed outright. There were also some who dropped their veils over their charms; but as the Wardour

Manuscript says these were fair ones of ten years' standing, it may be supposed that, having had their full share of such vanities, they were willing to withdraw their claim in order to give a fair chance to the rising beauties of the age.

At length the champion paused beneath the balcony in which the Lady Rowena was placed, and the expectation of the spectators was excited to the utmost.

It must be owned that, if an interest displayed in his success could have bribed the Disinherited Knight, the part of the lists before which he paused had merited his predilection. Cedric the Saxon, overjoyed at the discomfiture of the Templar, and still more so at the miscarriage of his two malevolent neighbors, Front-de-Bœuf and Malvoisin, had, with his body half-stretched over the balcony, accompanied the victor in each course not with his eyes only, but with his whole heart and soul. The Lady Rowena had watched the progress of the day with equal attention, though without openly betraying the same intense interest. Even the unmoved Athelstane had shown symptoms of shaking off his apathy, when, calling for a huge goblet of muscadine, he quaffed it to the health of the Disinherited Knight.

Whether from indecision or some other motive of hesitation, the champion of the day remained stationary for more than a minute, while the eyes of the silent audience were riveted upon his motions; and then, gradually and gracefully sinking the point of his lance, he deposited the coronet which it supported at the feet of the fair Rowena. The trumpets instantly sounded, while the heralds proclaimed the Lady Rowena the Queen of Beauty and of Love for the ensuing day, menacing with suitable penalties those who should be disobedient to her authority. They then repeated their cry of "Largesse," to which Cedric, in the height of his joy, replied by an ample donative, and to which Athelstane, though less promptly, added one equally large.

There was some murmuring among the damsels of Norman descent, who were as much unused to see the preference given to a Saxon beauty as the Norman nobles were to sustain defeat in the games of chivalry which they themselves had introduced. But these sounds of disaffection were drowned by the popular shout of "Long live the Lady Rowena, the chosen and lawful Queen of Love and of Beauty!" To which many in the lower area added, "Long live the Saxon Princess! long live the race of the immortal Alfred!"

However unacceptable these sounds might be to Prince John and to those around him, he saw himself nevertheless obliged to confirm the nomination of the victor, and accordingly calling to horse, he left his throne, and mounting his jennet, accompanied by his train, he again entered the lists.

Spurring his horse, as if to give vent to his vexation, he made the animal bound forward to the gallery where Rowena was seated, with the crown still at her feet.

"Assume," he said, "fair lady, the mark of your sovereignty, to which none vows homage more sincerely than ourself, John of Anjou; and if it please you to-day, with your noble sire and friends, to grace our banquet in the Castle of Ashby, we shall learn to know the empress to whose service we devote to-morrow."

Rowena remained silent, and Cedric answered for her in his native Saxon.

"The Lady Rowena," he said, "possesses not the language in which to reply to your courtesy, or to sustain her part in your festival. I also, and the noble Athelstane of Coningsburgh, speak only the language, and practice only the manners, of our fathers. We therefore decline with thanks your Highness's courteous invitation to the banquet. To-morrow, the Lady Rowena will take upon her the state to which she has been called by the free election of the victor Knight, confirmed by the acclamations of the people."

So saying, he lifted the coronet and placed it upon Rowena's head, in token of her acceptance of the temporary authority assigned to her.

In various routes, according to the different quarters from which they came, and in groups of various numbers, the spectators were seen retiring over the plain. By far the most numerous part streamed toward the town of Ashby, where many of the distinguished persons were lodged in the castle, and where others found accommodation in the town itself. Among these were most of the knights who had already appeared in the tournament, or who proposed to fight there the ensuing day, and who, as they rode slowly along, talking over the events of the day, were greeted with loud shouts by the populace. The same acclamations were bestowed upon Prince John, although he was indebted for them rather to the splendor of his appearance and train than to the popularity of his character.

A more sincere and more general, as well as a better merited acclamation, attended the victor of the day, until, anxious to withdraw himself from popular notice, he accepted the accommodation of one of those pavilions pitched at the extremities of the lists, the use of which was courteously tendered him by the marshals of the field. On his retiring to his tent, many who had lingered in the lists, to look upon and form conjectures concerning him, also dispersed.

The signs and sounds of a tumultuous concourse of men lately crowded together in one place, and agitated by the same passing events, were now exchanged for the distant hum of voices of different groups retreating in all directions, and these speedily died away in silence. No other sounds were heard save the voices of the menials who stripped the galleries of their cushions and tapestry, in order to put them in safety for the night, and wrangled among themselves for half-used bottles of wine and relics of the refreshments which had been served round to the spectators.

Beyond the precincts of the lists more than one forge was erected; and these now began to glimmer through the twilight, announcing the toil of the armorers, which was to continue through the whole night, in order to repair or alter the suits of armor to be used again on the morrow.

A strong guard of men-at-arms, renewed at intervals, from two hours to two hours, surrounded the lists, and kept watch during the night.

The Disinherited Knight had no sooner reached his pavilion than squires and pages in abundance tendered their services to disarm him, to bring fresh attire, and to offer him the refreshment of the bath. Their zeal on this occasion was perhaps sharpened by curiosity, since every one desired to know who the knight was that had gained so many laurels, yet had refused, even at the command of Prince John, to lift his visor or to name his name. But their officious inquisitiveness was not gratified. The Disinherited Knight refused all other assistance save that of his own squire, or rather yeoman—a clownish-looking man, who, wrapped in a cloak of dark-colored felt, and having his head and face half buried in a Norman bonnet made of black fur, seemed to affect the incognito as much as his master. All others being excluded from the tent, this attendant relieved his master from the more burdensome parts of his armor, and placed food and wine before him, which the exertions of the day rendered very acceptable.

The Knight had scarcely finished a hasty meal ere his menial announced to him that five men, each leading a barbed steed,[11] desired to speak

11. *Barbed*, or *barded*, is a term used of a war-horse, and means *furnished with armor*.

with him. The Disinherited Knight had exchanged his armor for the long robe usually worn by those of his condition, which, being furnished with a hood, concealed the features, when such was the pleasure of the wearer, almost as completely as the visor of the helmet itself; but the twilight, which was now fast darkening, would of itself have rendered a disguise unnecessary, unless to persons to whom the face of an individual chanced to be particularly well known.

The Disinherited Knight, therefore, stepped boldly forth to the front of his tent, and found in attendance the squires of the challengers, whom he easily knew by their russet and black dresses, each of whom led his master's charger, loaded with the armor in which he had that day fought.

"According to the laws of chivalry," said the foremost of these men, "I, Baldwin de Oyley, squire to the redoubted Knight Brian de Bois-Guilbert, make offer to you, styling yourself for the present the Disinherited Knight, of the horse and armor used by the said Brian de Bois-Guilbert in this day's passage of arms, leaving it with your nobleness to retain or to ransom the same, according to your pleasure; for such is the law of arms."

The other squires repeated nearly the same formula, and then stood to await the decision of the Disinherited Knight.

"To you four, sirs," replied the Knight, addressing those who had last spoken, "and to your honorable and valiant masters, I have one common reply. Commend me to the noble knights, your masters, and say, I should do ill to deprive them of steeds and arms which can never be used by braver cavaliers. I would I could here end my message to these gallant knights; but being, as I term myself, in truth and earnest, the Disinherited, I must be thus far bound to your masters, that they will, of their courtesy, be pleased to ransom their steeds and armor, since that which I wear I can hardly term mine own."

"We stand commissioned, each of us," answered the squire of Reginald Front-de-Bœuf, "to offer a hundred zecchins[12] in ransom of these horses and suits of armor."

"It is sufficient," said the Disinherited Knight. "Half the sum my present necessities compel me to accept; of the remaining half, distribute one moiety among yourselves, sir squires, and divide the other half between the heralds and the pursuivants, and minstrels, and attendants."

The squires, with cap in hand, and low reverences, expressed their deep sense of a courtesy and generosity not often practiced, at least upon a scale so extensive. The Disinherited Knight then addressed his discourse to Baldwin, the squire of Brian de Bois-Guilbert. "From your master," said he, "I will accept neither arms nor ransom. Say to him in my name, that our strife is not ended—no, not till we have fought as well with swords as with lances, as well on foot as on horseback. To this mortal quarrel he has himself defied me, and I shall not

12. A zecchin, or sequin, is worth about $2.25.

forget the challenge. Meantime, let him be assured that I hold him not as one of his companions, with whom I can with pleasure exchange courtesies; but rather as one with whom I stand upon terms of mortal defiance."

"My master," answered Baldwin, "knows how to requite scorn with scorn, and blows with blows, as well as courtesy with courtesy. Since

THE DISINHERITED KNIGHT CONFERS WITH THE SQUIRES

you disdain to accept from him any share of the ransom at which you have rated the arms of the other knights, I must leave his armor and his horse here, being well assured that he will never deign to mount the one nor wear the other."

"You have spoken well, good squire," said the Disinherited Knight—"well and boldly, as it beseemeth him to speak who answers for an absent master. Leave not, however, the horse and armor here. Restore them to thy master;

or, if he scorns to accept them, retain them, good friend, for thine own use. So far as they are mine, I bestow them upon you freely."

Baldwin made a deep obeisance, and retired with his companions; and the Disinherited Knight entered the pavilion.

Morning arose in unclouded splendor, and ere the sun was much above the horizon the idlest or the most eager of the spectators appeared on the common, moving to the lists as to a general centre, in order to secure a favorable situation for viewing the continuation of the expected games.

The marshals and their attendants appeared next on the field, together with the heralds, for the purpose of receiving the names of the knights who intended to joust, with the side which each chose to espouse. This was a necessary precaution in order to secure equality between the two bodies who should be opposed to each other.

According to due formality, the Disinherited Knight was to be considered as leader of the one body, while Brian de Bois-Guilbert, who had been rated as having done second-best in the preceding day, was named first champion of the other band. Those who had concurred in the challenge adhered to his party, of course, excepting only Ralph de Vipont, whom his fall had rendered unfit so soon to put on his armor. There was no want of distinguished and noble candidates to fill up the ranks on either side.

In fact, although the general tournament, in which all knights fought at once, was more dangerous than single encounters, they were, nevertheless, more frequented and practiced by the chivalry of the age. Many knights, who had not sufficient confidence in their own skill to defy a single adversary of high reputation, were, nevertheless, desirous of displaying their valor in the general combat, where they might meet others with whom they were more upon an equality. On the present occasion, about fifty knights were inscribed as desirous of combating upon each side, when the marshals declared that no more could be admitted, to the disappointment of several who were too late in preferring their claim to be included.

About the hour of ten o'clock the whole plain was crowded with horsemen, horsewomen, and foot-passengers, hastening to the tournament; and shortly after, a grand flourish of trumpets announced Prince John and his retinue, attended by many of those knights who meant to take share in the game, as well as others who had no such intention.

About the same time arrived Cedric the Saxon, with the Lady Rowena, unattended, however, by Athelstane. This Saxon lord had arrayed his tall and strong person in armor, in order to take his place among the combatants; and, considerably to the surprise of Cedric, had chosen to enlist himself on the part of the Knight Templar. The Saxon, indeed, had remonstrated strongly with his friend upon the injudicious choice he had made of his party; but he had only received that sort of answer usually given by those who are more obstinate in following their own course than strong in justifying it.

His best, if not his only, reason for adhering to the party of Brian de Bois-Guilbert, Athelstane had the prudence to keep to himself. Though his apathy of disposition prevented his taking any means to recommend himself to the Lady Rowena, he was, nevertheless, by no means insensible to her charms, and considered his union with her as a matter already fixed beyond doubt by the assent of Cedric and her other friends. It had, therefore, been with smothered displeasure that the proud though indolent Lord of Coningsburgh beheld the victor of the preceding day select Rowena as the object of that honor which it became his privilege to confer. In order to punish him for a preference which seemed to interfere with his own suit, Athelstane, confident of his strength, and to whom his flatterers, at least, ascribed great skill in arms, had determined not only to deprive the Disinherited Knight of his powerful succor, but, if an opportunity should occur, to make him feel the weight of his battle-axe.

De Bracy, and other knights attached to Prince John, in obedience to a hint from him, had joined the party of the challengers, John being desirous to secure, if possible, the victory to that side. On the other hand, many other knights, both English and Norman, natives and strangers, took part against the challengers, the more readily that the opposite band was to be led by so distinguished a champion as the Disinherited Knight had approved himself.

As soon as Prince John observed that the destined Queen of the day had arrived upon the field, assuming that air of courtesy which sat well upon him when he was pleased to exhibit it, he rode forward to meet her, doffed his bonnet, and, alighting from his horse, assisted the Lady Rowena from her saddle, while his followers uncovered at the same time, and one of the most distinguished dismounted to hold her palfrey.

"It is thus," said Prince John, "that we set the dutiful example of loyalty to the Queen of Love and Beauty, and are ourselves her guide to the throne which she must this day occupy. Ladies," he said, "attend your Queen, as you wish in your turn to be distinguished by like honors."

So saying, the Prince marshalled Rowena to the seat of honor opposite his own, while the fairest and most distinguished ladies present crowded after her to obtain places as near as possible to their temporary sovereign.

No sooner was Rowena seated than a burst of music, half-drowned by the shouts of the multitude, greeted her new dignity. Meantime, the sun shone fierce and bright upon the polished arms of the knights of either side, who crowded the opposite extremities of the lists, and held eager conference together concerning the best mode of arranging their line of battle and supporting the conflict.

The heralds then proclaimed silence until the laws of the tourney should be rehearsed. These were calculated in some degree to abate the dangers of the day—a precaution the more necessary as the conflict was to be maintained with sharp swords and pointed lances.

The champions were therefore prohibited to thrust with the sword, and were confined to striking. A knight, it was announced, might use a mace or battle-axe at pleasure; but the dagger was a prohibited weapon. A knight unhorsed might renew the fight on foot with any other on the opposite side in the same predicament; but mounted horsemen were in that case forbidden to assail him. When any knight could force his antagonist to the extremity of the lists, so as to touch the palisade with his person or arms, such opponent was obliged to yield himself vanquished, and his armor and horse were placed at the disposal of the conqueror. A knight thus overcome was not permitted to take further share in the combat. If any combatant was struck down, and unable to recover his feet, his squire or page might enter the lists and drag his master out of the press; but in that case the knight was adjudged vanquished, and his arms and horse declared forfeited. The combat was to cease as soon as Prince John should throw down his leading staff, or truncheon—another precaution usually taken to prevent the unnecessary effusion of blood by the too long endurance of a sport so desperate. Any knight breaking the rules of the tournament, or otherwise transgressing the rules of honorable chivalry, was liable to be stripped of his arms, and, having his shield reversed, to be placed in that posture astride upon the bars of the palisade, and exposed to public derision, in punishment of his unknightly conduct. Having announced these precautions, the heralds concluded with an exhortation to each good knight to do his duty, and to merit favor from the Queen of Beauty and Love.

This proclamation having been made, the heralds withdrew to their stations. The knights, entering at either end of the lists in long procession, arranged themselves in a double file, precisely opposite to each other, the leader of each party being in the center of the foremost rank, a post which he did not occupy until each had carefully arranged the ranks of his party, and stationed every one in his place.

It was a goodly, and at the same time an anxious, sight to behold so many gallant champions, mounted bravely and armed richly, stand ready prepared for an encounter so formidable, seated on their war-saddles like so many pillars of iron, and awaiting the signal of encounter with the same ardor as their generous steeds, which, by neighing and pawing the ground, gave signal of their impatience.

As yet the knights held their long lances upright, their bright points glancing to the sun, and the streamers with which they were decorated fluttering over the plumage of the helmets. Thus they remained while the marshals of the field surveyed their ranks with the utmost exactness, lest either party had more or fewer than the appointed number. The tale was found exactly complete. The marshals then withdrew from the lists, and William de Wyvil, with a voice of thunder, pronounced the signal words—"*Laissez aller!*"[13] The trumpets sounded as he spoke; the spears of the champions were at once lowered and placed in the rests; the spurs were dashed into the flanks of the horses; and the two foremost ranks of either party rushed upon each other in full gallop, and met in the middle of the lists with a shock the sound of which was heard at a mile's distance. The rear rank of each party advanced at a slower pace to sustain the defeated, and follow up the success of the victors, of their party.

The consequences of the encounter were not instantly seen, for the dust raised by the trampling of so many steeds darkened the air, and it was a minute ere the anxious spectators could see the fate of the encounter When the fight became visible, half the knights on each side were dismounted—some by the dexterity of their adversary's lance; some by the superior weight and strength of opponents, which had borne down both horse and man; some lay stretched on earth as if never more to rise; some had already gained their feet, and were closing hand to hand with those of their antagonists who were in the same predicament; and several on both sides, who had received wounds by which they were

13. *Laissez aller* means literally *Let go.*

HALF THE KNIGHTS WERE DISMOUNTED

disabled, were stopping their blood by their scarfs, and endeavoring to extricate themselves from the tumult. The mounted knights, whose lances had been almost all broken by the fury of the encounter, were now closely engaged with their swords, shouting their war-cries, and exchanging buffets, as if honor and life depended on the issue of the combat.

The tumult was presently increased by the advance of the second rank on either side, which, acting as a reserve, now rushed on to aid their companions. The followers of Brian de Bois-

Guilbert shouted—"*Ha! Beau-seant! Beau-seant!*[14] For the Temple! For the Temple!" The opposite shouted in answer—"*Desdichado! Desdichado!*" which watchword they took from the motto upon their leader's shield.

The champions thus encountering each other with the utmost fury, and with alternate success, the tide of battle seemed to flow now toward the southern, now toward the northern, extremity of the lists, as the one or the other party prevailed. Meantime the clang of the blows and the shouts of the combatants mixed fearfully with the sound of the trumpets, and drowned the groans of those who fell, and lay rolling defenceless beneath the feet of the horses. The splendid armor of the combatants was now defaced with dust and blood, and gave way at every stroke of the sword and battle-axe. The gay plumage, shorn from the crests, drifted upon the breeze like snowflakes. All that was beautiful and graceful in the martial array had disappeared, and what was now visible was only calculated to awake terror or compassion.

Yet such is the force of habit, that not only the vulgar spectators, who are naturally attracted by sights of horror, but even the ladies of distinction, who crowded the galleries. saw the conflict with a thrilling interest certainly, but without a wish to withdraw their eyes, from a sight so terrible. Here and there, indeed, a fair cheek might turn pale, or a faint scream

14. *Beau-seant* was the name given to the black and white banner of the Templars.

might be heard, as a lover, a brother, or a husband was struck from his horse. But, in general, the ladies around encouraged the combatants, not only by clapping their hands and waving their veils and kerchiefs, but even by exclaiming, "Brave lance! Good sword!" when any successful thrust or blow took place under their observation.

Such being the interest taken by the fair sex in this bloody game, that of the men is the more easily understood. It showed itself in loud acclamations upon every change of fortune, while all eyes were so riveted on the lists that the spectators seemed as if they themselves had dealt and received the blows which were there so freely bestowed. And between every pause was heard the voice of the heralds, exclaiming, "Fight on, brave knights! Man dies, but glory lives! Fight on; death is better than defeat! Fight on, brave knights! for bright eyes behold your deeds!"

Amid the varied fortunes of the combat, the eyes of all endeavored to discover the leaders of each band, who, mingling in the thick of the fight, encouraged their companions both by voice and example. Both displayed great feats of gallantry, nor did either Bois-Guilbert or the Disinherited Knight find in the ranks opposed to them a champion who could be termed their unquestioned match. They repeatedly endeavored to single out each other, spurred by mutual animosity, and aware that the fall of either leader might be considered as decisive of victory.

Such, however, was the crowd and confusion that, during the earlier part of the conflict, their efforts to meet were unavailing, and they were repeatedly separated by the eagerness of their followers, each of whom was anxious to win honor by measuring his strength against the leader of the opposite party.

But when the field became thin by the numbers on either side who had yielded themselves vanquished, had been compelled to the extremity of the lists, or been otherwise rendered incapable of continuing the strife, the Templar and the Disinherited Knight at length encountered hand to hand, with all the fury that mortal animosity, joined to rivalry of honor, could inspire. Such was the address of each in parrying and striking, that the spectators broke forth into a unanimous and involuntary shout, expressive of their delight and admiration.

But at this moment the party of the Disinherited Knight had the worst; the gigantic arm of Front-de-Bœuf on the one flank, and the ponderous strength of Athelstane on the other, bearing down and dispersing those immediately opposed to them. Finding themselves freed from their immediate antagonists, it seems to have occurred to both these knights at the same instant that they would render the most decisive advantage to their party by aiding the Templar in his contest with his rival. Turning their horses, therefore, at the same moment, the Norman spurred against the Disinherited Knight on the one side and the Saxon on the other. It was utterly impossible that the object of this unequal and unexpected assault could have sustained it, had he not been warned by a general cry from the spectators, who could not but take interest in one exposed to such disadvantage.

"Beware! beware! Sir Disinherited!" was shouted so universally that the knight became aware of his danger; and striking a full blow at the Templar, he reined back his steed in the same moment, so as to escape the charge of Athelstane and Front-de-Bœuf. These knights, therefore, their aim being thus eluded, rushed from opposite sides between the object of their attack and the Templar, almost running their horses against each other ere they could stop their career. Recovering their horses, however, and wheeling them round, the whole three pursued their united purpose of bearing to the earth the Disinherited Knight.

Nothing could have saved him except the remarkable strength and activity of the noble horse which he had won on the preceding day.

This stood him in the more stead, as the horse of Bois-Guilbert was wounded and those of Front-de-Bœuf and Athelstane were both tired with the weight of their gigantic masters, clad in complete armor, and with the preceding exertions of the day. The masterly horsemanship of the Disinherited Knight, and the activity of the noble animal which he mounted, enabled him for a few minutes to keep at sword's point his three antagonists, turning and wheeling with the agility of a hawk upon the wing, keeping his enemies as far separate as he could, and rushing now against the one, now against the other, dealing sweeping blows with his sword, without waiting to receive those which were aimed at him in return.

But although the lists rang with the applauses of his dexterity, it was evident that he must at last be overpowered; and the nobles around Prince John implored him with one voice to throw down his warder, and to save so brave a knight from the disgrace of being overcome by odds.

"Not I, by the light of Heaven!" answered Prince John: "this same springal,[15] who conceals his name and despises our proffered hospitality, hath already gained one prize, and may now afford to let others have their turn." As he spoke thus, an unexpected incident changed the fortune of the day.

There was among the ranks of the Disinherited Knight a champion in black armor, mounted on a black horse, large of size, tall, and to all appearance powerful and strong, like the rider by whom he was mounted. This knight, who bore on his shield no device of any kind, had hitherto evinced very little interest in the event of the fight, beating off with seeming ease those combatants who attacked him, but neither pursuing his advantages nor himself assailing any one. In short, he had hitherto acted the part rather of a spectator than of a party in the tournament, a circumstance which

15. *Springal* is an old word meaning *youth* or *young man*.

procured him among the spectators the name of *Le Noir Faineant*, or the Black Sluggard.

At once this knight seemed to throw aside his apathy, when he discovered the leader of his party so hard bested; for, setting spurs to his horse, which was quite fresh, he came to his assistance like a thunderbolt, exclaiming, in a voice like a trumpet-call, "*Desdichado*, to the rescue!" It was high time; for, while the Disinherited Knight was pressing upon the Templar, Front-de-Bœuf had got nigh to him with his uplifted sword; but ere the blow could descend, the Sable Knight dealt a stroke on his head, which, glancing from the polished helmet, lighted with violence scarcely abated on the chamfron[16] of the steed, and Front-de-Bœuf rolled on the ground, both horse and man equally stunned by the fury of the blow. *Le Noir Faineant* then turned his horse upon Athelstane of Coningsburgh; and his own sword having been broken in his encounter with Front-de-Bœuf, he wrenched from the hand of the bulky Saxon the battle-axe which he wielded, and, like one familiar with the use of the weapon, bestowed him such a blow upon the crest that Athelstane also lay senseless on the field. Having achieved this double feat, for which he was the more highly applauded that it was totally unexpected from him, the knight seemed to resume the sluggishness of his character, returning calmly to the northern extremity of the lists,

16. The chamfron is the defensive armor of the front part of the head of a war-horse.

leaving his leader to cope as he best could with Brian de Bois-Guilbert. This was no longer matter of so much difficulty as formerly. The Templar's horse had bled much, and gave way under the shock of the Disinherited Knight's charge. Brian de Bois-Guilbert rolled on the field, encumbered with the stirrup, from which he was unable to draw his foot. His antagonist sprung from horseback, waved his fatal sword over the head of his adversary, and commanded him to yield himself; when Prince John, more moved by the Templar's dangerous situation than he had been by that of his rival, saved him the mortification of confessing himself vanquished, by casting down his warder and putting an end to the conflict.

It was, indeed, only the relics and embers of the fight which continued to burn; for of the few knights who still continued in the lists, the greater part had, by tacit consent, forborne the conflict for some time, leaving it to be determined by the strife of the leaders.

The squires, who had found it a matter of danger and difficulty to attend their masters during the engagement, now thronged into the lists to pay their dutiful attendance to the wounded, who were removed with the utmost care and attention to the neighboring pavilions, or to the quarters prepared for them in the adjoining village.

Thus ended the memorable field of Ashby-de-la-Zouche, one of the most gallantly contested tournaments of that age; for although only four knights, including one who was smothered by the heat of his armor, had died upon the field, yet upward of thirty were desperately wounded, four or five of whom never recovered. Several more were disabled for life; and those who escaped best carried the marks of the conflict to the grave with them. Hence it is always mentioned in the old records as the "gentle and joyous passage of arms of Ashby."

It being now the duty of Prince John to name the knight who had done best, he determined that the honor of the day remained with the knight whom the popular voice had termed *Le Noir Faineant.* It was pointed out to the Prince, in impeachment of this decree, that the victory had been in fact won by the Disinherited Knight, who, in the course of the day, had overcome six champions with his own hand, and who had finally unhorsed and struck down the leader of the opposite party. But Prince John adhered to his own opinion, on the ground that the Disinherited Knight and his party had lost the day but for the powerful assistance of the Knight of the Black Armor, to whom, therefore, he persisted in awarding the prize.

To the surprise of all present, however, the knight thus preferred was nowhere to be found. He had left the lists immediately when the conflict ceased, and had been observed by some spectators to move down one of the forest glades with the same slow pace and listless and indifferent manner which had procured him the epithet of the Black Sluggard.[17] After he had been summoned twice by sound of trumpet and proclamation of the heralds, it became necessary to name another to receive the honors which had been assigned to him. Prince John had now no further excuse for resisting the claim of the Disinherited Knight, whom, therefore, he named the champion of the day.

Through a field slippery with blood and encumbered with broken armor and the bodies of slain and wounded horses, the marshals of the lists again conducted the victor to the foot of Prince John's throne.

"Disinherited Knight," said Prince John, "since by that title only you will consent to be known to us, we a second time award to you the honors of this tournament, and announce to you your right to claim and receive from the hands of the Queen of Love and Beauty the chaplet of honor which your valor has justly deserved."

The Knight bowed low and gracefully, but returned no answer.

While the trumpets sounded, while the heralds strained their voices in proclaiming honor to the brave and glory to the victor, while ladies waved their silken kerchiefs and embroidered veils, and while all ranks joined in a clamorous shout of exultation, the marshals conducted the Disinherited Knight across the lists to the foot of

17. The Black Sluggard was the king of England, Richard the Lion-Hearted, who had been absent from England on a Crusade and had come back without allowing his brother John to know of his return.

that throne of honor which was occupied by the Lady Rowena.

On the lower step of this throne the champion was made to kneel down. Indeed, his whole action since the fight had ended seemed rather to have been upon the impulse of those around him than from his own free will; and it was observed that he tottered as they guided him the second time across the lists. Rowena, descending from her station with a graceful and dignified step, was about to place the chaplet which she held in her hand upon the helmet of the champion, when the marshals exclaimed with one voice, "It must not be thus; his head must be bare." The knight muttered faintly a few words, which were lost in the hollow of his helmet; but their purport seemed to be a desire that his casque might not be removed.

Whether from love of form or from curiosity, the marshals paid no attention to his expressions of reluctance, but unhelmed him by cutting the laces of his casque, and undoing the fastening of his gorget. When the helmet was removed, the well-formed yet sun-burned features of a young man of twenty-five were seen, amid a profusion of short fair hair. His countenance was as pale as death, and marked in one or two places with streaks of blood.

Rowena had no sooner beheld him than she uttered a faint shriek; but at once summoning up the energy of her disposition, and compelling herself, as it were, to proceed, while her frame yet trembled with the violence of sudden emotion, she placed upon the drooping head of the victor the splendid chaplet which was the destined reward of the day, and pronounced in a clear and distinct tone these words: "I bestow on thee this chaplet, Sir Knight, as the meed of valor assigned to this day's victor." Here she paused a moment, and then firmly added, "And upon brows more worthy could a wreath of chivalry never be placed!"

The knight stooped his head and kissed the hand of the lovely Sovereign by whom his valor had been rewarded; and then, sinking yet further forward, lay prostrate at her feet.

There was a general consternation. Cedric, who had been struck mute by the sudden appearance of his banished son, now rushed forward, as if to separate him from Rowena. But this had been already accomplished by the marshals of the field, who, guessing the cause of Ivanhoe's swoon, had hastened to undo his armor, and found that the head of a lance had penetrated his breastplate and inflicted a wound in his side.

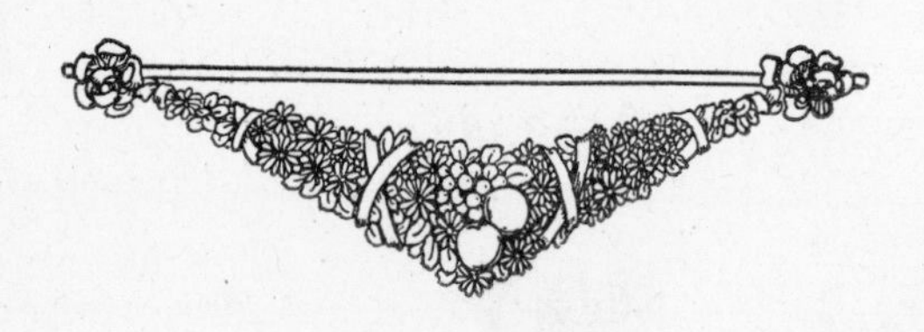

THE RAINBOW

THOMAS CAMPBELL

Triumphal arch, that fill'st the sky
  When storms prepare to part,
I ask not proud Philosophy
  To teach me what thou art.

Still seem, as to my childhood's sight,
  A midway station given,
For happy spirits to alight,
  Betwixt the earth and heaven.

Can all that optics teach, unfold
  Thy form to please me so,
As when I dreamt of gems and gold
  Hid in thy radiant bow?[1]

When science from creation's face
  Enchantment's veil withdraws,
What lovely visions yield their place
  To cold material laws!

And yet, fair bow, no fabling dreams,
  But words of the Most High,
Have told why first thy robe of beams
  Was woven in the sky.[2]

---

1. There was an old, old belief that a pot of gold was hidden at the end of the rainbow, and that whoever found his way to the spot might claim the gold. This superstition has existed in almost all lands, and references to it are constantly to be found in literature.

2. According to the account given in *Genesis IX*, God said to Noah after the flood:

"And I will establish my covenant with you; neither shall all flesh

When o'er the green undeluged earth
Heaven's covenant thou didst shine,
How came the world's gray fathers forth
To watch thy sacred sign!

And when its yellow lustre smiled
O'er mountains yet untrod,
Each mother held aloft her child
To bless the bow of God.

The earth to thee her incense yields,
The lark thy welcome sings,
When, glittering in the freshen'd fields,
The snowy mushroom springs.

How glorious is thy girdle, cast
O'er mountain, tower, and town,
Or mirror'd in the ocean vast
A thousand fathoms down!

As fresh in yon horizon dark,
As young thy beauties seem,
As when the eagle from the ark
First sported in thy beam.

---

be cut off any more by the waters of a flood; neither shall there any more be a flood to destroy the earth.

"This is the token of the covenant which I make between me and you, and every living creature that is with you for perpetual generations:

"I do set my bow in the cloud, and it shall be for a token of a covenant between me and the earth.

"And it shall come to pass, when I bring a cloud over the earth, that the bow shall be seen in the cloud:

"And I will remember my covenant, which is between me and you, and every living creature of all flesh; and the waters shall no more become a flood to destroy all flesh."

For, faithful to its sacred page,
  Heaven still rebuilds thy span;
Nor lets the type grow pale with age
  That first spoke peace to man.

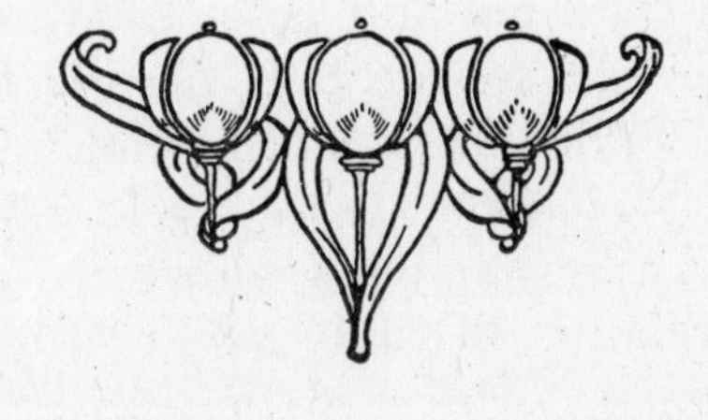

THE LION AND THE MISSIONARY

DAVID LIVINGSTONE

NOTE,—Few men have endured more hardship, dangers and excitement than did David Livingstone, missionary and African traveler, from whose writings this account of an adventure with a lion is taken. He penetrated to parts of Africa where no white man had ever been before, he suffered repeated attacks of African fever, he exposed himself to constant danger from wild beasts and wilder men; and he did none of this in his own interests. He was no merchant seeking for gold and diamonds, he was no discoverer seeking for fame; his only aim was to open up the continent of Africa so that civilization and Christianity might enter.

In 1840 Livingstone was sent as medical missionary to South Africa. Here he joined Robert Moffat, in Bechuanaland, where he worked for nine years. Learning from the natives that there was a large lake to the northward, he set out on his first exploring trip, and at length discovered Lake Ngami. Later, he undertook other journeys of exploration, on one of which he reached the Atlantic coast and then returned, crossing the entire continent. His greatest achievement was the exploration of the lake region of South Africa. So cut off was he, in the African jungles, from all the outer world that no communication was received from him for three years, and fears as to his safety were relieved only when Stanley, sent out by the *New York Herald* to search for Livingstone, reported that he had seen and assisted him.

In May, 1873, Livingstone died, at a village near Lake Bangweolo. His body was taken to England and laid in Westminster Abbey, but his heart was buried at the foot of the tree under whose branches he died.

RETURNING toward Kuruman, I selected the beautiful valley of Mabotsa (latitude 25° 14′ south, longitude 26° 30′) as the site of a missionary station, and thither I removed in 1843. Here an occurrence took place concerning which I have frequently been questioned in England, and which, but for the importunities of friends, I meant to have kept in store to tell my children when in my dotage. The Bakatla of the village Mabotsa were much troubled by lions, which leaped into the cattle pens by night and destroyed their cows. They even attacked the herds in open day. This was so unusual an occurrence that the people believed that they were bewitched,—"given," as they said, "into the power of the lions by a neighboring tribe." They went once to attack the animals, but, being rather a cowardly people compared to Bechuanas in general on such occasions, they returned without killing any.

It is well known that if one of a troop of lions is killed, the others take the hint and leave that part of the country. So, the next time the herds were attacked, I went with the people, in order to encourage them to rid themselves of the annoyance by destroying one of the marauders. We found the lions on a small hill about a quarter of a mile in length, and covered with trees. A circle of men was formed round it, and they gradually closed up, ascending pretty near to each other. Being down below on the plain with a native schoolmaster, named Mebálwe, a most excellent man, I saw one of the lions sitting on a piece of rock within the now closed circle of men. Mebálwe fired at him before I could, and the ball struck the rock on which the animal was sitting. He bit at the spot struck, as a dog does at a stick or stone thrown at him; then leaping away, broke through the opening circle and escaped unhurt. The men were afraid to attack him, perhaps on account of their belief in witchcraft. When the circle was re-formed, we saw two other lions in it; but we were afraid to fire lest we should strike the men, and they allowed the beasts to burst through also.

If the Bakatla had acted according to the custom of the country, they would have speared the lions in their attempt to get out. Seeing we could not get them to kill one of the lions, we bent our footsteps toward the village; in going round the end of the hill, however, I saw one of the beasts sitting on a piece of rock as before, but this time he had a little bush in front. Being about thirty yards off, I took a good aim at his body through the bush, and fired both barrels into it. The men then called out, "He is shot, he is shot!" Others cried, "He has been shot by another man too; let us go to him!" I did not see any one else shoot at him, but I saw the lion's tail erected in anger behind the bush, and turning to the people, said, "Stop a little, till I load again." When in the act of ramming down the bullets, I heard a shout. Starting, and looking half round, I saw the lion just in the act of springing upon me.

I was upon a little height; he caught my shoulder as he sprang, and we both came to the ground below together. Growling horribly close to my ear, he shook me as a terrier dog does a rat. The shock produced a stupor similar to that which seems to be felt by a mouse after the first shake of the cat. It caused a sort of dreaminess, in which there was no sense of pain nor feeling of terror, though I was quite conscious of all that was happening. It was like what patients partially under the influence of chloroform describe, who see all the operation, but feel not the knife. This singular condition was not the result of any mental process. The shake annihilated fear, and allowed no sense of horror in looking round at the beast. This peculiar state is probably produced in all animals killed by the carnivora; and if so, is a merciful provision by our benevolent Creator for lessening the pain of death. Turning round to relieve myself of the weight, as he had one paw on the back of my head, I saw his eyes directed to Mebálwe, who was trying to shoot him at a distance of ten or fifteen yards. His gun, a flint one, missed fire in both barrels; the lion immediately left me, and, attacking Mebálwe, bit his thigh. Another man, whose life I had saved before, after he had been tossed by a buffalo, attempted to spear the lion while he was biting Mebálwe. He left Mebálwe and caught this man by the shoulder, but at that moment the bullets he had received took effect, and he fell down dead. The whole was the work of a few moments, and must have been his paroxysms of dying rage. In order to take out the charm from him, the Bakátla on the following day made a huge bonfire over the carcass, which was declared to be that of the largest lion they had ever seen. Besides crunching the bone into splinters, he left eleven teeth wounds on the upper part of my arm.

A wound from this animal's tooth resembles a gunshot wound; it is generally followed by a great deal of sloughing and discharge, and pains are felt in the part, periodically ever afterward. I had on a tartan jacket on the occasion, and I believe that it wiped off all the virus from the teeth that pierced the flesh, for my two companions in this affray have both suffered from the peculiar pains, while I have escaped with only the inconvenience of a false joint in my limb. The man whose shoulder was wounded, showed me his wound actually burst forth afresh on the same month of the following year. This curious point certainly deserves the attention of inquirers.

THE MOSS ROSE

TRANSLATED FROM KRUMMACHER

The angel of the flowers, one day,
Beneath a rose-tree sleeping lay,—
That spirit to whose charge 'tis given
To bathe young buds in dews of heaven.
Awaking from his light repose,
The angel whispered to the rose:
"O fondest object of my care,
Still fairest found, where all are fair;
For the sweet shade thou giv'st to me
Ask what thou wilt, 'tis granted thee."
"Then," said the rose, with deepened glow,
"On me another grace bestow."
The spirit paused, in silent thought,—
What grace was there that flower had not?
'Twas but a moment,—o'er the rose
A veil of moss the angel throws,
And, robed in nature's simplest weed,
Could there a flower that rose exceed?

FOUR DUCKS ON A POND

WILLIAM ALLINGHAM

Four ducks on a pond,
A grass bank beyond,
A blue sky of spring,
White clouds on the wing;
What a little thing
To remember for years,
To remember with tears.

RAB AND HIS FRIENDS

JOHN BROWN, M. D.

FOUR and thirty years ago, Bob Ainslie and I were coming up Infirmary street from the high school, our heads together, and our arms intertwisted, as only lovers and boys know how or why. When we got to the top of the street, and turned north, we espied a crowd at the Tron-church. "A dog fight!" shouted Bob, and was off; and so was I, both of us all but praying that it might not be over before we got up! And is not this boy nature! and human nature too? and don't we all wish a house on fire not to be out before we see it? Dogs like fighting; old Isaac says they "delight" in it, and for the best of all reasons; and boys are not cruel because they like to see the fight. They see three of the great cardinal virtues of dog or man—courage, endurance, and skill—in intense action. This is very different from a love of making dogs fight, and enjoying, and aggravating, and making gain by their pluck. A boy—be he ever so fond himself of fighting, if he be a good boy, hates and despises all this, but he would have run off with Bob and me fast enough; it is a natural, and a not wicked, interest that all boys and men have in witnessing intense energy in action.

Does any curious and finely-ignorant woman wish to know how Bob's eye at a glance an-

"A DOG FIGHT!"

nounced a dog fight to his brain? He did not, he could not see the dogs fighting; it was a flash of an inference, a rapid induction. The crowd round a couple of dogs fighting, is a crowd masculine mainly, with an occasional active, compassionate woman, fluttering wildly round the outside, and using her tongue and her hands freely upon the men, as so many "brutes"; it is a crowd annular, compact and mobile; a crowd centripetal, having its eyes and its heads all bent downward and inward, to one common focus.

Well, Bob and I are up, and find it is not over; a small thoroughbred, white bull-terrier, is busy throttling a large shepherd's dog, unaccustomed to war, but not to be trifled with. They are hard at it; the scientific little fellow doing his work in great style, his pastoral enemy fighting wildly, but with the sharpest of teeth and a great courage. Science and breeding, however, soon had their own; the Game Chicken, as the premature Bob called him, working his way up, took his final grip of poor Yarrow's throat—and he lay gasping and done for. His master, a brown, handsome, big young shepherd from Tweedsmuir, would have liked to have knocked down any man, would "drink up Esil, or eat a crocodile," for that part, if he had a chance; it was no use kicking the little dog; that would only make him hold the closer. Many were the means shouted out in mouthfuls, of the best possible ways of ending it.

"Water!" but there was none near, and many cried for it who might have got it from the well at Blackfriars Wynd.

"Bite the tail!" and a large, vague, benevolent, middle-aged man, more desirous than wise, with some struggle got the bushy end of Yarrow's tail into his ample mouth, and bit it with all his might. This was more than enough for the much-enduring, much-perspiring shepherd, who, with a gleam of joy over his broad visage, delivered a terrific facer upon our large, vague, benevolent, middle-aged friend—who went down like a shot.

Still the Chicken holds; death not far off.

"Snuff! a pinch of snuff!" observed a calm,

highly-dressed young buck, with an eye-glass in his eye. "Snuff, indeed!" growled the angry crowd, affronted and glaring.

"Snuff! a pinch of snuff!" again observes the buck, but with more urgency; whereupon were produced several open boxes, and from a mull which may have been at Culloden, he took a pinch, knelt down, and presented it to the nose of the Chicken. The laws of physiology and of snuff take their course; the Chicken sneezes, and Yarrow is free.

The young pastoral giant stalks off with Yarrow in his arms—comforting him.

But the bull-terrier's blood is up, and his soul unsatisfied; he grips the first dog he meets, and discovering she is not a dog, in Homeric phrase, he makes a brief sort of *amende*,[1] and is off. The boys, with Bob and me at their head, are after him; down Niddry street he goes, bent on mischief; up the Cowgate like an arrow—Bob and I, and our small men, panting behind.

There, under the single arch of the South bridge is a huge mastiff, sauntering down the middle of the causeway, as if with his hands in his pockets; he is old, gray, brindled, as big as a little Highland bull, and has the Shakespearian dew-laps shaking as he goes.

The Chicken makes straight at him, and fastens on his throat. To our astonishment, the great creature does nothing but stand still, hold himself up, and roar—yes, roar; a long,

1. *Amende* means *apology*.

serious, remonstrative roar. How is this? Bob and I are up to them. *He is muzzled!* The bailies had proclaimed a general muzzling, and his master, studying strength and economy mainly, had encompassed his huge jaws in a homemade apparatus, constructed out of the leather of some ancient breechin. His mouth was open as far as it could; his lips curled up in rage—a sort of terrible grin; his teeth gleaming, ready, from out the darkness; the strap across his mouth tense as a bow string; his whole frame stiff with indignation and surprise; his roar asking us all round, "Did you ever see the like of this?"

He looked a statue of anger and astonishment, done in Aberdeen granite.

We soon had a crowd; the Chicken held on. "A knife!" cried Bob; and a cobbler gave him his knife; you know the kind of knife, worn away obliquely to a point, and always keen. I put its edge to the tense leather; it ran before it; and then!—one sudden jerk of that enormous head, a sort of dirty mist about his mouth, no noise, and the bright and fierce little fellow is dropped, limp, and dead. A solemn pause; this was more than any of us had bargained for. I turned the little fellow over, and saw he was quite dead; the mastiff had taken him by the small of the back, like a rat, and broken it.

He looked down at his victim appeased, ashamed and amazed; snuffed him all over, stared at him, and taking a sudden thought, turned round and trotted off.

HE LOOKED A STATUE OF ANGER

Bob took the dead dog up, and said, "John, we'll bury him after tea."

"Yes," said I, and was off after the mastiff. He made up the Cowgate at a rapid swing; he had forgotten some engagement. He turned up the Candlemaker Row, and stopped at the Harrow Inn.

There was a carrier's cart ready to start, and a keen, thin, impatient, black-a-vised little man, his hand at his gray horse's head looking about angrily for something.

"Rab, ye thief!" said he, aiming a kick at my great friend, who drew cringing up, and avoiding the heavy shoe with more agility than dignity, and watching his master's eye, slunk dismayed under the cart—his ears down, and as much as he had of tail down too.

What a man this must be—thought I—to whom my tremendous hero turns tail! The carrier saw the muzzle hanging, cut and useless, from his neck, and I eagerly told him the story which Bob and I always thought, and still think, Homer, or King David, or Sir Walter, alone were worthy to rehearse. The severe little man was mitigated, and condescended to say, "Rab, ma man, puir Rabbie"—whereupon the stump of a tail rose up, the ears were cocked, the eyes filled, and were comforted; the two friends were reconciled. "Hupp!" and a stroke of the whip were given to Jess; and off went the three.

Bob and I buried the Game Chicken that night (we had not much of a tea) in the back-green of his house in Melville street, No. 17, with considerable gravity and silence; and being at the time in the Iliad, and, like all boys, Trojans, we called him Hector of course.

* * * * *

Six years have passed—a long time for a boy and a dog: Bob Ainslie is off to the wars; I am a medical student, and clerk at Minto House Hospital.

Rab I saw almost every week, on the Wednesday; and we had much pleasant intimacy. I found the way to his heart by frequent scratching of his huge head, and an occasional bone. When I did not notice him he would plant himself straight before me, and stand wagging that bud of a tail, and looking up, with his head a little to the one side. His master I occasionally saw; he used to call me "Maister John," but was laconic as any Spartan.

One fine October afternoon, I was leaving the hospital when I saw the large gate open, and in walked Rab with that great and easy saunter of his. He looked as if taking general possession of the place; like the Duke of Wellington entering a subdued city, satiated with victory and peace. After him came Jess, now white from age, with her cart; and in it a woman, carefully wrapped up—the carrier leading the horse anxiously, and looking back.

When he saw me, James (for his name was James Noble) made a curt and grotesque "boo," and said, "Maister John, this is the mistress; she's got a trouble in her breest—some kind of an income we're thinkin'."

By this time I saw the woman's face; she was sitting on a sack filled with straw, her husband's plaid round her, and his big-coat, with its large white metal buttons, over her feet.

I never saw a more unforgettable face—pale, serious, *lonely*, delicate, sweet, without being at all what we call fine. She looked sixty, and had on a mutch, white as snow, with its black ribbon; her silvery, smooth hair setting off her dark-gray eyes—eyes such as one sees only twice or thrice in a lifetime, full of suffering, full also of the overcoming of it; her eyebrows black and delicate, and her mouth firm, patient, and contented, which few mouths ever are.

As I have said, I never saw a more beautiful countenance, or a more subdued or settled quiet. "Ailie," said James, "this is Maister John, the young doctor; Rab's freend, ye ken. We often speak aboot you, doctor."

She smiled, and made a movement, but said nothing; and prepared to come down, putting her plaid aside and rising. Had Solomon, in all his glory, been handing down the Queen of Sheba at his palace gate, he could not have done it more daintily, more tenderly, more like a gentleman, than did James the Howgate carrier, when he lifted down Ailie, his wife.

The contrast of his small, swarthy, weather-beaten, keen, worldly face to hers—pale, subdued, and beautiful—was something wonderful. Rab looked on concerned and puzzled, but ready for anything that might turn up—were it to strangle the nurse, the porter, or even me. Ailie and he seemed great friends.

"As I was sayin', she's got a kind o' trouble in her breest, doctor; wull ye tak' a look at it?" We walked into the consulting-room, all four; Rab grim and comic, willing to be happy and confidential if cause could be shown, willing also to be the reverse on the same terms. Ailie sat down, undid her open gown and her lawn handkerchief round her neck, and, without a word, showed me her right breast. I looked at and examined it carefully, she and James watching me, and Rab eying all three. What could I say? There it was that had once been so soft, so shapely, so white, so gracious and bountiful, so "full of all blessed conditions"—hard as a stone, a center of horrid pain, making that pale face, with its gray, lucid, reasonable eyes, and its sweet resolved mouth, express the full measure of suffering overcome. Why was that gentle, modest, sweet woman, clean and lovable, condemned by God to bear such a burden?"

I got her away to bed.

"May Rab and me bide?" said James.

"*You* may; and Rab, if he will behave himself."

"I'se warrant he's do that, doctor;" and in slunk the faithful beast.

I wish you could have seen him. There are no such dogs now. He belonged to a lost tribe. As I have said, he was brindled, and gray like Rubislaw granite; his hair short, hard, and close, like a lion's; his body thickset, like a little bull—a sort of compressed Hercules of a dog. He must have been ninety pounds' weight, at the least; he had a large blunt head; his muzzle black as night, his mouth blacker than any night, a tooth or two—being all he had—gleaming out of his jaws of darkness. His head was scarred with the records of old wounds, a sort of series of fields of battle all over it; one eye out, one ear cropped as close as was Archbishop Leighton's father's; the remaining eye had the power of two; and above it, and in constant communication with it, was a tattered rag of an ear, which was forever unfurling itself, like an old flag; and then that bud of a tail, about one inch long, if it could in any sense be said to be long, being as broad as long—the mobility, the instantaneousness of that bud were very funny and surprising, and its expressive twinklings and winkings, the intercommunications between the eye, the ear, and it, were of the oddest and swiftest.

Rab had the dignity and simplicity of great size; and having fought his way all along the road to absolute supremacy, he was as mighty in his own line as Julius Cæsar or the Duke of Wellington, and had the gravity of all great fighters.

You must have often observed the likeness of certain men to certain animals, and of certain dogs to men. Now, I never looked at Rab without thinking of the great Baptist preacher, Andrew Fuller. The same large, heavy, menacing, combative, sombre, honest countenance, the same deep inevitable eye, the same look—as of thunder asleep, but ready—neither a dog nor a man to be trifled with.

Next day, my master, the surgeon, examined Ailie. There was no doubt it must kill her, and soon. It could be removed—it might never return—it would give her speedy relief—she should have it done.

She curtsied, looked at James, and said, "When?"

"To-morrow," said the kind surgeon—a man of few words.

She and James and Rab and I retired. I noticed that he and she spoke a little, but seemed to anticipate everything in each other. The following day at noon, the students came in, hurrying up the great stair. At the first landing-place, on a small well-known blackboard, was a bit of paper fastened by wafers and many remains of old wafers beside it. On the paper were the words—"An operation to-day. J. B., *Clerk.*"

Up ran the youths, eager to secure good places; in they crowded, full of interest and talk.

"What's the case? Which side is it?"

Don't think them heartless; they are neither better nor worse than you or I; they get over their professional horrors, and into their proper work; and in them pity—as an *emotion,* ending in itself or at best in tears and a long-drawn breath, lessens, while pity as a *motive* is quickened, and gains power and purpose. It is well for poor human nature that it is so.

The operating theatre is crowded; much talk and fun, and all the cordiality and stir of youth. The surgeon with his staff of assistants is there. In comes Ailie; one look at her quiets and abates the eager students. The beautiful old woman is too much for them. They sit down, and are dumb, and gaze at her. These rough boys feel the power of her presence. She walks in quickly, but without haste; dressed in her mutch, her neckerchief, her white dimity short-gown, her black bombazine petticoat, showing her white worsted stockings and her carpet-shoes. Behind her was James with Rab. James sat down in the distance, and took that huge and noble head between his knees. Rab looked perplexed and dangerous; forever cocking his ear and dropping it as fast.

Ailie stepped up on a seat, and laid herself on the table, as her friend the surgeon told her; arranged herself, gave a rapid look at James, shut her eyes, rested herself on me, and took my hand. The operation was at once begun; it was necessarily slow; and chloroform—one of God's best gifts to his suffering children—was then unknown. The surgeon did his work. The pale face showed its pain, but was still and silent. Rab's soul was working within him; he saw that something strange was going on—blood flowing from his mistress, and she suffering; his ragged ear was up, and importunate; he growled and gave now and then a sharp impatient yelp; he would have liked to have done something to that man. But James had him firm, and gave him a *glower*[2] from time to time, and an intimation of a possible kick;—all the better for James, it kept his eye and his mind off Ailie.

It is over; she is dressed, steps gently and decently down from the table, looks for James; then, turning to the surgeon and the students, she curtsies—and in a low, clear voice, begs their pardon if she has behaved ill. The students—all of us—wept like children; the surgeon happed her up carefully—and, resting on James and me, Ailie went to her room, Rab following. We put her to bed. James took off his heavy shoes, crammed with tackets, heel-capt and toe-capt, and put them carefully under the table, saying, "Maister John, I'm for nane o' yer strynge nurse bodies for Ailie. I'll be her nurse, and I'll gang about on my stockin' soles as canny as pussy."

And so he did; handy and clever, and swift and tender as any woman, was that horny-handed, snell, peremptory little man. Everything she got he gave her; he seldom slept; and often I saw his small, shrewd eyes out of the darkness, fixed on her. As before, they spoke little.

Rab behaved well, never moving, showing us how meek and gentle he could be, and occasionally, in his sleep, letting us know that he was demolishing some adversary. He took a walk

2. *Glower*, a Scotch word meaning a savage stare.

with me every day, generally to the Candlemaker Row; but he was sombre and mild; declined doing battle, though some fit cases offered, and indeed submitted to sundry indignities; and was always very ready to turn and came faster back, and trotted up the stair with much lightness, and went straight to that door.

Jess, the mare, had been sent, with her weatherworn cart, to Howgate, and had doubtless her own dim and placid meditations and confusions, on the absence of her master and Rab, and her unnatural freedom from the road and her cart.

For some days Ailie did well. The wound healed "by the first intention;" for as James said, "Our Ailie's skin's ower clean to beil." The students came in quiet and anxious, and surrounded her bed. She said she liked to see their young, honest faces. The surgeon dressed her, and spoke to her in his own short, kind way, pitying her through his eyes, Rab and James outside the circle—Rab being now reconciled, and even cordial, and having made up his mind that as yet nobody required worrying, but as you may suppose *semper paratus.*[3]

So far well; but four days after the operation my patient had a sudden and long shivering, a "groosin'," as she called it. I saw her soon after; her eyes were too bright, her cheek colored; she was restless, and ashamed of being so; the

3. *Semper paratus* means *always ready.*

balance was lost; mischief had begun. On looking at the wound, a blush of red told the secret; her pulse was rapid, her breathing anxious and quick, she wasn't herself, as she said, and was vexed at her restlessness. We tried what we could, James did everything, was everywhere; never in the way, never out of it. Rab subsided under the table into a dark place, and was motionless, all but his eye, which followed every one. Ailie got worse; began to wander in her mind, gently; was more demonstrative in her ways to James, rapid in her questions, and sharp at times. He was vexed, and said, "She was never that way afore; no, never."

For a time she knew her head was wrong, and was always asking our pardon—the dear, gentle old woman; then delirium set in strong, without pause. Her brain gave way, and then came that terrible spectacle,

"The intellectual power, through words and
things,
Went sounding on its dim and perilous way;"

she sang bits of old songs and psalms, stopping suddenly, mingling the Psalms of David, and the diviner words of his Son and Lord, with homely odds and ends and scraps of ballads.

Nothing more touching, or in a sense more strangely beautiful, did I ever witness. Her tremulous, rapid, affectionate, eager, Scotch voice—the swift, aimless, bewildered mind, the baffled utterance, the bright and perilous eye; some wild words, some household cares, something for James, the names of the dead, Rab called rapidly and in a "fremyt"[4] voice, and he starting up, surprised, and slinking off as if he were to blame somehow, or had been dreaming he heard. Many eager questions and beseechings which James and I could make nothing of, and on which she seemed to set her all, and then sink back ununderstood. It was very sad, but better than many things that are not called sad. James hovered about, put out and miserable, but active and exact as ever; read to her, when there was a lull, short bits from the Psalms, prose and metre, chanting the latter in his own rude and serious way, showing great knowledge of the fit words, bearing up like a man, and doating over her as his "ain Ailie," "Ailie, ma woman!" "Ma ain bonnie wee dawtie!"

The end was drawing on: the golden bowl was breaking; the silver cord was fast being loosed—that *animula blandula, vagula, hospes, comesque*[5] was about to flee. The body and the soul—companions for sixty years—were being sundered, and taking leave. She was walking, alone, through the valley of that shadow, into which one day we must all enter—and yet she was not alone, for we knew whose rod and staff were comforting her.

4. *Fremyt* means *trembling, querulous.*

5. *Animula blandula, vagula, hospes, comesque,* means *sweet fleeting life, companion and sojourner.*

One night she had fallen quiet, and as we hoped, asleep; her eyes were shut. We put down the gas and sat watching her. Suddenly she sat up in bed, and taking a bedgown which was lying on it rolled up, she held it eagerly to her breast—to the right side. We could see her eyes bright with surpassing tenderness and joy, bending over this bundle of clothes. She held it as a woman holds her sucking child; opening out her nightgown impatiently, and holding it close, and brooding over it, and murmuring foolish little words, as one whom his mother comforteth, and who sucks and is satisfied. It was pitiful and strange to see her wasting dying look, keen and yet vague—her immense love.

"Preserve me!" groaned James, giving away. And then she rocked back and forward, as if to make it sleep, hushing it, and wasting on it her infinite fondness.

"Wae's me, doctor; I declare she's thinkin' it's that bairn."

"What bairn?"

"The only bairn we ever had; our wee Mysie, and she's in the Kingdom, forty years and mair."

It was plainly true: the pain in the breast telling its urgent story to a bewildered, ruined brain, was misread, and mistaken; it suggested to her the uneasiness of a breast full of milk, and then the child; and so again once more they were together, and she had her ain wee Mysie in her bosom.

This was the close. She sank rapidly: the

THIS WAS THE CLOSE

delirium left her; but, as she whispered, she was "clean silly"; it was the lightening before the final darkness. After having for some time lain still—her eyes shut, she said, "James!"

He came close to her, and lifting up her calm, clear, beautiful eyes, she gave him a long look, turned to me kindly but shortly, looked for Rab but could not see him, then turned to her husband again, as if she would never leave off looking, shut her eyes and composed herself. She lay for some time breathing quick, and passed away so gently, that when we thought she was gone, James, in his old-fashioned way, held the mirror to her face. After a long pause, one small spot of dimness was breathed out; it vanished away, and never returned, leaving the blank clear darkness of the mirror without a stain. "What is your life? it is even a vapor, which appeareth for a little time, and then vanisheth away."

Rab all this time had been full awake and motionless; he came forward beside us; Ailie's hand, which James had held, was hanging down; it was soaked with his tears; Rab licked it all over carefully, looked at her, and returned to his place under the table.

James and I sat, I don't know how long, but for some time—saying nothing: he started up, abruptly, and with some noise went to the table, and putting his right fore and middle fingers each into a shoe, pulled them out, and put them on, breaking one of the leather latchets, and muttering in anger, "I never did the like o' that afore."

I believe he never did; nor after either. "Rab!" he said roughly, and pointing with his thumb to the bottom of the bed. Rab leaped up, and settled himself; his head and eye to the dead face. "Maister John, ye'll wait for me," said the carrier, and disappeared in the darkness, thundering downstairs in his heavy shoes. I ran to a front window: there he was, already round the house, and out at the gate fleeing like a shadow.

I was afraid about him, and yet not afraid; so I sat down beside Rab, and being wearied, fell asleep. I awoke from a sudden noise outside. It was November, and there had been a heavy fall of snow. Rab was *in statu quo*;[6] he heard the noise too, and plainly knew it, but never moved. I looked out, and there, at the gate, in the dim morning—for the sun was not up—was Jess and the cart—a cloud of steam rising from the old mare. I did not see James; he was already at the door, and came up to the stairs, and met me. It was less than three hours since he left, and he must have posted out—who knows how—to Howgate, full nine miles off; yoked Jess, and driven her astonished into town. He had an armful of blankets, and was streaming with perspiration. He nodded to me, spread out on the floor two pairs of clean old blankets, having at their corners "A. G., 1794," in large letters in red worsted. These were the initials of Alison Græme, and James may have looked in at her from without—himself unseen but not unthought of—when he was "wat, wat and weary," and after having walked many a mile over the hills, may have seen her sitting, while "a' the lave were sleepin';" and by the firelight working her name on the blankets, for her ain James' bed.

He motioned Rab down, and taking his wife in his arms, laid her in the blankets, and happed her carefully and firmly up, leaving the face uncovered; and then lifting her, he nodded again sharply to me, and with a resolved but utterly miserable face, strode along the passage, and

6. *In statu quo* means *in the same position.*

downstairs, followed by Rab. I followed with a light; but he didn't need it. I went out, holding stupidly the candle in my hand in the calm frosty air; we were soon at the gate. I could have helped him, but I saw he was not to be meddled with, and he was strong, and did not need it. He laid her down as tenderly, as safely, as he had lifted her out ten days before—as tenderly as when he had her first in his arms when she was only "A. G."—sorted her, leaving that beautiful sealed face open to the heavens; and then taking Jess by the head, he moved away. He did not notice me, neither did Rab, who presided behind the cart.

I stood till they passed through the long shadow of the College, and turned up Nicholson Street. I heard the solitary cart sound through the streets, and die away and come again; and I returned, thinking of that company going up Libberton Brae, then along Roslin Muir, the morning light touching the Pentlands and making them on-looking ghosts; then down the hill through Auchindinny woods, past "haunted Woodhouselee"; and as daybreak came sweeping up the bleak Lammermuirs, and fell on his own door, the company would stop, and James would take the key, and lift Ailie up again, laying her on her own bed, and, having put Jess up, would return with Rab and shut the door.

James buried his wife, with his neighbors mourning, Rab inspecting the solemnity from a distance. It was snow, and that black ragged hole would look strange in the midst of the swelling spotless cushion of white. James looked after everything; then rather suddenly fell ill, and took to bed; was insensible when the doctor came, and soon died. A sort of low fever was prevailing in the village, and his want of sleep, his exhaustion, and his misery, made him apt to take it. The grave was not difficult to reopen. A fresh fall of snow had again made all things white and smooth; Rab once more looked on, and slunk home to the stable.

And what of Rab? I asked for him next week of the new carrier who got the goodwill of James's business, and was now master of Jess and her cart.

"How's Rab?"

He put me off, and said rather rudely, "What's *your* business wi' the dowg?"

I was not to be so put off.

"Where's Rab?"

He, getting confused and red, and intermeddling with his hair, said, "'Deed sir, Rab's died."

"Dead! what did he die of?"

"Well, sir," said he, getting redder, "he didna exactly dee; he was killed. I had to brain him wi' a rack-pin; there was nae doing wi' him. He lay in the treviss wi' the mear, and wadna come oot. I tempit him wi' the kail and meat, but he wad tak naething, and keepit me frae feedin' the beast, and he was aye gur gurrin', and grup gruppin' me by the legs. I was laith to make awa wi' the old dowg, his like wasne atween this and Thornhill—but, 'deed, sir, I could do naething else."

I believed him. Fit end for Rab, quick and complete. His teeth and his friends gone, why should he keep the peace and be civil?

ANNIE LAURIE

NOTE,—Concerning the history of this song it is stated on good authority that there did really live, in the seventeenth century, an Annie Laurie. She was a daughter of Sir Robert Laurie, first baronet of the Maxwelton family, and was celebrated for her beauty. We should be glad to hear that Annie Laurie married the Mr. Douglas whose love for her inspired the writing of this poem, but records show that she became the wife of another man.

Only the first two verses were composed by Douglas; the last was added by an unknown author.

MAXWELTON braes are bonnie
Where early fa's the dew,
And it's there that Annie Laurie
Gie'd me her promise true,—
Gie'd me her promise true,
Which ne'er forgot will be;
And for bonnie Annie Laurie
I'd lay me doune and dee.

Her brow is like the snaw drift;
Her throat is like the swan;
Her face it is the fairest
That e'er the sun shone on,—
That e'er the sun shone on;
And dark blue is her ee;
And for bonnie Annie Laurie
I'd lay me doune and dee.

Like dew on the gowan lying
Is the fa' o' her fairy feet;
And like winds in summer sighing,
Her voice is low and sweet,—
Her voice is low and sweet;
And she's a' the world to me;
And for bonnie Annie Laurie
I'd lay me doune and dee.

THE BLIND LASSIE

T. C. LATTO

O hark to the strain that sae[1] sweetly is ringin',
And echoing clearly o'er lake and o'er lea,[2]
Like some fairy bird in the wilderness singin';
It thrills to my heart, yet nae[3] minstrel I see.
Round yonder rock knittin', a dear child is sittin',
Sae toilin' her pitifu' pittance[4] is won,
Hersel' tho' we see nae,[5] 'tis mitherless[6] Jeanie—
The bonnie[7] blind lassie that sits i' the sun.

Five years syne come autumn[8] she cam'[9] wi' her mither,
A sodger's[10] puir[11] widow, sair[12] wasted an' gane;[13]
As brown fell the leaves, sae wi' them did she wither,
And left the sweet child on the wide world her lane.[14]

1. *Sae* is the Scotch word for *so*.
2. A lea is a grassy field or meadow.
3. *Nae* means *no*.
4. *Pittance* means small *earnings*.

She left Jeanie weepin', in His holy keepin'
Wha[15] shelters the lamb frae[16] the cauld[17] wintry win';
We had little siller,[18] yet a' were good till her,
The bonnie blind lassie that sits i' the sun.

An' blythe now an' cheerfu', frae mornin' to e'enin
She sits thro' the simmer, an' gladdens ilk[19] ear,
Baith[20] auld and young daut[21] her, sae gentle and winnin';
To a' the folks round the wee lassie is dear.
Braw[22] leddies[23] caress her, wi' bounties would press her;
The modest bit[24] darlin' their notice would shun;
For though she has naething, proud-hearted this wee thing,
The bonnie blind lassie that sits i' the sun.

---

5. *Nae* is *not*.
6. *Mither* is the Scotch form of *mother*.
7. *Bonnie* means *pretty*.
8. *Since come autumn;* that is, it will be nine years next autumn.
9. *Cam'* is a contraction of *came*.
10. *Sodger's* is *soldier's*.
11. *Puir* is the Scotch spelling of *poor*.
12. *Sair* is *sore*, that is, *sadly*.
13. *Gane* means *gone*.
14. *Her lane* means *by herself*.
15. *Wha* is Scotch for *who*.
16. *Frae* means *from*.
17. *Cauld* is the Scotch form of *cold*.
18. *Siller* means *silver money*, or simply *money*.
19. *Ilk* means *every*.
20. *Baith* is Scotch for *both*.
21. *Daut* means *pet*.
22. *Braw* means *fine*, or *gay*.
23. *Leddies* is the Scotch form of *ladies*.
24. *Bit* means *little*.

BOYHOOD

WASHINGTON ALLSTON

Ah, then how sweetly closed those crowded
days!
The minutes parting one by one like rays,
That fade upon a summer's eve.
But O, what charm or magic numbers
Can give me back the gentle slumbers
Those weary, happy days did leave?
When by my bed I saw my mother kneel,
And with her blessing took her nightly kiss;
Whatever Time destroys, he cannot this;—
E'en now that nameless kiss I feel.

SWEET AND LOW

NOTE,—In Tennyson's long poem *The Princess* is a little lullaby so wonderfully sweet that all who have read it wish to read it again. It is one that we all love, no matter whether we are little children and hear it sung to us or are older children and look back to the evenings when we listened to mother's loving voice as she led us gently into the land of dreams while she watched patiently for father's return.

Here are the stanzas which are usually known by the name *Sweet and Low:*

Sweet and low, sweet and low,
Wind of the western sea,
Low, low, breathe and blow,
Wind of the western sea!

Over the rolling waters go,
Come from the dying moon, and blow,
  Blow him again to me;
While my little one, while my pretty one
    sleeps.

Sleep and rest, sleep and rest,
  Father will come to thee soon;
Rest, rest, on mother's breast,
  Father will come to thee soon;
Father will come to his babe in the nest,
Silver sails all out of the west
  Under the silver moon:
Sleep, my little one, sleep, my pretty one,
    sleep.

It is interesting to try to determine just how a great poet makes us feel so strongly the thing that he tells us. In this case Tennyson thinks of a mother in England and a father who is somewhere in the West, out on the broad Atlantic, but is coming home to his little one. The mother dreams only of the home-coming of her husband, and she wishes the baby to learn to love its father as much as she does, so as she sings the little one to sleep, she pours out her love for both in beautiful melody.

To express this mother-love and anxious care the poet has chosen simple words that have rich, musical sounds, that can be spoken easily and smoothly and that linger on the tongue. He speaks of the sea, the gentle wind, the rolling waters, the dying moon and the silver sails, all of which call up ideas that rest us and make us happy, and then with rare skill he arranges the words so that when we read the lines we can feel the gentle rocking movement that lulls the little one, the pretty one into its gentle slumbers.

CHILDHOOD[1]

DONALD G. MITCHELL

ISABEL and I—she is my cousin, and is seven years old, and I am ten—are sitting together on the bank of a stream, under an oak tree that leans half way over to the water. I am much stronger than she, and taller by a head. I hold in my hands a little alder rod, with which I am fishing for the roach and minnows, that play in the pool below us.

She is watching the cork tossing on the water, or playing with the captured fish that lie upon the bank. She has auburn ringlets that fall down upon her shoulders; and her straw hat lies back upon them, held only by the strip of ribbon, that passes under her chin. But the sun does not shine upon her head; for the oak tree above us is full of leaves; and only here and there, a dimple of the sunlight plays upon the pool, where I am fishing.

Her eye is hazel, and bright; and now and then she turns it on me with a look of girlish curiosity, as I lift up my rod—and again in playful menace, as she grasps in her little fingers one of the dead fish, and threatens to throw it back upon the stream. Her little feet hang over the edge of the bank; and from time to time,

1. From *Reveries of a Bachelor*, by Donald G. Mitchell (Ik Marvel).

UNDER THE OAK TREE

she reaches down to dip her toe in the water; and laughs a girlish laugh of defiance, as I scold her for frightening away the fishes.

"Bella," I say, "what if you should tumble in the river?"

"But I won't."

"Yes, but if you should?"

"Why then you would pull me out."

"But if I wouldn't pull you out?"

"But I know you would; wouldn't you, Paul?"

"What makes you think so, Bella?"

"Because you love Bella."

"How do you know I love Bella?"

"Because once you told me so; and because

you pick flowers for me that I cannot reach; and because you let me take your rod, when you have a fish upon it."

"But that's no reason, Bella."

"Then what is, Paul?"

"I'm sure I don't know, Bella."

A little fish has been nibbling for a long time at the bait; the cork has been bobbing up and down —and now he is fairly hooked, and pulls away toward the bank, and you cannot see the cork.

"Here, Bella, quick!"—and she springs eagerly to clasp her little hands around the rod. But the fish has dragged it away on the other side of me; and as she reaches farther, and farther, she slips, cries—"Oh, Paul!" and falls into the water.

The stream, they told us when we came, was over a man's head—it is surely over little Isabel's. I fling down the rod, and thrusting one hand into the roots that support the overhanging bank, I grasp at her hat, as she comes up; but the ribbons give way, and I see the terribly earnest look upon her face as she goes down again. Oh, my mother—thought I—if you were only here!

But she rises again; this time, I thrust my hand into her dress, and struggling hard, keep her at the top, until I can place my foot down upon a projecting root; and so bracing myself, I drag her to the bank, and having climbed up, take hold of her belt firmly with both hands, and drag her out; and poor Isabel, choked, chilled, and wet, is lying upon the grass.

I commence crying aloud. The workmen in the fields hear me, and come down. One takes Isabel in his arms, and I follow on foot to our uncle's home upon the hill.

—"Oh, my dear children!" says my mother; and she takes Isabel in her arms; and presently with dry clothes, and blazing wood-fire, little Bella smiles again. I am at my mother's knee.

"I told you so, Paul," says Isabel—"aunty, doesn't Paul love me?"

"I hope so, Bella," said my mother.

"I know so," said I; and kissed her cheek.

And how did I know it? The boy does not ask; the man does. Oh, the freshness, the honesty, the vigor of a boy's heart! how the memory of it refreshes like the first gush of spring, or the break of an April shower!

But boyhood has its PRIDE, as well as its LOVES.

My uncle is a tall, hard-faced man; I fear him when he calls me—"child;" I love him when he calls me—"Paul." He is almost always busy with his books; and when I steal into the library door, as I sometimes do, with a string of fish, or a heaping basket of nuts to show to him—he looks for a moment curiously at them, sometimes takes them in his fingers—gives them back to me, and turns over the leaves of his book. You are afraid to ask him if you have not worked bravely; yet you want to do so.

You sidle out softly, and go to your mother; she scarce looks at your little stores; but she draws you to her with her arm, and prints a kiss upon your forehead. Now your tongue is unloosed; that kiss and that action have done it; you will tell what capital luck you have had; and you hold up your tempting trophies; "are they not great, mother?" But she is looking in your face, and not at your prize.

"Take them, mother," and you lay the basket upon her lap.

"Thank you, Paul, I do not wish them: but you must give some to Bella."

And away you go to find laughing, playful, cousin Isabel. And we sit down together on the grass, and I pour out my stores between us. "You shall take, Bella, what you wish in your apron, and then when study hours are over, we will have such a time down by the big rock in the meadow!"

"But I do not know if papa will let me," says Isabel.

"Bella," I say, "do you love your papa?"

"Yes," says Bella, "why not?"

"Because he is so cold; he does not kiss you, Bella, so often as my mother does; and besides, when he forbids your going away, he does not say, as mother does—my little girl will be tired, she had better not go—but he says only—Isabel must not go. I wonder what makes him talk so?"

"Why Paul, he is a man, and doesn't—at any rate, I love him, Paul. Besides, my mother is sick, you know."

"But Isabel, my mother will be your mother, too. Come, Bella, we will go ask her if we may go."

And there I am, the happiest of boys, pleading with the kindest of mothers. And the young heart leans into that mother's heart—none of the void now that will overtake it like an opening Korah gulf, in the years that are to come. It is joyous, full, and running over!

"You may go," she says, "if your uncle is willing."

"But mamma, I am afraid to ask him; I do not believe he loves me."

"Don't say so, Paul," and she draws you to her side; as if she would supply by her own love the lacking love of a universe.

"Go, with your cousin Isabel, and ask him kindly; and if he says no—make no reply."

And with courage, we go hand in hand, and steal in at the library door. There he sits—I seem to see him now—in the old wainscoted room, covered over with books and pictures; and he wears his heavy-rimmed spectacles, and is poring over some big volume, full of hard words, that are not in any spelling-book. We step up softly; and Isabel lays her little hand upon his arm; and he turns, and says—"Well, my little daughter?"

I ask if we may go down to the big rock in the meadow?

He looks at Isabel, and says he is afraid—"we cannot go."

"But why, uncle? It is only a little way, and we will be very careful."

"I am afraid, my children; do not say any

more: you can have the pony, and Tray, and play at home."

"But, uncle——"

"You need say no more, my child."

I pinch the hand of little Isabel, and look in her eye—my own half filling with tears. I feel that my forehead is flushed, and I hide it behind Bella's tresses—whispering to her at the same time—"Let us go."

"What, sir," says my uncle, mistaking my meaning—"do you persuade her to disobey?"

Now I am angry, and say blindly—"No, sir, I didn't!" And then my rising pride will not let me say, that I wished only Isabel should go out with me.

Bella cries; and I shrink out; and am not easy until I have run to bury my head in my mother's bosom. Alas! pride cannot always find such covert! There will be times when it will harass you strangely; when it will peril friendships—will sever old, standing intimacy; and then—no resource but to feed on its own bitterness. Hateful pride!—to be conquered, as a man would conquer an enemy, or it will make whirlpools in the current of your affections—nay, turn the whole tide of the heart into rough and unaccustomed channels.

But boyhood has its GRIEF, too, apart from PRIDE.

You love the old dog, Tray; and Bella loves him as well as you. He is a noble old fellow, with shaggy hair, and long ears, and big paws, that he will put up into your hand, if you ask him. And he never gets angry when you play with him, and tumble him over in the long grass, and pull his silken ears. Sometimes, to be sure, he will open his mouth, as if he would bite, but when he gets your hand fairly in his jaws, he will scarce leave the print of his teeth upon it. He will swim, too, bravely, and bring ashore all the sticks you throw upon the water; and when you fling a stone to tease him, he swims round and round, and whines, and looks sorry, that he cannot find it.

He will carry a heaping basket full of nuts, too, in his mouth, and never spill one of them; and when you come out to your uncle's home in the spring, after staying a whole winter in the town, he knows you—old Tray does! And he leaps upon you, and lays his paws on your shoulder, and licks your face; and is almost as glad to see you, as cousin Bella herself. And when you put Bella on his back for a ride, he only pretends to bite her little feet—but he wouldn't do it for the world. Ay, Tray is a noble old dog!

But one summer, the farmers say that some of their sheep are killed, and that the dogs have worried them; and one of them comes to talk with my uncle about it.

But Tray never worried sheep; you know he never did; and so does nurse; and so does Bella; for in the spring, she had a pet lamb, and Tray never worried little Fidele.

And one or two of the dogs that belong to the neighbors are shot; though nobody knows who shot them; and you have great fears about poor

HE WILL CARRY A BASKET

Tray; and try to keep him at home, and fondle him more than ever. But Tray will sometimes wander off; till finally, one afternoon, he comes back whining piteously, and with his shoulder all bloody.

Little Bella cries loud; and you almost cry, as nurse dresses the wound; and poor old Tray whines very sadly. You pat his head, and Bella pats him; and you sit down together by him on the floor of the porch, and bring a rug for him to lie upon; and try and tempt him with a little milk, and Bella brings a piece of cake for him—but he will eat nothing. You sit up till very late, long after Bella has gone to bed, patting his head, and wishing you could do something for poor Tray; but he only licks your hand, and whines more piteously than ever.

In the morning, you dress early, and hurry downstairs; but Tray is not lying on the rug; and you run through the house to find him, and whistle, and call—Tray—Tray! At length you see him lying in his old place, out by the cherry tree, and you run to him; but he does not start; and you lean down to pat him—but he is cold, and the dew is wet upon him—poor Tray is dead!

You take his head upon your knees, and pat again those glossy ears, and cry; but you cannot bring him to life. And Bella comes, and cries with you. You can hardly bear to have him put in the ground; but uncle says he must be buried. So one of the workmen digs a grave under the cherry tree, where he died—a deep grave, and

POOR TRAY IS DEAD

they round it over with earth, and smooth the sods upon it—even now I can trace Tray's grave.

You and Bella together put up a little slab for a tombstone; and she hangs flowers upon it, and ties them there with a bit of ribbon. You can scarce play all that day; and afterward, many weeks later, when you are rambling over the fields, or lingering by the brook, throwing off sticks into the eddies, you think of old Tray's shaggy coat, and of his big paw, and of his honest eye; and the memory of your boyish grief comes upon you; and you say with tears, "Poor Tray!" And Bella too, in her sad sweet tones, says—"Poor old Tray—he is dead!"

FROM THE IMITATION OF CHRIST

THOMAS À KEMPIS

OF FOLLOWING CHRIST AND DESPISING ALL WORLDLY VANITIES

UR Lord saith: he that followeth me walketh not in darkness.

These are the words of Christ in the which we are admonished to follow his life and his manners if we would be truly enlightened and be delivered from all manner of blindness of heart.

Wherefore let our chief study be upon the life of Jesus Christ.

Sublime words make not a man holy and righteous, but it is a virtuous life that maketh him dear to God.

I desire rather to know compunction than its definition. If thou knewest all the sayings of all the philosophers, what should that avail thee without charity and grace?

All other things in the world, save only to love God and serve him, are vanity of vanities and all vanity.

And it is vanity also to desire honour and for a man to lift himself on high.

And it is vanity to follow the desires of the flesh and to desire the thing for which man must afterward grievously be punished.

And it is vanity to desire a long life and to take no care to live a good life.

And it is vanity for a man to take heed only to this present life and not to see before those things that are to come.

Study therefore to withdraw thy heart from love of things visible and turn thee to things invisible.

For they that follow their senses stain their consciences and lose the grace of God.

OF A HUMBLE OPINION OF OURSELVES

Every man naturally desireth knowledge; but knowledge without love and fear of God, what availeth it?

Certainly the meek plow-man that serveth God is much better than the proud philosopher that, taking no heed of his own living, studies the course of the stars.

He that knoweth himself well is lowly in his own sight and hath no delight in man's praises.

If I knew all things that are in the world and had not charity, what should that help me before God who shall judge me according to my deeds?

Unwise is he that more attendeth to other things than to the health of his soul.

Many words fill not the soul; but a good life refresheth the mind and a pure conscience giveth a great confidence in God.

The more thou canst do and the better that thou canst do, the more grievously thou shalt be judged unless thou live holily.

Think not highly of thyself but rather acknowledge thine ignorance.

If thou wilt learn and know anything profitably, love to be unknown and to be accounted as of little worth.

OF THE TEACHING OF TRUTH

Blissful is he whom truth itself teacheth, not by figures or voices, but as it is.

What availeth great searching of dark and hidden things for the which we shall not be blamed in the judgment though we know them not?

He to whom the Word Everlasting speaketh is delivered from a multitude of opinions. Of one Word came all things, and all things speak one word; that is the Beginning that speaketh to us. No man without the Word understandeth or judgeth righteously.

He to whom all things are one and who draweth all things to one and seeth all things in one may be quiet in heart and peaceably abide in God.

O God of truth, make me one with thee in everlasting love!

Ofttimes it wearieth me to hear and read many things; in thee Lord is all that I wish and can desire.

Let all teachers hold their peace and all manner of creatures keep their silence in thy sight: Speak thou alone to me!

Who hath a stronger battle than he that useth force to overcome himself? This should be our occupation, to overcome ourselves and every day to be stronger and somewhat holier.

Meek knowing of thyself is more acceptable to God than deep inquiry after knowledge.

Knowledge or bare and simple knowing of things is not to be blamed, the which, in itself considered, is good and ordained of God: but a good conscience and a virtuous life is ever to be preferred.

And aforasmuch as many people study more to have knowledge than to live well, therefore ofttimes they err and bring forth little fruit or none.

Certainly at the day of doom it shall not be asked of us what we have read, but what we have done; nor what good we have spoken but how religiously we have lived.

Verily he is great that in himself is little and meek and setteth at naught all height of honour. Verily he is great that hath great love. Verily he is prudent that deemeth all earthly things foul so that he may win Christ. And he is verily well learned that doth the will of God and forsaketh his own will.

OF WISDOM IN MAN'S ACTIONS

It is not fit to give credence to every word nor to every suggestion, but every thing is to be weighed according to God, warily and in leisure.

Alas, rather is evil believed of another man than good; we are so weak.

But the perfect believe not easily all things that men tell, for they know man's infirmity, ready to speak evil and careless enough in words.

Hereto it belongeth also not to believe every man's words, nor to tell other men what we hear or carelessly believe.

Have thy counsel with a wise man and a man of conscience and seek rather to be taught by thy betters than to follow thine own inventions.

Good life maketh a man wise in God's sight and expert in many things.

The more meek that a man is and the more subject to God the more wise shall he be in all things—and the more patient.

OF READING THE SCRIPTURES

Truth is to be sought in holy writings, not in eloquence. Every holy writing ought to be read with the same spirit wherewith it was made.

We ought in Scriptures rather to seek profitableness than subtle language.

We ought as gladly to read simple and devout books as high and profound ones.

Let not the authority of him that writeth, whether he be of great name or little, change thy thought, but let the love of pure truth draw thee to read.

Ask not who said this, but take heed what is said. Man passeth, but the truth of the Lord abideth everlastingly.

God speaketh to us in diverse ways without respect to persons.

If thou wilt draw profit in reading, read meekly, simply and truly, not desiring to have a reputation for knowledge.

OF INORDINATE AFFECTIONS

Whenever a man coveteth anything inordinately, anon is he disquieted in himself.

The proud man and covetous hath never rest: the poor and the meek in spirit dwell in peace.

The man that is not perfectly dead to himself is soon tempted and soon overcome by small things and things of little price.

In withstanding passions and not in serving them, standeth peace of heart.

There is no peace in the heart of the carnal man nor in him that is all given to outward things; but in the fervent, spiritual man is peace.

OF SHUNNING TOO GREAT FAMILIARITY

Show not thy heart to every man but bring thy cause to him that is wise and feareth God.

Converse rarely with young people and strangers.

Flatter not rich men and seek not great men; but keep company thyself with meek and simple men and talk of such things as will edify.

Be not familiar to any woman; but generally commend all good women to God.

Desire to be familiar with God and with his angels and avoid knowledge of men. Love is to be given to all men, but familiarity is not expedient.

It happeneth some times that a person unknown shineth by his bright fame, whose presence offendeth and maketh dark the eyes of the beholders. We often hope to please others by our being and living with them, but often we displease them through the bad manners they find in us.

OF SHUNNING MANY WORDS

Avoid noise and the press of men as much as thou mayest: for talking of worldly deeds, though they be brought forth with true and simple intention, hindereth much: for we be soon defiled and led into vanity.

I have wished myself ofttimes to have held my peace and not to have been among men. Why speak we and talk we together so gladly, since seldom we come home without hurting of conscience?

We talk so oft together because by such speaking we seek comfort each from the other and to relieve the heart that is made weary with many thoughts; and we speak much of such things as we love or desire or such things as we dislike. But, alas, it is ofttimes vainly and fruitlessly, for such outward comfort is a great hindering to inward and heavenly consolation. Therefore we ought to watch and pray that our time pass not idly by.

OF FLEEING FROM VAIN HOPE AND ELATION

He is vain that putteth his hope in men or in other created things.

Be not ashamed to serve other men for the love of Jesus Christ and to be considered poor in this world. Stand not upon thyself but set thy trust in God. Do what in thee is and God shall be nigh to thy good will.

Trust not in thine own knowledge nor in the skill of any man living; but rather in the grace of God that helpeth meek folk and maketh low them that are proud.

Rejoice thee not in riches if thou have any, nor in friends if they be mighty; but in God that giveth all things and above all things desireth to give Himself.

Rejoice not for thy greatness nor for the beauty of that body which is corrupted and disfigured with a little sickness.

Please not thyself for thy ability or for thy wit lest thou displease God of whom cometh all the good that thou hast naturally.

Account not thyself better than others, lest peradventure thou be held worse in the sight of God that knoweth what is in man.

Be not proud of good works; for God's judgments are otherwise than thine. Ofttimes what pleaseth man displeaseth God.

If thou hast any good things in thee believe better things of others that thou mayest keep thy humility.

It hurteth thee not to be set under all men: it might hinder thee if thou settest thyself afore others.

Continual peace is with the meek man, but in the heart of the proud man are often envy and indignation.

Thomas a Kempis was born in the latter part of the fourteenth century and lived to a good old age. His name in full was Thomas Haemercken, but as he was born in the town of Kempen he has been generally known by the title above given. The *Imitation* was written slowly, a little at a time, and as the result of reading, reflection and prayer.

The very brief selections given above are condensed from the first ten chapters of the first book. While in the main following the best translation of the original, the language has been simplified in a few places.

THE DESTRUCTION OF SENNACHERIB

LORD BYRON

NOTE,—Byron takes for granted his readers' knowledge of the events with which this poem deals; that is, he does not tell the whole story. Indeed, he gives us very few facts. Is there, for instance, in the poem any hint as to who Sennacherib was, or as to who the enemy was that the Assyrians came against? But if we turn to the eighteenth and nineteenth chapters of *Second Kings*, we shall find the whole account of Sennacherib, king of Assyria, and his expedition against the Hebrew people. The climax of the story, with which this poem deals, is to be found in *Second Kings*, XIX, 35:

"And it came to pass that night, that the angel of the LORD went out, and smote in the camp of the Assyrians an hundred fourscore and five thousand; and when they arose early in the morning, behold, they were all dead corpses."

The Assyrian came down like the wolf on the
fold,
And his cohorts were gleaming in purple and
gold,
And the sheen of their spears was like stars on
the sea,
When the blue wave rolls nightly on deep Galilee.

Like the leaves of the forest when summer is
green,
That host with their banners at sunset were seen;
Like the leaves of the forest when autumn hath
blown,
That host on the morrow lay wither'd and strown.

For the Angel of Death spread his wings on the
blast,
And breathed in the face of the foe as he pass'd;
And the eyes of the sleepers wax'd deadly and
chill,
And their hearts but once heaved, and forever
grew still.

And there lay the steed with his nostril all wide,
But through it there roll'd not the breath of his
pride:
And the foam of his gasping lay white on the turf,
And cold as the spray of the rock-beating surf.

And there lay the rider, distorted and pale,
With the dew on his brow, and the rust on his
mail;
And the tents were all silent, the banners alone,
The lances unlifted, the trumpet unblown.

And the widows of Ashur[1] are loud in their wail,
And the idols are broke in the temple of Baal,[2]
And the might of the Gentile, unsmote by the sword,
Hath melted like snow in the glance of the Lord!

THE BUGLE SONG.

ALFRED TENNYSON

The splendor falls on castle walls
And snowy summits old in story:
The long light shakes across the lakes,
And the wild cataract leaps in glory.
Blow, bugle, blow, set the wild echoes flying,
Blow, bugle; answer, echoes, dying, dying, dying.

O hark, O hear! how thin and clear,
And thinner, clearer, farther going!
O sweet and far from cliff and scar
The horns of Elfland faintly blowing!
Blow, let us hear the purple glens replying:
Blow, bugle; answer, echoes, dying, dying, dying.

O love, they die in yon rich sky,
They faint on hill or field or river:
Our echoes roll from soul to soul,
And grow for ever and for ever.
Blow, bugle, blow, set the wild echoes flying,
And answer, echoes, answer, dying, dying, dying.

1. *Ashur* is the Assyrian form of our word *Assyria*.
2. Baal was the chief god of the Assyrians.

RUTH

NOTE,—This charming story may be found complete in the book of *Ruth* in the Old Testament by those who wish the literal Bible narrative as it is there given.

Little is known as to the date of the writing of the book of *Ruth*. Some authorities believe that it was written earlier than 500 B. C., while others contend that it was not written until much later. As to the purpose, also, there are differences of opinion; is the book merely a religious romance, told to point a moral, or is it an historical narrative meant to give information as to the ancestry of David? Whichever is true, the story is a delightful one, and we enjoy reading it just as we do any other story, apart from its Biblical interest.

I

NOW it came to pass in the days when the judges ruled in Judah that there was a famine in the land, and a certain man of Beth-lehem-Judah went to sojourn in the country of Moab, he, and his wife and his two sons. Together they came into the land and continued there; but the man died, and the wife was left, and her two sons.

And they took them wives of the women of Moab; the name of the one was Orpah, and the name of the other was Ruth; and they dwelled there about ten years. Then the two sons died also both of them; and the woman, Naomi, their mother, alone was left of the family that came into Moab.

Then she arose with her daughters-in-law, that she might return from the country of Moab; for she had heard in the country of Moab how that the Lord had visited his people in giving them bread. Wherefore she went forth out of the place where she was, and her two daughters-in-law with her; and they went on the way to return unto the land of Judah.

But Naomi said unto her two daughters-in-law, "Go, return each to her mother's house. The Lord deal kindly with you, as ye have dealt with the dead, and with me. The Lord grant you that ye may find rest again, each in the house of her husband."

Then she kissed them; and they lifted up their voices and wept, and said unto her, "Surely we will return with thee unto thy people."

Naomi said, "Turn again, my daughters, why will you go with me? Have I yet any more sons that may be your husbands? Nay, it grieveth me much for your sakes that the hand of the Lord is gone out against me. Turn again my daughters; go your way."

Again they lifted up their voice and wept, and Orpah kissed her mother-in-law, but Ruth clave unto her.

"WHITHER THOU GOEST, I WILL GO."

Naomi said, "Behold, thy sister-in-law is gone back unto her people, and unto her gods; return thou after thy sister-in-law."

And Ruth said, "Entreat me not to leave thee, or to return from following after thee: for whither thou goest, I will go; and where thou lodgest, I will lodge: thy people shall be my people, and thy God my God: where thou diest, will I die, and there will I be buried: the Lord do so to me, and more also, if ought but death part thee and me."

When Naomi saw that Ruth was steadfastly minded to go with her, then she left speaking unto her. So they two went until they came to Bethlehem.

There it came to pass that all the city was moved about them, and the people said, "Is this Naomi?"

"Call me not Naomi," she said unto them. "Call me Mara: for the Almighty hath dealt very bitterly with me.[1] I went out full and the Lord hath brought me home again empty: why then call me Naomi, seeing the Lord hath testified against me, and the Almighty hath afflicted me?"

So Naomi returned, and Ruth the Moabitess, her daughter-in-law, with her, which returned out of the country of Moab: and they came to Bethlehem in the beginning of barley harvest.

II

NAOMI had a kinsman of her husband's, a mighty man of wealth; and his name was Boaz.

And Ruth said unto Naomi, "Let me now go to the field, and glean ears of corn after him in whose sight I shall find grace." And Naomi answered, "Go, my daughter."

And she went, and came, and gleaned in the field after the reapers: and her hap was to light on a part of the field belonging unto Boaz.

And, behold, Boaz came from Bethlehem and said unto the reapers, "The Lord be with you."

1. *Naomi* means *pleasant*, while *Mara* means *bitter*.

RUTH GLEANING

And the reapers answered him, "The Lord bless thee."

Then said Boaz unto his servant that was set over the reapers, "Whose damsel is this?"

And the servant answered and said, "It is the Moabitish damsel that came back with Naomi out of the country of Moab. And she said, 'I pray you, let me glean and gather after the reapers among the sheaves': so she came, and hath continued even from the morning until now, that she tarried a little in the house."

Boaz said unto Ruth, "Hearest thou not, my daughter? Go not to glean in another field, neither go from hence, but abide here fast by my maidens. Let thine eyes be on the field that they do reap, and go thou after them: have I not charged the young men that they shall not touch thee? and when thou art athirst, go unto the vessels, and drink of that which the young men have drawn."

Then she fell on her face and bowed herself to the ground, and said unto him, "Why have I found grace in thine eyes, that thou shouldest take knowledge of me, seeing I am a stranger?"

And Boaz answered and said unto her, "It hath fully been shewed me, all that thou hast done unto thy mother-in-law since the death of thine husband: and how thou hast left thy father and thy mother, and the land of thy nativity, and art come unto a people which thou knewest not heretofore. The Lord recompense thy work, and a full reward be given thee of the Lord God of Israel, under whose wings thou art come to trust."

Then she said, "Let me find favour in thy sight, my lord; for that thou hast comforted me, and for that thou hast spoken friendly unto thine handmaid, though I be not like unto one of thine handmaidens."

And Boaz said unto her, "At mealtime come

thou hither, and eat of the bread and dip thy morsel in the vinegar."

And she sat beside the reapers; and he reached her parched corn, and she did eat, and was sufficed and left.

And when she was risen up to glean again, Boaz commanded his young men, saying, "Let her glean even among the sheaves and reproach her not; and let fall also some handfuls of purpose for her, and leave them that she may glean them, and rebuke her not."

So she gleaned in the field until even, and beat out that she had gleaned: and it was about an ephah[2] of barley. And she took it up, and went into the city: and her mother-in-law saw what she had gleaned.

And her mother-in-law said unto her, "Where hast thou gleaned to-day? and where wroughtest thou? blessed be he that did take knowledge of thee."

And she showed her mother-in-law with whom she had wrought, and said, "The man's name with whom I wrought to-day is Boaz."

And Naomi said unto her daughter-in-law, "Blessed be he of the Lord, who hath not left off his kindness to the living and to the dead." And Naomi said unto her, "The man is near of kin unto us, one of our next kinsmen."

And Ruth the Moabitess said, "He said unto me also, 'Thou shalt keep fast by my young men, until they have ended all my harvest.'"

And Naomi said unto Ruth, her daughter-in-

2. The *ephah* was equal to about two pecks and five quarts.

law, "It is good, my daughter, that thou go out with his maidens, that they meet thee not in any other field."

So she kept fast by the maidens of Boaz to glean unto the end of barley harvest and of wheat harvest; and dwelt with her mother-in-law.

III

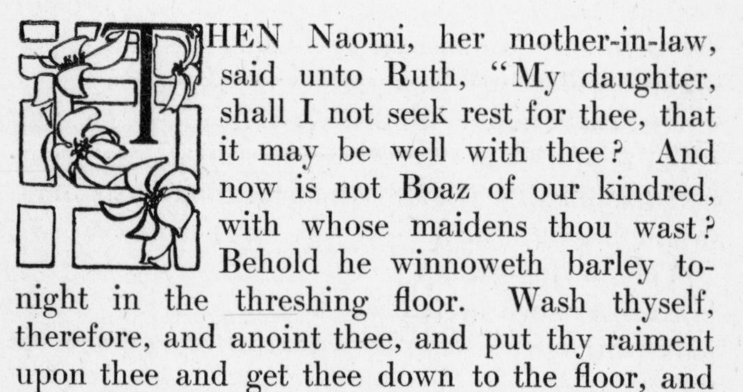

THEN Naomi, her mother-in-law, said unto Ruth, "My daughter, shall I not seek rest for thee, that it may be well with thee? And now is not Boaz of our kindred, with whose maidens thou wast? Behold he winnoweth barley to-night in the threshing floor. Wash thyself, therefore, and anoint thee, and put thy raiment upon thee and get thee down to the floor, and he will tell thee what to do."

And Ruth said, "All that thou sayest unto me, that will I do."

Therefore went she down unto the threshing floor and did according to all that her mother-in-law bade her. And Boaz saw her and loved her and asked her, "Who art thou?"

She answered, "I am Ruth, thy handmaid."

And Boaz said, "Blessed be thou of the Lord, my daughter, and fear not, for all the city of my people doth know thou art a virtuous woman. And now it is true that I am thy near kinsman: howbeit, there is a kinsman nearer than I. Tarry this night, and it shall be in the morning that if he will perform unto thee the part of a kinsman, well; let him do the kinsman's part. But if he will not do the part of a kinsman to thee, then will I do the part of the kinsman to thee, as the Lord liveth. Bring now the vail that thou hast upon thee and hold it."

And when she held it, he measured six measures of barley, and laid it on her, and she returned into the city.

When now she came to her mother, Naomi asked, "Who art thou?" And Ruth told her all that the man had said and done, and said, "These six measures of barley gave he me, for he said to me, 'Go not empty unto thy mother-in-law.'"

Then said Naomi, "Sit still, my daughter, until thou know how the matter will fall; for the man will not be in rest until he have finished the thing this day."

IV

THEN went Boaz up to the gate and sat him down there; and, behold, the kinsman of whom Boaz spoke, came by; unto whom Boaz said, "Ho, such a one! turn aside, sit down here." And he turned aside and sat down.

And Boaz took also ten men of the elders of the city and said, "Sit ye down here." And they sat down.

Then said Boaz unto the kinsman, "Naomi, that is come again out of the land of Moab, selleth a parcel of land, which was our brother's. And I thought to ask thee to buy it before the inhabitants and before the elders of my people. If thou wilt redeem it, redeem it; but if thou wilt not redeem it, then tell me, that I may know: for there is none to redeem it beside thee, and I am after thee. And what day thou buyest it of the hand of Naomi, thou must buy it also of Ruth the Moabitess, the wife of the dead."

And the kinsman said, "I cannot redeem it for myself, lest I mar mine own inheritance; redeem thou my right to thyself: for I cannot redeem it."

Now this was the manner in former time in Israel, concerning redeeming and concerning changing, for to confirm all things: a man plucked off his shoe and gave it to his neighbor; and this was a testimony in Israel. Therefore the kinsman said unto Boaz, "Buy it for thee." So he drew off his shoe.

And Boaz said unto the elders and all the people, "Ye are witnesses this day that I have bought all that was Naomi's husband's and all that was her son's of the hand of Naomi. Moreover, Ruth the Moabitess, the wife of my kinsman that is dead, have I purchased to be my wife, that the name of the dead be not cut off from among his brethren, and from the gate of his place: ye are witnesses this day."

And all the people that were there in the gate, and the elders, said, "We are witnesses. The Lord make the woman that is come into thine house like Rachel and like Leah, which two did

HE DREW OFF HIS SHOE

build the house of Israel: and do thou worthily and be famous in Bethlehem."

So Boaz took Ruth, and she was his wife, and she bare him a son. And the women said unto Naomi, "Blessed be the Lord that hath not left thee this day without a kinsman, that his name may be famous in Israel. And he shall be unto thee a restorer of thy life, and a nourisher of thine old age; for thy daughter-in-law which loveth thee, which is better to thee than seven sons, hath born him."

And Naomi took the child and laid it in her bosom, and became nurse unto it. And the women, her neighbors, gave it a name, saying, "There is a son born to Naomi, and his name is Obed."

This same Obed is the father of Jesse, who is the father of David.

THE VISION OF BELSHAZZAR

LORD BYRON

NOTE,—According to the account given in the fifth chapter of *Daniel*, Belshazzar was the last king of Babylon, and the son of the great king Nebuchadnezzar, who had destroyed Jerusalem and taken the Jewish people captive to Babylon. The dramatic incident with which the second stanza of Byron's poem deals is thus described:

"In the same hour came forth fingers of a man's hand, and wrote over against the candlestick upon the plaister of the wall of the king's palace; and the king saw the part of the hand that wrote."

After all the Babylonian wise men had tried in vain to read the writing, the "captive in the land," Daniel, was sent for, and he interpreted the mystery.

"And this is the writing that was written, MENE, MENE, TEKEL, UPHARSIN.

"This is the interpretation of the thing: MENE; God hath numbered thy kingdom, and finished it.

"TEKEL; Thou art weighed in the balances, and art found wanting.

"PERES; Thy kingdom is divided, and given to the Medes and Persians."

The fulfillment of the prophecy thus declared by Daniel is described thus briefly: "In that night was Belshazzar the king of the Chaldeans slain. And Darius the Median took the kingdom."

The King was on his throne,
  The Satraps[1] throng'd the hall;
A thousand bright lamps shone
  O'er that high festival.
A thousand cups of gold,
  In Judah deem'd divine—
Jehovah's vessels hold[2]
  The godless Heathen's wine.

In that same hour and hall
  The fingers of a Hand
Came forth against the wall,
  And wrote as if on sand:
The fingers of a man;—
  A solitary hand
Along the letters ran,
  And traced them like a wand.

The monarch saw, and shook,
  And bade no more rejoice;
All bloodless wax'd his look,
  And tremulous his voice:—
"Let the men of lore appear,
  The wisest of the earth,
And expound the words of fear,
  Which mar our royal mirth."

---

1. The satraps were the governors of the provinces, who ruled under the king and were accountable to him.

2. These were the sacred "vessels that were taken out of the temple of the house of God which was at Jerusalem."

THE WRITING ON THE WALL

Chaldea's[3] seers are good,
  But here they have no skill;
And the unknown letters stood
  Untold and awful still.
And Babel's[4] men of age
  Are wise and deep in lore;
But now they were not sage,
  They saw—but knew no more.

3. The terms *Chaldea* and *Babylonia* were used practically synonymously.

4. *Babel* is a shortened form of *Babylon*.

A Captive in the land,
  A stranger and a youth,
He heard the king's command,
  He saw that writing's truth;
The lamps around were bright,
  The prophecy in view;
He read it on that night,—
  The morrow proved it true!

"Belshazzar's grave is made,
  His kingdom pass'd away,
He, in the balance weigh'd,
  Is light and worthless clay;
The shroud, his robe of state;
  His canopy, the stone:
The Mede is at his gate!
  The Persian on his throne!"

SOHRAB AND RUSTEM

RUSTEM

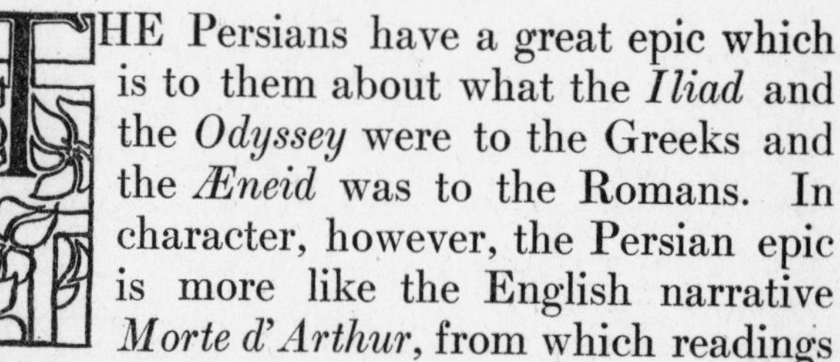

THE Persians have a great epic which is to them about what the *Iliad* and the *Odyssey* were to the Greeks and the *Æneid* was to the Romans. In character, however, the Persian epic is more like the English narrative *Morte d'Arthur*, from which readings will be found elsewhere in these volumes. This wonderful poem, the *Shah Nameh*, relates exploits of the Shahs of Persia for a period that is supposed to extend over more than three thousand years. It was written by Firdusi, a famous Persian poet, toward the close of the tenth century, and is filled with tales of the marvelous adventures and stirring achievements of national heroes. Fierce monsters like those that appear in the legendary tales of all nations stalk through its pages, and magicians, good and bad, work their enchantments for and against the devoted Persians. The imagination of Eastern writers is more vivid than that of the Europeans, and for that reason the stories are more full of thrilling episodes and supernatural occurrences.

Chief among the heroes is Rustem, who seems to have lived through many centuries, and to have been the one great defender of the Persian throne. From the cradle he was marked for renown, for he was larger, stronger and healthier than any other babe that was ever born. His mother alone could not feed him, and ten nurses were required to satisfy the infant's hunger. His father, Zal, the white-haired, looked with pride upon his growing son, who as soon as he was weaned fell upon bread and meat as his only diet and required as much of them as would feed five ordinary men. Such a child ought to make a wonderful man, and this one fulfilled the highest hopes of his parents, for he became taller in stature, broader in shoulders, deeper in the chest and stronger in all his muscles than any other man the Persian race had ever known.

His childish exploits were quite as wonderful as those of his later years. One night he was awakened from his slumbers by hearing the servants say that the great white elephant on which his father rode on state occasions had broken loose and was running about the royal gardens, mad with rage, pulling up the trees, tearing down buildings and killing every one that came in his way. Not a man dared stand against the fierce beast, and though the archers had tried again and again their weapons had no effect upon him.

Rustem rose from his couch, put on his clothes, caught from the wall the huge club his grandfather had owned, and made for the door of his chamber.

"Where are you going? What will you do?" cried the frightened servants.

"Open the door. I must stop that elephant

before he does greater damage," answered the boy.

One of his serving men, braver than the rest, opposed the boy. "I dare not obey you," said the man; "your father would never forgive me if I let you go forth to be slain by that ferocious beast whose broken chains clank about his legs and whose huge trunk brings destruction to everything it strikes. You will be knocked down and trampled to death. This is pure folly!"

"Out of my way," cried the enraged Rustem. "You rush upon your own doom."

Almost blind with anger, the furious youth swung his club about him and struck the faithful servant so fearful a blow that his head was knocked from his body and rolled along the floor like a huge ball. The other servants fled to the corners of the room and gave Rustem a clear path. One blow from his great club broke the iron balls from the door and sent it flying from its hinges. Shouldering his club Rustem hurried into the garden, where he soon found the maddened elephant in the midst of the ruin he was making. When the unwieldy animal saw the boy approaching it rushed at him with savage bellowings, swinging its long, powerful trunk from side to side in great circles. The terrible spectacle frightened Rustem not in the least, and the dauntless youth rushed forward and struck the elephant a single blow full in its forehead. The great legs trembled and bent, the huge body tottered and fell, making a mountain of quivering flesh. Rustem calmly shouldered his club, returned to his chamber, and finished his sleep.

As Rustem grew to manhood he became the owner of a great horse little less wonderful than his master. Raksh, for that was the animal's name, not only carried Rustem in war and in the chase, but he fought for his master in every conflict, watched over him in his sleep, and defended him with human intelligence. On one of his expeditions Rustem lay down to sleep near the den of a lion, that as he came forth to hunt at night saw the horse and rider asleep before him. The lion, knowing that if he could kill the horse the man could not get away, made ready to spring upon Raksh, but that wary animal was sleeping with one eye open and met the leaping lion more than half way with two great hoofs planted squarely in his face. Before the astonished animal could recover his senses Raksh seized him by the back and beat his life out upon the ground.

Of Rustem's countless struggles with dragons, witches, genii and other strange beings, and of the wonderful battles by which he defended the throne of Persia, we cannot stop to read. They were all very similar in one respect at least, for always he escaped from deadly peril by his own wisdom and strength, aided often, as we have said, by Raksh. But there is one part of his life, one series of more than human adventures that we ought to know.

One day Rustem was hunting over a plain

on the borders of Tartary when he discovered a large herd of wild asses. No animal could outstrip Raksh, and so his master was soon among the herd, killing the animals to right and left. Some he slew with the arrows of his strong bow, others he lassoed and killed with his trusty club. When his love for hunting was satisfied he built a fire, roasted one of the asses and prepared for a great feast. In time even his sharp appetite was quenched, and lying down upon his blanket he was soon buried in a sound slumber.

As he slept Raksh wandered about the plains quietly feeding. Without noticing it he strayed far away from his master, and in fact quite out of sight. Then it happened that seven Tartars who had been following Raksh made a dash at him and tried to capture him with their lassoes. The noble horse fought them manfully, killing two of them with the blows of his forefeet and biting the head from the shoulders of another. But the ropes from the lassoes became tangled with his legs, and even the marvelous Raksh was at last thrown, overpowered and led struggling away.

When Rustem awoke his first thought was for his horse, but though he looked everywhere the faithful animal was not in sight. Such a thing had never happened before, and Rustem grew pale with sorrow and dread.

"What can I do without my noble charger?" he said. "How can I carry my arrows, club and other weapons? How can I defend myself? Moreover, I shall be the laughingstock of friends and enemies alike, for all will say that in my carelessness I slept and allowed my horse to be stolen."

At last he discovered the tracks of Raksh in the dust of the plain, and following them with difficulty he found himself at the town of Samengan. The king and nobles of the town knew Rustem, but seemed surprised to see him come walking. The wanderer explained what had happened, and the wily monarch answered, "Have no fear, noble Rustem. Every one knows your wonderful horse Raksh, and soon some one will come and bring him to you. I will even send many men to search for him. In the meantime, rest with us and be happy. We will entertain you with the best, and in pleasure you will forget your loss till Raksh is returned to you."

This plan pleased Rustem, and the king kept his word in royal entertainments in which he served his guest with grave humility. Moreover, the princess Tehmina likewise served Rustem with becoming grace and dignity. No maiden was ever more beautiful. She was tall as the cypress and as graceful as a gazelle. Her neck and shoulders were like ivory; her hair, black and shiny as a raven's wings, hung in two long braids down her back, as the Persian horseman loops his lasso to his saddle bow; her lips were like twin rubies, and her black brilliant eyes glanced from highly-arched eyebrows.

Rustem fell deeply in love with the fair maiden as soon as he saw her, and at the first opportunity told her of his affection. Tehmina then confessed that she had long loved Rustem from the reports she had heard of his noble character and deeds of great prowess. The capture of Raksh was a part of her plan for meeting the owner, for she felt sure he would follow the animal's track to her father's capital. All this served to make more strong the love of Rustem, who impatiently demanded of the king his daughter's hand in marriage. The king, glad enough to have so powerful a man for his son, consented willingly to the match, and after they were married amid great rejoicings, Rustem settled down at the court in quiet enjoyment of his new-found home.

A powerful man like Rustem cannot always remain in idleness, however, and when news came to him that the Persian king was in need of his greatest warrior, Rustem took his lasso, his bow and arrows and his club, mounted Raksh and rode away. Before going, however, he took from his arm an onyx bracelet that had been his father's, and calling Tehmina to him handed it to her, saying:

"Take this bracelet, my dear one, and keep it. If we have a child and it be a girl, weave the bracelet in her hair and she will grow tall, beautiful and good; if our child be a boy, fasten the bracelet on his arm, and he will become strong and courageous, a mighty warrior and a wise counsellor."

SOHRAB

WHEN Rustem had gone Tehmina wept bitterly, but consoled herself with the thought that her husband would soon return. After her child was born, she devoted herself to the wonderful boy and waited patiently for the father that never returned. She remembered the parting words of Rustem, and fastened upon the arm of her infant son the magic bracelet of his race.

He was a marvelous boy, this son of Rustem and Tehmina. Beautiful in face as the moon when it rides the heavens in its fullness, he was large, well-formed, with limbs as straight as the arrows of his father. He grew at an astonishing rate. When he was but a month old he was as tall as any year-old baby; at three years of age he could use the bow, the lasso and the club with the skill of a man; at five he was as brave as a lion, and at ten not a man in the kingdom was his match in strength and agility.

Tehmina, rejoicing in the intelligent, shining face of her boy, had named him Sohrab, but as she feared that Rustem might send for his son if he knew that he had so promising a one, she sent word to her husband that her child was a girl. Disappointed in this, Rustem paid no attention to his offspring, who grew up unknown to his parent, and himself ignorant of the name of his father.

When Sohrab was about ten years old he began to notice that, unlike the other young men, he seemed to have no father. Accordingly he went to his mother and questioned her.

"What shall I say," he inquired, "when the young men ask me who is my father? Must I always tell them that I do not know? Whose son am I?"

"My son, you ask and you have a right to know. You need feel no shame because of your father. He is the mighty Rustem, the greatest of Persian warriors, the noblest man that ever lived. But I beg you to tell no one lest word should come to Rustem, for I know he would take you from me and I should never see you again."

Sohrab was overjoyed to hear of his noble parentage and felt his heart swell with pride, for he had heard all his life of the heroic deeds of his father.

"Such a thing as this cannot be kept secret," he cried. "Sooner or later every one in the world will know that I am Rustem's son. But not now will we tell the tale. I will gather a great army of Tartars and make war upon Kaoos, the Persian king. When I have defeated him I will set my father Rustem upon the throne, and then I will overthrow Afrasiab, King of the Turanians, and take his throne myself. There is room in the world for but two kings, my father Rustem and myself."

The youthful warrior began his preparations immediately. First he sought far and wide for a horse worthy to carry him, and at last succeeded in finding a noble animal of the same breed as the famous Raksh. Mounted on this splendid steed he rode about and rapidly collected an army of devoted followers.

The noise of these preparations spread abroad and soon came to the ears of Afrasiab, who saw in this war an opportunity for profit to himself and humiliation for Kaoos. Accordingly, he sent offers of assistance to Sohrab, who accepted them willingly and received among his followers the hosts of the Turanian king. But Afrasiab was a wily monarch, and sent to Sohrab two astute counsellors, Haman and Barman, with instructions to watch the young leader carefully and to keep from him all knowledge of his father.

"If possible," said the treacherous monarch, "bring the two together and let them fight, neither knowing who the other is. Then may Sohrab slay his mighty father and we be left to rule the youthful and inexperienced son by our superior cunning and wisdom. If on the other hand Rustem shall slay his son, his heart will fail him, and he will die in despair."

When the army was fully in readiness Sohrab set forth against Persia. In his way lay the great White Fort whose chief defender was the mighty Hujir. The Persians felt only contempt for the boyish leader and had no fear of his great army. As they approached, Hujir rode forth to meet them and called aloud in derision,

"Let the mighty Sohrab come forth to meet

me alone. I will slay him with ease and give his body to the vultures for food."

Undismayed by these threats Sohrab met the doughty Persian and unhorsed him in the first encounter. Springing from his horse Sohrab raised his sword to strike, but the Persian begged so lustily for quarter that he was granted his life, though sent a prisoner to the king.

Among those who watched the defeat of Hujir was Gurdafrid, the daughter of the old governor of the White Fort. She was stronger than any warrior in the land and fully accustomed to the use of arms. When she became aware that Hujir was indeed vanquished she hastily clothed herself in full armor, thrust her long hair under her helmet and rode gallantly out to meet Sohrab. The girl shot a perfect shower of arrows at Sohrab, but all glanced harmlessly from his armor. Seeing that she could not find a weak spot in his mail she put her shield in rest and charged valiantly at her foe. However, she was no match for her antagonist and was borne from her saddle by the fierce lance of her enemy. As she fell, however, she drew her sword and severed the spear of Sohrab. Before he could change weapons she had mounted her horse and was galloping wildly toward the fort with her late antagonist in full pursuit. Long ere the castle walls were reached Sohrab overtook her and seized her by the helmet, when its fastenings gave way and her long hair fell about her shoulders, disclosing the fact that he had been fighting with a woman.

Struck by the beauty of the girl and ashamed that he had been fighting with her, Sohrab released her after she had promised that she would make no further resistance and that the castle would surrender at his approach. The fierce Gurdafrid, however, had no idea of giving up the fort, but as soon as she was within, the gates were closed, and she, mounting upon the walls, jeered at the waiting Sohrab.

"It is now too late to fight, but when morning comes I will level your fort to the earth and leave not one stone upon the other." With these words the incensed warrior galloped back to his camp. When in the morning he marched his army against the fort he found that his prey had escaped, for during the night Gurdafrid had led the whole garrison out through a secret passage and had gone to warn King Kaoos of the approach of the mighty Sohrab and his powerful army. The allied Tartars and Turanians followed as rapidly as they might, but it was some time before they could come anywhere near the Persian capital.

What was happening in Persia has been very well told by Alfred J. Church in his story of Sohrab and Rustem:

"When King Kaoos heard that there had appeared among the Tartars a mighty champion, against whom, such was the strength of his arms, no one could stand; how he had overthrown and taken their champion and now threatened to overrun and conquer the whole land of Persia, he was greatly troubled, and calling a scribe, said to him, 'Sit down and write a letter to Rustem.'

"So the scribe sat down and wrote. The letter was this: 'There has appeared among the Tartars a great champion, strong as an elephant and as fierce as a lion. No one can stand against him. We look to you for help. It is of your doing that our warriors hold their heads so high. Come, then, with all the speed that you can use, so soon as you shall have read this letter. Be it night or day, come at once; do not open your mouth to speak; if you have a bunch of roses in your hand do not stop to smell it, but come; for the warrior of whom I write is such that you only can meet him.'

"King Kaoos sealed the letter and gave it to a warrior named Giv. At the same time he said, 'Haste to Rustem. Tarry not on the way; and when you are come, do not rest there for an hour. If you arrive in the night, depart again the next morning.'

"So Giv departed, and traveled with all his speed, allowing himself neither sleep nor food. When he approached Zabulistan, the watchman said, 'A warrior comes from Persia riding like the wind.' So Rustem, with his chiefs, went out to meet him. When they had greeted each other, they returned together to Rustem's palace.

"Giv delivered his message, and handed the king's letter, telling himself much more that he had heard about the strength and courage of this Tartar warrior. Rustem heard him with astonishment, and said, 'This champion is like, you say, to the great San, my grandfather. That such a man should come from the free Persians is possible; but that he should be among those slaves the Tartars, is past belief. I have myself a child, whom the daughter of a Tartar king bore to me; but the child is a girl. This, then, that you tell me is passing strange; but for the present let us make merry.'

"So they made merry with the chiefs that were assembled in Rustem's palace. But after a while Giv said again: 'King Kaoos commanded me, saying, "You must not sleep in Zabulistan; if you arrive in the night, set out again the next morning. It will go ill with us if we have to fight before Rustem comes." It is necessary, then, great hero, that we set out in all haste for Persia.'

"Rustem said, 'Do not trouble yourself about this matter. We must all die some day. Let us, therefore, enjoy the present. Our lips are dry, let us wet them with wine. As to this Tartar, fortune will not always be with him. When he sees my standard, his heart will fail him.'

"So they sat, drinking the red wine and singing merry songs, instead of thinking of the king and his commands. The next day Rustem passed in the same fashion, and the third also. But on the fourth Giv made preparations to depart, saying to Rustem, 'If we do not make haste to set out, the king will be wroth, and his anger is terrible.'

"Rustem said, 'Do not trouble yourself; no man dares to be wroth with me.' Nevertheless, he bade them saddle Raksh and set out with his companions.

"When they came near the king's palace, a great company of nobles rode out to meet them, and conducted them to the king, and they paid their homage to him. But the king turned away from them in a rage. 'Who is Rustem,' he cried, 'that he forgets his duty to me, and disobeys my commands? If I had a sword in my hand this moment, I would cut off his head, as a man cuts an orange in half. Take him, hang him up alive on gallows, and never mention his name again in my presence.'

"Giv answered, 'Sir, will you lay hands upon Rustem?'

"The king burst out again in rage against Giv and Rustem, crying to one of his nobles, 'Take these two villains and hang them alive on gallows.' And he rose up from his throne in fury.

"The noble to whom he had spoken laid his hand upon Rustem, wishing to lead him out of the king's presence, lest Kaoos in his rage should do him an injury. But Rustem cried out, 'What a king are you! Hang this Tartar, if you can, on your gallows. Keep such things for your enemies. All the world has bowed itself before me and Raksh, my horse. And you—you are king by my grace.'

"Thus speaking, he struck away the hand that the noble had laid upon him so fiercely that the man fell headlong to the ground, and he passed over his body to go from the presence of the king. And as he mounted on Raksh, he cried: 'What is Kaoos that he should deal with me in this fashion? It is God who has given me strength and victory, and not he or his army. The nobles would have given me the throne of Persia long since, but I would not receive it; I kept the right before my eyes. Verily, had I not done so, you, Kaoos, would not be sitting upon the throne.' Then he turned to the Persians that stood by, and said, 'This brave Tartar will come. Look out for yourselves how you may save your lives. Me you shall see no more in the land of Persia.'

"The Persians were greatly troubled to hear such words; for they were sheep, and Rustem was their shepherd. So the nobles assembled, and said to each other: 'The king has forgotten all gratitude and decency. Does he not remember that he owes to Rustem his throne—nay, his very life? If the gallows be Rustem's reward, what shall become of us?'

"So the oldest among them came and stood before the king, and said: 'O king, have you forgotten what Rustem has done for you and this land—how he conquered Mazanieran and its king and the White Genius; how he gave you back the sight of your eyes? And now you have commanded that he shall be hanged alive upon a gallows. Are these fitting words for a king?'

"The king listened to the old man, and said: 'You speak well. The words of a king should be words of wisdom. Go now to Rustem, and speak good words to him, and make him forget my anger.'

"So the old man rode after Rustem, and many of the nobles went with him. When they had overtaken him, the old man said, 'You know that the king is a wrathful man, and that in his rage he speaks hard words. But you know also that he soon repents. But now he is ashamed of what he said. And if he has offended, yet the Persians have done no wrong that you should thus desert them.'

"Rustem answered, 'Who is the king that I should care for him? My saddle is my throne and my helmet is my crown, my corselet is my robe of state. What is the king to me but a grain of dust? Why should I fear his anger? I delivered him from prison; I gave him back his crown. And now my patience is at an end.'

"The old man said, 'This is well. But the king and his nobles will think, "Rustem fears this Tartar," and they will say, "If Rustem is afraid, what can we do but leave our count y?" I pray you therefore not to turn your back upon the king, when things are in such a plight. Is it well that the Persians should become the slaves of the infidel Tartars?'

"Rustem stood confounded to hear such words. 'If there were fear in my heart, then I would tear my soul from my body. But you know that it is not; only the king has treated me with scorn.'

"But he perceived that he must yield to the

old man's advice. So he went back with the nobles.

"As soon as the king saw him, he leaped upon his feet, and said, 'I am hard of soul, but a man must grow as God has made him. My heart was troubled by the fear of this new enemy. I looked to you for safety, and you delayed your coming. Then I spoke in my wrath; but I have repented, and my mouth is full of dust.'

"Rustem said, 'It is yours to command, O king, and ours to obey. You are the master, and we are the slaves. I am but as one of those who open the door for you, if indeed I am worthy to be reckoned among them. And now I come to execute your commands.'

"Kaoos said, 'It is well. Now let us feast. To-morrow we will prepare for war.'

"So Kaoos, and Rustem, and the nobles feasted till the night had passed and the morning came. The next day King Kaoos and Rustem, with a great army, began their march."

Matthew Arnold, the great English critic, scholar and poet, has used the incidents that follow as the subject of one of his most interesting poems. To that poem we will look for a continuation of the story. Arnold alters the story at times to suit the needs of his poem, and he often employs a slightly different spelling of proper names from that used in the above account.

SOHRAB AND RUSTUM

AN EPISODE

MATTHEW ARNOLD

ND the first gray of morning fill'd the east,
And the fog rose out of the Oxus[1] stream.
But all the Tartar camp along the stream
Was hush'd, and still the men were plunged in sleep;
Sohrab alone, he slept not; all night long
He had lain wakeful, tossing on his bed;
But when the gray dawn stole into his tent,
He rose, and clad himself, and girt his sword,
And took his horseman's cloak, and left his tent,
And went abroad into the cold wet fog,
Through the dim camp to Peran-Wisa's[2] tent.

Through the black Tartar tents he pass'd, which stood
Clustering like beehives on the low flat strand
Of Oxus, where the summer floods o'erflow
When the sun melts the snows in high Pamere;[3]

---

1. The Oxus, 1300 miles long, is the chief river of Central Asia, and one of the boundaries of Persia.

2. Peran-Wisa was the commander of King Afrasiab's troops, a Turanian chief who ruled over the many wild Tartar tribes whose men composed his army.

3. Pamir or Pamere is a high tableland called by the natives "the roof of the world." In it lies the source of the Oxus. Arnold has named many places for the purpose of giving an air of reality to the

Through the black tents he pass'd, o'er that low
strand,
And to a hillock came, a little back
From the stream's brink—the spot where first a
boat,
Crossing the stream in summer, scrapes the land.
The men of former times had crown'd the top
With a clay fort; but that was fall'n, and now
The Tartars built there Peran-Wisa's tent,
A dome of laths, and over it felts were spread.
And Sohrab came there, and went in, and stood
Upon the thick piled carpets in the tent,
And found the old man sleeping on his bed
Of rugs and felts, and near him lay his arms.
And Peran-Wisa heard him, though the step
Was dull'd; for he slept light, an old man's
sleep;
And he rose quickly on one arm, and said:—
"Who art thou? for it is not yet clear dawn.
Speak! is there news, or any night alarm?"
But Sohrab came to the bedside, and said:—
"Thou know'st me, Peran-Wisa! it is I.
The sun is not yet risen, and the foe
Sleep; but I sleep not; all night long I lie
Tossing and wakeful, and I come to thee.
For so did King Afrasiab bid me seek
Thy counsel and to heed thee as thy son,
In Samarcand,[4] before the army march'd;
And I will tell thee what my heart desires.

poem. It is not necessary to locate them accurately in order to understand the poem, and so the notes will refer to them only as the story is made clearer by the explanation.

4. Samarcand is a city of Turkistan, now a center of learning and of commerce.

Thou know'st if, since from Ader-baijan first
I came among the Tartars and bore arms,
I have still served Afrasiab well, and shown,
At my boy's years, the courage of a man.
This too thou know'st, that while I still bear on
The conquering Tartar ensigns through the
world,
And beat the Persians back on every field,
I seek one man, one man, and one alone—
Rustum, my father; who I hoped should greet,
Should one day greet, upon some well-fought field,
His not unworthy, not inglorious son.
So I long hoped, but him I never find.
Come then, hear now, and grant me what I ask.
Let the two armies rest to-day; but I
Will challenge forth the bravest Persian lords
To meet me man to man; if I prevail,
Rustum will surely hear it; if I fall—
Old man, the dead need no one, claim no kin.
Dim is the rumor of a common[5] fight,
Where host meets host, and many names are
sunk;
But of a single combat fame speaks clear."
He spoke; and Peran-Wisa took the hand
Of the young man in his, and sigh'd, and said:—
"O Sohrab, an unquiet heart is thine!
Canst thou not rest among the Tartar chiefs,
And share the battle's common chance with us

---

5. *Common* here means *general.* The idea is that little fame comes to him who fights in a general combat in which numbers take part. What is the real reason for Sohrab's desire to fight in single combat? Arnold gives a different reason from that in the *Shah Nameh.* In the latter case it is that by defeating their champion Sohrab may frighten the Persians into submission.

PERAN-WISA HEARD HIM

Who love thee, but must press forever first,
In single fight incurring single risk,
To find a father thou hast never seen?
That were far best, my son, to stay with us
Unmurmuring; in our tents, while it is war,
And when 'tis truce, then in Afrasiab's towns.
But, if this one desire indeed rules all,
To seek out Rustum—seek him not through fight!
Seek him in peace and carry to his arms,
O Sohrab, carry an unwounded son!
But far hence seek him, for he is not here.
For now it is not as when I was young,
When Rustum was in front of every fray;
But now he keeps apart, and sits at home,
In Seistan,[6] with Zal, his father old.
Whether that[7] his own mighty strength at last
Feels the abhorr'd approaches of old age,
Or in some quarrel with the Persian King.
There go!—Thou wilt not? Yet my heart forbodes
Danger or death awaits thee on this field.
Fain would I know thee safe and well, though lost
To us; faint herefore send thee hence, in peace
To seek thy father, not seek single fights
In vain;—but who can keep the lion's cub
From ravening, and who govern Rustum's son?
Go, I will grant thee what thy heart desires."

---

6. Seistan was the province in which Rustem and his father Zal had ruled for many years, subjects of the King of Persia.

7. *Whether that* and *Or in* beginning the second line below may be understood to read *Either because* and *Or because of*.

So said he, and dropped Sohrab's hand and left
His bed, and the warm rugs whereon he lay;
And o'er his chilly limbs his woolen coat
He passed, and tied his sandals on his feet,
And threw a white cloak round him, and he took
In his right hand a ruler's staff, no sword;
And on his head he set his sheepskin cap,
Black, glossy, curl'd, the fleece of Kara-Kul;
And raised the curtain of his tent, and call'd
His herald to his side and went abroad.

The sun by this had risen, and cleared the fog
From the broad Oxus and the glittering sands.
And from their tents the Tartar horsemen filed
Into the open plain; so Haman bade—
Haman, who next to Peran-Wisa ruled
The host, and still was in his lusty prime.
From their black tents, long files of horse, they stream'd;
As when some gray November morn the files,
In marching order spread, of long-neck'd cranes
Stream over Casbin and the southern slopes
Of Elburz, from the Aralian estuaries,
Or some frore[8] Caspian reed bed, southward bound
For the warm Persian seaboard—so they streamed.
The Tartars of the Oxus, the King's guard,
First, with black sheepskin caps and with long spears;

8. *Frore* means *frozen*.

Large men, large steeds; who from Bokhara come
And Khiva, and ferment the milk of mares.[9]
Next, the more temperate Toorkmuns of the south,
The Tukas, and the lances of Salore,
And those from Attruck and the Caspian sands;
Light men and on light steeds, who only drink
The acrid milk of camels, and their wells.
And then a swarm of wandering horse, who came
From far, and a more doubtful service own'd;
The Tartars of Ferghana, from the banks
Of the Jaxartes, men with scanty beards
And close-set skullcaps; and those wilder hordes
Who roam o'er Kipchak and the northern waste,
Kalmucks and unkempt Kuzzacks, tribes who stray
Nearest the Pole, and wandering Kirghizzes,
Who come on shaggy ponies from Pamere;
These all filed out from camp into the plain.
And on the other side the Persians form'd;—
First a light cloud of horse, Tartars they seem'd,
The Ilyats of Khorassan; and behind,
The royal troops of Persia, horse and foot,
Marshal'd battalions bright in burnish'd steel.
But Peran-Wisa with his herald came,
Threading the Tartar squadrons to the front,
And with his staff kept back the foremost ranks.
And when Ferood, who led the Persians, saw
That Peran-Wisa kept the Tartars back,
He took his spear, and to the front he came,

9. From mares' milk is made koumiss, a favorite fermented drink of Tartar tribes.

And check'd his ranks, and fix'd[10] them where
they stood.
And the old Tartar came upon the sand
Betwixt the silent hosts, and spake, and said:—
"Ferood, and ye, Persians and Tartars, hear!
Let there be truce between the hosts to-day,

PERAN-WISA GIVES SOHRAB'S CHALLENGE

But choose a champion from the Persian lords
To fight our champion Sohrab, man to man."
As, in the country, on a morn in June,
When the dew glistens on the pearled ears,
A shiver runs through the deep corn[11] for joy—
So, when they heard what Peran-Wisa said,

10. *Fix'd* means *halted.* He caused his army to remain stationary while he rode forward.

11. The *corn* is grain of some kind, not our maize or Indian corn.

A thrill through all the Tartar squadrons ran
Of pride and hope for Sohrab, whom they loved.
But as a troop of peddlers, from Cabool,
Cross underneath the Indian Caucasus,
That vast sky-neighboring mountain of milk
snow;
Crossing so high, that, as they mount, they pass
Long flocks of traveling birds dead on the snow,
Choked by the air, and scarce can they them-
selves
Slake their parch'd throats with sugar'd mul-
berries—
In single file they move, and stop their breath,
For fear they should dislodge the o'erhanging
snows—
So the pale Persians held their breath with fear.
And to Ferood his brother chiefs came up
To counsel; Gudurz and Zoarrah came,
And Feraburz, who ruled the Persian host
Second, and was the uncle of the King;
These came and counsel'd, and then Gudurz
said:—
"Ferood, shame bids us take their challenge up,
Yet champion have we none to match this youth.
He has the wild stag's foot, the lion's heart.
But Rustum came last night; aloof he sits
And sullen, and has pitch'd his tents apart.
Him will I seek, and carry to his ear
The Tartar challenge, and this young man's
name.
Haply he will forget his wrath, and fight.
Stand forth the while, and take their challenge
up."

So spake he; and Ferood stood forth and cried:—
"Old man, be it agreed as thou hast said!
Let Sohrab arm, and we will find a man."
He spake: and Peran-Wisa turn'd, and strode
Back through the opening squadrons to his tent.
But through the anxious Persians Gudurz ran,
And cross'd the camp which lay behind, and reach'd
Out on the sand beyond it, Rustum's tents.
Of scarlet cloth they were, and glittering gay,
Just pitch'd; the high pavilion in the midst
Was Rustum's and his men lay camp'd around.
And Gudurz enter'd Rustum's tent, and found
Rustum; his morning meal was done, but still
The table stood before him, charged with food—
A side of roasted sheep, and cakes of bread,
And dark-green melons, and there Rustum sate
Listless, and held a falcon on his wrist,
And play'd with it; but Gudurz came and stood
Before him; and he look'd, and saw him stand,
And with a cry sprang up and dropped the bird,
And greeted Gudurz with both hands, and said:—
"Welcome! these eyes could see no better sight.
What news? but sit down first, and eat and drink."
But Gudurz stood in the tent door, and said:—
"Not now! a time will come to eat and drink,
But not to-day; to-day has other needs.
The armies are drawn out, and stand at gaze;
For from the Tartars is a challenge brought
To pick a champion from the Persian lords

To fight their champion—and thou know'st his
name—
Sohrab men call him, but his birth is hid.
O Rustum, like thy might is this young man's!
He has the wild stag's foot, the lion's heart;
And he is young, and Iran's chiefs are old,
Or else too weak; and all eyes turn to thee.
Come down and help us, Rustum, or we lose!"

He spoke; but Rustum answer'd with a
smile:—
"Go to! if Iran's chiefs are old, then I
Am older; if the young are weak, the King
Errs strangely; for the King, for Kai Khosroo,[12]
Himself is young, and honors younger men,
And lets the aged molder to their graves.
Rustum he loves no more, but loves the young—
The young may rise at Sohrab's vaunts, not I.
For what care I, though all speak Sohrab's fame?
For would that I myself had such a son,
And not that one slight helpless girl I have—
A son so famed, so brave, to send to war,
And I to tarry with the snow-hair'd Zal,[13]
My father, whom the robber Afghans vex,

12. Kai Khosroo was one of the Persian kings who lived in the sixth century B. C., and is now understood to be Cyrus. He was the grandson of Kai Kaoos, in whose reign the *Shah Nameh* places the episode of Sohrab and Rustem. Here as elsewhere Arnold alters the legend to suit his convenience and to make the poem more effective. For instance, he compresses the combat into a single day, while in the Persian epic, the battle lasts three days. This change gives greater vitality and more rapid action to the poem.

13. Zal was born with snowy hair, a most unusual thing among the black-haired Persians. His father was so angered by the appearance of his son that he abandoned the innocent babe in the Elburz mountains, where, however, a great bird or griffin miraculously preserved the infant and in time returned it to its father, who had repented of his hasty action.

And clip his borders short, and drive his herds,
And he has none to guard his weak old age.
There would I go, and hang my armor up,
And with my great name fence that weak old man,
And spend the goodly treasures I have got,
And rest my age, and hear of Sohrab's fame,
And leave to death the hosts of thankless kings,
And with these slaughterous hands draw sword no more."

He spoke, and smiled; and Gudurz made reply:—
"What then, O Rustum, will men say to this,
When Sohrab dares our bravest forth, and seeks
Thee most of all, and thou, whom most he seeks,
Hidest thy face? Take heed lest men should say:
'Like some old miser, Rustum hoards his fame,
And shuns to peril it with younger men.'"

And, greatly moved, then Rustum made reply:—
"O Gudurz, wherefore dost thou say such words?
Thou knowest better words than this to say.
What is one more, one less, obscure or famed,
Valiant or craven, young or old, to me?
Are not they mortal, am not I myself?
But who for men of naught would do great deeds?
Come, thou shalt see how Rustum hoards his fame!
But I will fight unknown, and in plain arms;
Let not men say of Rustum, he was match'd
In single fight with any mortal man."

He spoke, and frown'd; and Gudurz turn'd, and ran
Back quickly through the camp in fear and joy—
Fear at his wrath, but joy that Rustum came.
But Rustum strode to his tent door, and call'd
His followers in, and bade them bring his arms,
And clad himself in steel; the arms he chose
Were plain, and on his shield was no device,
Only his helm was rich, inlaid with gold,
And, from the fluted spine atop, a plume
Of horsehair waved, a scarlet horsehair plume.
So arm'd, he issued forth; and Ruksh,[14] his horse,
Follow'd him like a faithful hound at heel—
Ruksh, whose renown was noised through all the earth,
The horse, whom Rustum on a foray once
Did in Bokhara by the river find
A colt beneath its dam, and drove him home,
And rear'd him; a bright bay, with lofty crest,
Dight with a saddlecloth of broider'd green
Crusted with gold, and on the ground were work'd
All beasts of chase, all beasts which hunters know.
So follow'd, Rustum left his tents, and cross'd
The camp, and to the Persian host appear'd.
And all the Persians knew him, and with shouts
Hail'd; but the Tartars knew not who he was.
And dear as the wet diver to the eyes
Of his pale wife who waits and weeps on shore,
By sandy Bahrein, in the Persian Gulf,

14. *Ruksh*, also spelled *Raksh*.

Plunging all day in the blue waves, at night,
Having made up his tale[15] of precious pearls,
Rejoins her in their hut upon the sands—
So dear to the pale Persians Rustum came.
And Rustum to the Persian front advanced,
And Sohrab arm'd in Haman's tent, and came.
And as afield the reapers cut a swath
Down through the middle of a rich man's corn,
And on each side are squares of standing corn,
And in the midst a stubble, short and bare—
So on each side were squares of men, with spears
Bristling, and in the midst, the open sand.
And Rustum came upon the sand, and cast
His eyes toward the Tartar tents, and saw
Sohrab come forth, and eyed him as he came.
As some rich woman, on a winter's morn,
Eyes through her silken curtains the poor drudge
Who with numb blacken'd fingers makes her fire—
At cock-crow, on a starlit winter's morn,
When the frost flowers the whiten'd window-panes—
And wonders how she lives, and what the thoughts
Of that poor drudge may be; so Rustum eyed
The unknown adventurous youth, who from afar
Came seeking Rustum, and defying forth
All the most valiant chiefs; long he perused
His spirited air, and wonder'd who he was.
For very young he seem'd, tenderly rear'd;

15. *Tale* means *count* or *reckoning*. The diver had gathered all the pearls required from him for the day.

Like some young cypress, tall, and dark, and
straight,
Which in a queen's secluded garden throws
Its slight dark shadow on the moonlit turf,
By midnight, to a bubbling fountain's sound—
So slender Sohrab seem'd, so softly rear'd.[16]
And a deep pity enter'd Rustum's soul
As he beheld him coming; and he stood,
And beckon'd to him with his hand, and said:—
"O thou young man, the air of heaven is soft,
And warm, and pleasant; but the grave is cold!
Heaven's air is better than the cold dead grave.
Behold me! I am vast, and clad in iron,
And tried; and I have stood on many a field
Of blood, and I have fought with many a foe—
Never was that field lost, or that foe saved.
O Sohrab, wherefore wilt thou rush on death?
Be govern'd![17] quit the Tartar host, and come
To Iran, and be as my son to me,
And fight beneath my banner till I die!
There are no youths in Iran brave as thou."
So he spake, mildly; Sohrab heard his voice,
The mighty voice of Rustum, and he saw
His giant figure planted on the sand,
Sole, like some single tower, which a chief
Hath builded on the waste in former years
Against the robbers; and he saw that head,
Streak'd with its first gray hairs;—hope fill'd
his soul,

16. This description by Arnold scarcely tallies with the idea we have obtained of the powerful Sohrab from reading the accounts taken from the *Shah Nameh*. Arnold's is the more poetic idea, and increases the reader's sympathy for Sohrab.

17. *Be governed*, that is, *take my advice*.

And he ran forward and embraced his knees,
And clasp'd his hand within his own, and said:—
"Oh, by thy father's head! by thine own soul!
Art thou not Rustum? speak! art thou not he?"
But Rustum eyed askance the kneeling youth,
And turn'd away, and spake to his own soul:—
"Ah me, I muse what this young fox may mean!
False, wily, boastful, are these Tartar boys.
For if I now confess this thing he asks,
And hide it not, but say: 'Rustum is here!'
He will not yield indeed, nor quit our foes,
But he will find some pretext not to fight,
And praise my fame, and proffer courteous gifts,
A belt or sword perhaps, and go his way.
And on a feast tide, in Afrasiab's hall,
In Samarcand, he will arise and cry:
'I challenged once, when the two armies camp'd
Beside the Oxus, all the Persian lords
To cope with me in single fight; but they
Shrank, only Rustum dared; then he and I
Changed gifts, and went on equal terms away.'
So will he speak, perhaps, while men applaud;
Then were the chiefs of Iran shamed through me."
And then he turn'd, and sternly spake aloud:—
"Rise! wherefore dost thou vainly question thus
Of Rustum? I am here, whom thou hast call'd
By challenge forth; make good thy vaunt, or yield!
Is it with Rustum only thou wouldst fight?
Rash boy, men look on Rustum's face and flee!
For well I know, that did great Rustum stand

Before thy face this day, and were reveal'd,
There would be then no talk of fighting more.
But being what I am, I tell thee this—
Do thou record it in thine inmost soul:
Either thou shalt renounce thy vaunt and yield,
Or else thy bones shall strew this sand, till winds
Bleach them, or Oxus with his summer floods,
Oxus in summer wash them all away."

He spoke; and Sohrab answer'd, on his feet:—
"Art thou so fierce? Thou wilt not fright me so!
I am no girl, to be made pale by words.
Yet this thou hast said well, did Rustum stand
Here on this field, there were no fighting then.
But Rustum is far hence, and we stand here.
Begin! thou art more vast, more dread than I,
And thou art proved, I know, and I am young—
But yet success sways with the breath of heaven.
And though thou thinkest that thou knowest sure
Thy victory, yet thou canst not surely know.
For we are all, like swimmers in the sea,
Poised on the top of a huge wave of fate,
Which hangs uncertain to which side to fall.
And whether it will heave us up to land,
Or whether it will roll us out to sea,
Back out to sea, to the deep waves of death,
We know not, and no search will make us know;
Only the event will teach us in its hour."

He spoke, and Rustum answer'd not, but hurl'd
His spear; down from the shoulder, down it came,
As on some partridge in the corn a hawk,
That long has tower'd in the airy clouds,

Drops like a plummet; Sohrab saw it come,
And sprang aside, quick as a flash; the spear
Hiss'd, and went quivering down into the sand,
Which it sent flying wide;—then Sohrab threw
In turn, and full struck Rustum's shield; sharp rang,
The iron plates rang sharp, but turn'd the spear.
And Rustum seized his club, which none but he
Could wield; an unlopp'd trunk it was, and huge,
Still rough—like those which men in treeless plains
To build them boats fish from the flooded rivers,
Hyphasis or Hydaspes, when, high up
By their dark springs, the wind in winter time
Hath made in Himalayan forests wrack,
And strewn the channels with torn boughs—so huge
The club which Rustum lifted now, and struck
One stroke; but again Sohrab sprang aside,
Lithe as the glancing snake, and the club came
Thundering to earth, and leapt from Rustum's hand.
And Rustum follow'd his own blow, and fell
To his knees, and with his fingers clutch'd the sand;
And now might Sohrab have unsheathed his sword,
And pierced the mighty Rustum while he lay
Dizzy, and on his knees, and choked with sand;
But he look'd on, and smiled, nor bared his sword,
But courteously drew back, and spoke, and said:—

"Thou strik'st too hard! that club of thine will float
Upon the summer floods, and not my bones.
But rise, and be not wroth! not wroth am I;
No, when I see thee, wrath forsakes my soul.
Thou say'st, thou art not Rustum; be it so!
Who art thou then, that canst so touch my soul?
Boy as I am, I have seen battles too—
Have waded foremost in their bloody waves,
And heard their hollow roar of dying men;
But never was my heart thus touch'd before.
Are they from Heaven, these softenings of the heart?
O thou old warrior, let us yield to Heaven!
Come, plant we here in earth our angry spears,
And make a truce, and sit upon this sand,
And pledge each other in red wine, like friends,
And thou shalt talk to me of Rustum's deeds.
There are enough foes in the Persian host,
Whom I may meet, and strike, and feel no pang;
Champions enough Afrasiab has, whom thou
Mayst fight; fight *them*, when they confront thy spear!
But oh, let there be peace 'twixt thee and me!"

He ceased, but while he spake, Rustum had risen,
And stood erect, trembling with rage; his club
He left to lie, but had regained his spear,
Whose fiery point now in his mail'd right hand
Blazed bright and baleful, like that autumn star,
The baleful sign of fevers; dust had soil'd
His stately crest, and dimm'd his glittering arms.

His breast heaved, his lips foam'd, and twice his voice
Was choked with rage; at last these words broke way:—
"Girl! nimble with thy feet, not with thy hands!
Curl'd minion, dancer, coiner of sweet words!
Fight, let me hear thy hateful voice no more!
Thou art not in Afrasiab's gardens now
With Tartar girls, with whom thou art wont to dance;
But on the Oxus sands, and in the dance
Of battle, and with me, who make no play
Of war; I fight it out, and hand to hand.
Speak not to me of truce, and pledge, and wine!
Remember all thy valor; try thy feints
And cunning! all the pity I had is gone;
Because thou hast shamed me before both the hosts
With thy light skipping tricks, and thy girl's wiles."
He spoke, and Sohrab kindled at his taunts,
And he too drew his sword; at once they rush'd
Together, as two eagles on one prey
Come rushing down together from the clouds,
One from the east, one from the west; their shields
Dash'd with a clang together, and a din
Rose, such as that the sinewy woodcutters
Make often in the forest's heart at morn,
Of hewing axes, crashing trees—such blows
Rustum and Sohrab on each other hail'd.
And you would say that sun and stars took part

THE SPEAR RENT THE TOUGH PLATES

In that unnatural[18] conflict; for a cloud
Grew suddenly in heaven, and dark'd the sun
Over the fighters' heads; and a wind rose
Under their feet, and moaning swept the plain,
And in a sandy whirlwind wrapp'd the pair.

18. It is not natural for father and son to fight thus.

In gloom they twain were wrapp'd, and they alone;
For both the onlooking hosts on either hand
Stood in broad daylight, and the sky was pure,
And the sun sparkled on the Oxus stream.
But in the gloom they fought, with bloodshot eyes
And laboring breath; first Rustum struck the shield
Which Sohrab held stiff out; the steel-spiked spear
Rent the tough plates, but fail'd to reach the skin,
And Rustum pluck'd it back with angry groan.
Then Sohrab with his sword smote Rustum's helm,
Nor clove its steel quite through; but all the crest
He shore away, and that proud horsehair plume,
Never till now defiled, sank to the dust;
And Rustum bow'd his head; and then the gloom
Grew blacker, thunder rumbled in the air,
And lightnings rent the cloud; and Ruksh, the horse,
Who stood at hand, utter'd a dreadful cry;—
No horse's cry was that, most like the roar
Of some pain'd desert lion, who all day
Hath trail'd the hunter's javelin in his side,
And comes at night to die upon the sand.
The two hosts heard that cry, and quaked for fear,
And Oxus curdled as it cross'd his stream.
But Sohrab heard, and quail'd not, but rush'd on,
And struck again; and again Rustum bow'd
His head; but this time all the blade, like glass,

Sprang in a thousand shivers on the helm,
And in the hand the hilt remain'd alone.
Then Rustum raised his head; his dreadful eyes
Glared, and he shook on high his menacing spear,
And shouted: "Rustum!"—Sohrab heard that shout,
And shrank amazed: back he recoil'd one step,
And scann'd with blinking eyes the advancing form;
And then he stood bewilder'd, and he dropp'd
His covering shield, and the spear pierced his side.[19]
He reel'd, and, staggering back, sank to the ground;
And then the gloom dispersed, and the wind fell,
And the bright sun broke forth, and melted all
The cloud; and the two armies saw the pair—
Saw Rustum standing, safe upon his feet,
And Sohrab, wounded, on the bloody sand.
Then, with a bitter smile, Rustum began:—
"Sohrab, thou thoughtest in thy mind to kill
A Persian lord this day, and strip his corpse,
And bear thy trophies to Afrasiab's tent;
Or else that the great Rustum would come down
Himself to fight, and that thy wiles would move
His heart to take a gift, and let thee go;
And then that all the Tartar host would praise
Thy courage or thy craft, and spread thy fame,
To glad thy father in his weak old age.
Fool, thou art slain, and by an unknown man!

19. In the *Shah Nameh* Rustem overpowers Sohrab and slays him by his superior power and skill. Arnold takes the more poetic view that Sohrab's arm is powerless when he hears his father's name.

Dearer to the red jackals shalt thou be
Than to thy friends, and to thy father old."
  And, with a fearless mien, Sohrab replied:—
"Unknown thou art; yet thy fierce vaunt is vain.
Thou dost not slay me, proud and boastful man!
No! Rustum slays me, and this filial heart.
For were I match'd with ten such men as thee,
And I were that which till to-day I was,
They should be lying here, I standing there.
But that beloved name unnerved my arm—
That name, and something, I confess, in thee,
Which troubles all my heart, and made my shield
Fall; and thy spear transfix'd an unarm'd foe.
And now thou boastest, and insult'st my fate.
But hear thou this, fierce man, tremble to hear:
The mighty Rustum shall avenge my death!
My father, whom I seek through all the world,
He shall avenge my death, and punish thee!"
  As when some hunter in the spring hath found
A breeding eagle sitting on her nest,
Upon the craggy isle of a hill lake,
And pierced her with an arrow as she rose,
And follow'd her to find her where she fell
Far off;—anon her mate comes winging back
From hunting, and a great way off descries
His huddling young left sole;[20] at that, he checks
His pinion, and with short uneasy sweeps
Circles above his eyry, with loud screams
Chiding his mate back to her nest; but she
Lies dying, with the arrow in her side,
In some far stony gorge out of his ken,
A heap of fluttering feathers—never more

20. *Sole* means *solitary, alone.*

Shall the lake glass[21] her, flying over it;
Never the black and dripping precipices
Echo her stormy scream as she sails by—
As that poor bird flies home, nor knows his loss,
So Rustum knew not his own loss, but stood
Over his dying son, and knew him not.

But, with a cold incredulous voice, he said:—
"What prate is this of fathers and revenge?
The mighty Rustum never had a son."

And, with a failing voice, Sohrab replied:—
"Ah yes, he had! and that lost son am I.
Surely the news will one day reach his ear,
Reach Rustum, where he sits, and tarries long,
Somewhere, I know not where, but far from here;
And pierce him like a stab, and make him leap
To arms, and cry for vengeance upon thee.
Fierce man, bethink thee, for an only son!
What will that grief, what will that vengeance be?
Oh, could I live till I that grief had seen!
Yet him I pity not so much, but her,
My mother, who in Ader-baijan dwells
With that old king, her father, who grows gray
With age, and rules over the valiant Koords.
Her most I pity, who no more will see
Sohrab returning from the Tartar camp,
With spoils and honor, when the war is done.
But a dark rumor will be bruited up,
From tribe to tribe, until it reach her ear;
And then will that defenseless woman learn
That Sohrab will rejoice her sight no more,
But that in battle with a nameless foe,
By the far-distant Oxus, he is slain."

21. *Glass her* means *reflect her* as in a mirror.

He spoke; and as he ceased, he wept aloud,
Thinking of her he left, and his own death.
He spoke; but Rustum listen'd, plunged in
thought.
Nor did he yet believe it was his son
Who spoke, although he call'd back names he
knew;
For he had had sure tidings that the babe,
Which was in Ader-baijan born to him,
Had been a puny girl, no boy at all—
So that sad mother sent him word, for fear
Rustum should seek the boy, to train in arms.
And so he deem'd that either Sohrab took,
By a false boast, the style of Rustum's son;
Or that men gave it him, to swell his fame.
So deem'd he: yet he listen'd, plunged in
thought;
And his soul set to grief, as the vast tide
Of the bright rocking Ocean sets to shore
At the full moon; tears gather'd in his eyes;
For he remember'd his own early youth,
And all its bounding rapture; as, at dawn,
The shepherd from his mountain lodge descries
A far, bright city, smitten by the sun,
Through many rolling clouds—so Rustum saw
His youth; saw Sohrab's mother, in her bloom;
And that old king, her father, who loved well
His wandering guest, and gave him his fair child
With joy; and all the pleasant life they led,
They three, in that long-distant summer time—
The castle, and the dewy woods, and hunt
And hound, and morn on those delightful hills
In Ader-baijan. And he saw that youth,

Of age and looks to be his own dear son,[22]
Piteous and lovely, lying on the sand,
Like some rich hyacinth which by the scythe
Of an unskillful gardener has been cut,
Mowing the garden grassplots near its bed,
And lies, a fragrant tower of purple bloom,
On the mown, dying grass—so Sohrab lay,
Lovely in death, upon the common sand.
And Rustum gazed on him with grief, and said:—
"O Sohrab, thou indeed art such a son
Whom Rustum, wert thou his, might well have loved!
Yet here thou errest, Sohrab, or else men
Have told thee false—thou art not Rustum's son.
For Rustum had no son; one child he had—
But one—a girl; who with her mother now
Plies some light female task, nor dreams of us—
Of us she dreams not, nor of wounds, nor war."

But Sohrab answer'd him in wrath; for now
The anguish of the deep-fix'd spear grew fierce,
And he desired to draw forth the steel,
And let the blood flow free, and so to die—
But first he would convince his stubborn foe;
And, rising sternly on one arm, he said:—
"Man, who art thou who dost deny my words?
Truth sits upon the lips of dying men,
And falsehood, while I lived, was far from mine.
I tell thee, prick'd upon this arm I bear
That seal which Rustum to my mother gave,

22. He sees that this young man, as far as age and appearance are concerned, might be a son of his.

That she might prick it on the babe she bore."[23]
He spoke: and all the blood left Rustum's cheeks,
And his knees totter'd, and he smote his hand
Against his breast, his heavy mailed hand,
That the hard iron corselet clank'd aloud;
And to his heart he press'd the other hand,
And in a hollow voice he spake, and said:—
"Sohrab, that were a proof which could not lie!
If thou show this, then art thou Rustum's son."
Then, with weak hasty fingers, Sohrab loosed
His belt, and near the shoulder bared his arm,
And show'd a sign in faint vermilion points
Prick'd; as a cunning workman, in Pekin,
Pricks with vermilion some clear porcelain vase,
An emperor's gift—at early morn he paints,
And all day long, and, when night comes, the lamp
Lights up his studious forehead and thin hands—
So delicately prick'd the sign appear'd
On Sohrab's arm, the sign of Rustum's seal.
It was that griffin,[24] which of old rear'd Zal,
Rustum's great father, whom they left to die,
A helpless babe, among the mountain rocks;
Him that kind creature found, and rear'd and loved—
Then Rustum took it for his glorious sign.
And Sohrab bared that image on his arm,
And himself scann'd it long with mournful eyes,
And then he touch'd it with his hand, and said:—

23. Again Arnold departs from the Persian tale, in which Sohrab wears a bracelet or amulet on his arm. Arnold's work gives a more certain identification.

24. The griffin spoken of in note 13.

"How say'st thou? Is that sign the proper sign
Of Rustum's son, or of some other man's?"
He spoke; but Rustum gazed, and gazed, and stood
Speechless; and then he utter'd one sharp cry:
"O boy—thy father!" and his voice choked there.
And then a dark cloud pass'd before his eyes,
And his head swam, and he sank down to earth.
But Sohrab crawl'd to where he lay, and cast
His arms about his neck, and kiss'd his lips,
And with fond faltering fingers stroked his cheeks,
Trying to call him back to life; and life
Came back to Rustum, and he oped his eyes,
And they stood wide with horror; and he seized
In both his hands the dust which lay around,
And threw it on his head, and smirch'd his hair,—
His hair, and face, and beard, and glittering arms;
And strong convulsive groanings shook his breast,
And his sobs choked him; and he clutch'd his sword,
To draw it, and forever let life out.
But Sohrab saw his thought, and held his hands,
And with a soothing voice he spake, and said:—
"Father, forbear! for I but meet to-day
The doom which at my birth was written down
In heaven, and thou art heaven's unconscious hand.

Surely my heart cried out that it was thou,
When first I saw thee; and thy heart spoke too,
I know it! but fate trod those promptings down
Under its iron heel; fate, fate engaged
The strife, and hurl'd me on my father's spear.
But let us speak no more of this! I find
My father; let me feel that I have found!
Come, sit beside me on the sand, and take
My head betwixt thy hands, and kiss my cheeks,
And wash them with thy tears, and say: 'My son!'
Quick! quick! for number'd are my sands of life,
And swift; for like the lightning to this field
I came, and like the wind I go away—
Sudden, and swift, and like a passing wind.
But it was writ in heaven that this should be."
So said he, and his voice released the heart
Of Rustum, and his tears broke forth; he cast
His arms round his son's neck, and wept aloud,
And kiss'd him. And awe fell on both the hosts,
When they saw Rustum's grief; and Ruksh, the horse,
With his head bowing to the ground and mane
Sweeping the dust, came near, and in mute woe
First to the one then to the other moved
His head, as if inquiring what their grief
Might mean; and from his dark, compassionate eyes,
The big warm tears roll'd down, and caked the sand.
But Rustum chid him with stern voice, and said:—

"Ruksh, now thou grievest; but, O Ruksh, thy feet
Should first have rotted on their nimble joints,
Or ere they brought thy master to this field!"
But Sohrab look'd upon the horse, and said:—
"Is this, then, Ruksh? How often, in past days,
My mother told me of thee, thou brave steed,
My terrible father's terrible horse! and said,
That I should one day find thy lord and thee.
Come, let me lay my hand upon thy mane!
O Ruksh, thou art more fortunate than I;
For thou hast gone where I shall never go,
And snuff'd the breezes of my father's home.
And thou hast trod the sands of Seistan,
And seen the River of Helmund, and the Lake
Of Zirrah; and the aged Zal himself
Has often stroked thy neck, and given thee food,
Corn in a golden platter soak'd with wine,
And said: 'O Ruksh! bear Rustum well,'—but I
Have never known my grandsire's furrow'd face,
Nor seen his lofty house in Seistan,
Nor slaked my thirst at the clear Helmund stream;
But lodged among my father's foes, and seen
Afrasiab's cities only, Samarcand,
Bokhara, and lone Khiva in the waste,
And the black Toorkmun tents; and only drunk
The desert rivers, Moorghab and Tejend,
Kohik, and where the Kalmuks feed their sheep,
The northern Sir; and this great Oxus stream,
The yellow Oxus, by whose brink I die."

Then, with a heavy groan, Rustum bewail'd:—
"Oh, that its waves were flowing over me!
Oh, that I saw its grains of yellow silt
Roll tumbling in the current o'er my head!"
But, with a grave mild voice, Sohrab replied:—
"Desire not that, my father! thou must live.
For some are born to do great deeds, and live,
As some are born to be obscured, and die.
Do thou the deeds I die too young to do,
And reap a second glory in thine age;
Thou art my father, and thy gain is mine.
But come! thou seest this great host of men
Which follow me; I pray thee, slay not these!
Let me entreat for them; what have they done?
They follow'd me, my hope, my fame, my star.
Let them all cross the Oxus back in peace.
But me thou must bear hence, not send with them,
But carry me with thee to Seistan,
And place me on a bed, and mourn for me,
Thou, and the snow-hair'd Zal, and all thy friends.
And thou must lay me in that lovely earth,
And heap a stately mound above my bones,[25]
And plant a far-seen pillar over all.
That so the passing horseman on the waste
May see my tomb a great way off, and cry:
'Sohrab, the mighty Rustum's son, lies there,
Whom his great father did in ignorance kill!'
And I be not forgotten in my grave."

25. The Persian tradition is that over the spot where Sohrab was buried a huge mound, shaped like the hoof of a horse, was erected.

And, with a mournful voice, Rustum replied:—
"Fear not! as thou hast said, Sohrab, my son,
So shall it be; for I will burn my tents,
And quit the host, and bear thee hence with me,
And carry thee away to Seistan,
And place thee on a bed, and mourn for thee,
With the snow-headed Zal, and all my friends.
And I will lay thee in that lovely earth,
And heap a stately mound above thy bones,
And plant a far-seen pillar over all,
And men shall not forget thee in thy grave.
And I will spare thy host; yea, let them go!
Let them all cross the Oxus back in peace!
What should I do with slaying any more?
For would that all that I have ever slain
Might be once more alive; my bitterest foes,
And they who were call'd champions in their time,
And through whose death I won that fame I have—
And I were nothing but a common man,
A poor, mean soldier, and without renown,
So thou mightest live too, my son, my son!
Or rather would that I, even I myself,
Might now be lying on this bloody sand,
Near death, and by an ignorant stroke of thine,
Not thou of mine! and I might die, not thou;
And I, not thou, be borne to Seistan;
And Zal might weep above my grave, not thine;
And say: 'O son, I weep thee not too sore,
For willingly, I know, thou met'st thine end!'
But now in blood and battles was my youth,
And full of blood and battles is my age,
And I shall never end this life of blood."

Then, at the point of death, Sohrab replied:—
"A life of blood indeed, thou dreadful man!
But thou shalt yet have peace; only not now,
Not yet! but thou shalt have it on that day[26]
When thou shalt sail in a high-masted ship,
Thou and the other peers of Kai Khosroo,
Returning home over the salt blue sea,
From laying thy dear master in his grave."
And Rustum gazed in Sohrab's face, and said:—
"Soon be that day, my son, and deep that sea!
Till then, if fate so wills, let me endure."
He spoke; and Sohrab smiled on him, and took
The spear, and drew it from his side, and eased
His wound's imperious anguish; but the blood
Came welling from the open gash, and life
Flow'd with the stream;—all down his cold white side
The crimson torrent ran, dim now and soil'd,
Like the soil'd tissue of white violets
Left, freshly gather'd, on their native bank,
By children whom their nurses call with haste
Indoors from the sun's eye; his head droop'd low,
His limbs grew slack; motionless, white, he lay—
White, with eyes closed; only when heavy gasps,
Deep heavy gasps quivering through all his frame,
Convulsed him back to life, he open'd them,
And fix'd them feebly on his father's face;

26. It is said that shortly after the death of Sohrab the king himself died while on a visit to a famous spring far in the north, and as the nobles were returning with his corpse all were lost in a great tempest. Unfortunately for Sohrab's prophecy, Persian traditions do not include Rustem among the lost.

RUSTUM SORROWS OVER SOHRAB

Till now all strength was ebb'd, and from his
limbs
Unwillingly the spirit fled away,
Regretting the warm mansion which it left,
And youth, and bloom, and this delightful world.
So, on the bloody sand, Sohrab lay dead;

And the great Rustum drew his horseman's cloak
Down o'er his face, and sate by his dead son.
As those black granite pillars, once high-rear'd
By Jemshid in Persepolis, to bear
His house, now 'mid their broken flights of steps
Lie prone, enormous, down the mountain side—
So in the sand lay Rustum by his son.
And night came down over the solemn waste,
And the two gazing hosts, and that sole pair,
And darken'd all; and a cold fog, with night,
Crept from the Oxus. Soon a hum arose,
As of a great assembly loosed, and fires
Began to twinkle through the fog; for now
Both armies moved to camp, and took their meal;
The Persians took it on the open sands
Southward, the Tartars by the river marge;
And Rustum and his son were left alone.

But the majestic river floated on,
Out of the mist and hum of that low land,
Into the frosty starlight, and there moved,
Rejoicing, through the hush'd Chorasmian waste,
Under the solitary moon;—he flow'd
Right for the polar star, past Orgunjè,
Brimming, and bright, and large; then sands begin
To hem his watery march, and dam his streams,
And split his currents; that for many a league
The shorn and parcel'd Oxus strains along
Through beds of sand and matted rushy isles—
Oxus, forgetting the bright speed he had
In his high mountain cradle in Pamere,
A foil'd circuitous wanderer—till at last

The long'd-for dash of waves is heard, and
wide
His luminous home of waters opens, bright
And tranquil, from whose floor the new-bathed
stars
Emerge, and shine upon the Aral Sea.[27]

---

27. This beautiful stanza makes a peculiarly artistic termination to the poem. After the storm and stress of the combat and the heart-breaking pathos of Sohrab's death, the reader willingly rests his thought on the majestic Oxus that still flows on, unchangeable, but ever changing. The suggestion is that after all nature is triumphant, that our pains and losses, our most grievous disappointments and greatest griefs are but incidents in the great drama of life, and that, though like the river Oxus, we for a time become "foiled, circuitous wanderers," we at last see before us the luminous home, bright and tranquil under the shining stars.

Matthew Arnold was one of England's purest and greatest men. As scholar, teacher, poet and critic he labored zealously for the betterment of his race and sought to bring them back to a clearer, lovelier spiritual life and to win them from the base and sordid schemes that make only for material success.

He was born in 1822 and was the son of Doctor Thomas Arnold, the great teacher who was so long headmaster of the famous Rugby school, and whose scholarly and Christian influence is so faithfully brought out in Hughes's ever popular story *Tom Brown's School Days.*

Matthew Arnold received his preparatory education in his father's school at Rugby, and his college training at Oxford. He was always a student and always active in educational work, as an inspector of schools, and for ten years as professor of poetry at Oxford. He twice visited the United States and both times lectured here. His criticisms of America and Americans were severe, for he saw predominant the spirit of money-getting, the thirst for material prosperity and the absence of spiritual interests. In 1888, while at the house of a friend in Liverpool, he died suddenly and peacefully from an attack of heart disease.

Arnold was one of the most exacting and critical of English writers, a man who applied to his own works the same severe standards that he set up for others. As a result his writings have become one of the standards of purity and taste in style.

The story of *Sohrab and Rustum* pleased him, and he enjoyed writing the poem, as may be seen from a letter to his mother, written in 1853. He says:

"All my spare time has been spent on a poem which I have just finished, and which I think by far the best thing I have yet done, and I think it will be generally liked; though one can never be sure of this.

I have had the greatest pleasure in composing it, a rare thing with me, and, as I think, a good test of the pleasure what you write is likely to afford to others. But the story is a very noble and excellent one."

Two men, both competent to judge, have given at length their opinion of Matthew Arnold's character. So admirable a man deserves to be known by the young, although most of his writings will be understood and appreciated only by persons of some maturity in years. Mr. John Morley says:

"He was incapable of sacrificing the smallest interest of anybody to his own; he had not a spark of envy or jealousy; he stood well aloof from all the hustlings and jostlings by which selfish men push on; he bore life's disappointments—and he was disappointed in some reasonable hopes—with good nature and fortitude; he cast no burden upon others, and never shrank from bearing his own share of the daily load to the last ounce of it; he took the deepest, sincerest, and most active interest in the well-being of his country and his countrymen."

Mr. George E. Woodbury in an essay on Arnold remarks concerning the man as shown in his private letters:

"A nature warm to its own, kindly to all, cheerful, fond of sport and fun, and always fed from pure fountains, and with it a character so founded upon the rock, so humbly serviceable, so continuing in power and grace, must wake in all the responses of happy appreciation and leave the charm of memory.

"He did his duty as naturally as if it required neither resolve nor effort, nor thought of any kind for the morrow, and he never failed, seemingly, in an act or word of sympathy, in little or great things; and when to this one adds the clear ether of intellectual life where he habitually moved in his own life apart, and the humanity of his home, the gift that these letters bring may be appreciated. That gift is the man himself, but set in the atmosphere of home, with sonship and fatherhood, sisters and brothers, with the bereavements of years full accomplished, and those of babyhood and boyhood—a sweet and wholesome English home, with all the cloud and sunshine of the English world drifting over its roof trees, and the soil of England beneath its stones, and English duties for the breath of its being."

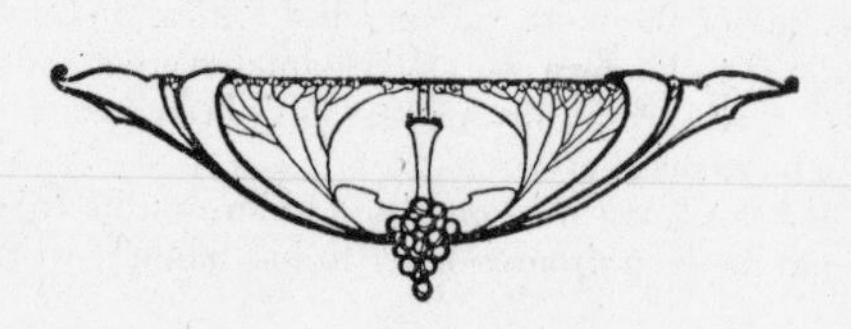

MATTHEW ARNOLD

THE POET AND THE PEASANT

FROM THE FRENCH OF EMILE SOUVESTRE

YOUNG man was walking through a forest, and in spite of the approach of night, in spite of the mist that grew denser every moment, he was walking slowly, paying no heed either to the weather or to the hour.

His dress of green cloth, his buckskin gaiters, and the gun slung across his shoulder might have caused him to be taken for a sportsman, had not the book that half protruded from his game-bag betrayed the dreamer, and proved that Arnold de Munster was less occupied with observing the track of wild game than in communing with himself.

For some moments his mind had been filled with thoughts of his family and of the friends he had left in Paris. He remembered the studio that he had adorned with fantastic engravings, strange paintings, curious statuettes; the German songs that his sister had sung, the melancholy verses that he had repeated in the subdued light of the evening lamps, and the long talks in which every one confessed his inmost feelings, in which all the mysteries of thought were discussed and translated into impassioned or graceful words! Why had he abandoned these choice pleasures to bury himself in the country?

He was aroused at last from his meditations by the consciousness that the mist had changed into rain and was beginning to penetrate his shooting-coat. He was about to quicken his steps, but in looking around him he saw that he had lost his way, and he tried vainly to determine the direction he must take. A first attempt only succeeded in bewildering him still more. The daylight faded, the rain fell more heavily, and he continued to plunge at random into unknown paths.

He had begun to be discouraged, when the sound of bells reached him through the leafless trees. A cart driven by a big man in a blouse had appeared at an intersecting road and was coming toward the one that Arnold had just reached.

Arnold stopped to wait for the man and asked him if he were far from Sersberg.

"Sersberg!" repeated the carter; "you don't expect to sleep there to-night?"

"Pardon me, but I do," answered the young man.

"At Sersberg?" went on his interlocutor; "you'll have to go by train, then! It is six good leagues from here to the gate; and considering the weather and the roads, they are equal to twelve."

The young man uttered an exclamation. He had left the château that morning and did not think that he had wandered so far; but he had been on the wrong path for hours, and in thinking to take the road to Sersberg he had continued to turn his back upon it. It was too late to make good such an error; so he was forced to accept the shelter offered by his new companion, whose farm was fortunately within gunshot.

He accordingly regulated his pace to the carter's and attempted to enter into conversation with him; but Moser was not a talkative man and was apparently a complete stranger to the young man's usual sensations. When, on issuing from the forest, Arnold pointed to the magnificent horizon purpled by the last rays of the setting sun, the farmer contented himself with a grimace.

"Bad weather for to-morrow," he muttered, drawing his cloak about his shoulders.

"One ought to be able to see the entire valley from here," went on Arnold, striving to pierce the gloom that already clothed the foot of the mountain.

"Yes, yes," said Moser, shaking his head; "the ridge is high enough for that. There's an invention for you that isn't good for much."

"What invention?"

"The mountains."

"You would rather have everything level?"

"What a question!" cried the farmer, laughing. "You might as well ask me if I would not rather ruin my horses."

"True," said Arnold in a tone of somewhat contemptuous irony. "I had forgotten the horses! It is clear that God should have thought principally of them when he created the world."

"I don't know as to God," answered Moser

quietly, "but the engineers certainly made a mistake in forgetting them when they made the roads. The horse is the laborer's best friend, monsieur—without disrespect to the oxen, which have their value too."

Arnold looked at the peasant.

"So you see in your surroundings only the advantages you can derive from them?" he asked gravely. "The forest, the mountains, the clouds, all say nothing to you? You have never paused before the setting sun or at the sight of the woods lighted by the stars?"

"I?" cried the farmer. "Do you take me for a maker of almanacs? What should I get out of your starlight and the setting sun? The main thing is to earn enough for three meals a day and to keep one's stomach warm. Would monsieur like a drink of cognac? It comes from the other side of the Rhine."

He held out a little wicker-covered bottle to Arnold, who refused by a gesture. The positive coarseness of the peasant had rekindled his regret and his contempt. Were they really men such as he was, these unfortunates, doomed to unceasing labor, who lived in the bosom of nature without heeding it and whose souls never rose above the most material sensations? Was there one point of resemblance which could attest their original brotherhood to such as he? Arnold doubted this more and more each moment.

These thoughts had the effect of communicating to his manner a sort of contemptuous indifference toward his conductor, to whom he ceased to talk. Moser showed neither surprise nor pain and set to whistling an air, interrupted from time to time by some brief word of encouragement to his horses.

Thus they arrived at the farm, where the noise of the bells announced their coming. A young boy and a woman of middle age appeared on the threshold.

"Ah, it is the father!" cried the woman, looking back into the house, where could be heard the voices of several children, who came running to the door with shouts of joy and pressed around the peasant.

"Wait a moment, youngsters," interrupted the father in his big voice as he rummaged in the cart and brought forth a covered basket. "Let Fritz unharness."

But the children continued to besiege the farmer, all talking at once. He bent to kiss them, one after another; then rising suddenly:

"Where is Jean?" he asked with a quickness that had something of uneasiness in it.

"Here, father, here," answered a shrill little voice from the farm-house door; "mother doesn't want me to go out in the rain."

"Stay where you are," said Moser, throwing the traces on the backs of the horses; "I will go to you, little son. Go in, the rest of you, so as not to tempt him to come out."

The three children went back to the doorway, where little Jean was standing beside his mother.

He was a poor little creature, so cruelly deformed that at the first glance one could not have told his age or the nature of his infirmity. His whole body, distorted by sickness, formed a curved, not to say a broken line. His disproportionately large head was sunken between two unequally rounded shoulders, while his body was sustained by two little crutches; these took the place of the shrunken legs, which could not support him.

At the farmer's approach he held out his thin arms with an expression of love that made Moser's furrowed face brighten. The father lifted him in his strong arms with an exclamation of tender delight.

"Come!" he cried, "hug your father—with both arms—hard! How has he been since yesterday?"

The mother shook her head.

"Always the cough," she answered in a low tone.

"It's nothing, father," the child answered in his shrill voice. "Louis had drawn me too fast in my wheeled chair; but I am well, very well; I feel as strong as a man."

The peasant placed him carefully on the ground, set him upon his little crutches, which had fallen, and looked at him with an air of satisfaction.

"Don't you think he's growing, wife?" he asked in the tone of a man who wishes to be encouraged. "Walk a bit, Jean; walk, boy! He walks more quickly and more strongly. It'll all come right, wife; we must only be patient."

The farmer's wife made no reply, but her eyes turned toward the feeble child with a look of despair so deep that Arnold trembled; fortunately Moser paid no heed.

"Come, the whole brood of you," he went on, opening the basket he had taken from the cart; "here is something for every one! In line and hold out your hands."

The peasant had displayed three small white rolls glazed in the baking; three cries of joy burst forth simultaneously and six hands advanced to seize the rolls, but they all paused at the word of command.

"And Jean?" asked the childish voices.

"To the devil with Jean," answered Moser gayly; "there is nothing for him to-night. Jean shall have his share another time."

But the child smiled and tried to get up to look into the basket. The farmer stepped back a pace, took off the cover carefully, and lifting his arm with an air of solemnity, displayed before the eyes of all a cake of gingerbread garnished with almonds and pink and white sugarplums.

There was a general shout of admiration. Jean himself could not restrain a cry of delight; a slight flush rose to his pale face and he held out his hands with an air of joyful expectancy.

"Ah, you like it, little mole!" cried the peasant, whose face was radiant at the sight of the child's pleasure; "take it, old man, take it; it is nothing but sugar and honey."

He placed the gingerbread in the hands of the

little hunchback, who trembled with happiness, watched him hobble off, and turning to Arnold when the sound of the crutches was lost in the house, said with a slight break in his voice:

"He is my eldest. Sickness has deformed him a little, but he's a shrewd fellow and it only depends upon us to make a gentleman of him."

While speaking he had crossed the first room on the ground-floor and led his guest into a species of dining-room, the whitewashed walls of which were decorated only with a few rudely colored prints. As he entered, Arnold saw Jean seated on the floor and surrounded by his brothers, among whom he was dividing the cake given him by his father. But each one objected to the size of his portion and wished to lessen it; it required all the little hunchback's eloquence to make them accept what he had given them. For some time the young sportsman watched this dispute with singular interest, and when the children had gone out again he expressed his admiration to the farmer's wife.

"It is quite true," she said with a smile and a sigh, "that there are times when it seems as though it were a good thing for them to see Jean's infirmity. It is hard for them to give up to each other, but not one of them can refuse Jean anything; it is a constant exercise in kindness and devotion."

"Great virtue, that!" interrupted Moser. "Who could refuse anything to such a poor, afflicted little innocent? It's a silly thing for a man to say; but, look you, monsieur, that child there always makes me want to cry. Often when I am at work in the fields, I begin all at once to think about him. I say to myself Jean is ill! or Jean is dead! and then I have to find some excuse for coming home to see how it is. Then he is so weak and so ailing! If we did not love him more than the others, he would be too unhappy."

"Yes," said the mother gently, "the poor child is our cross and our joy at the same time. I love all my children, monsieur, but whenever I hear the sound of Jean's crutches on the floor, I always feel a rush of happiness. It is a sign that the good God has not yet taken our darling away from us. It seems to me as though Jean brought happiness to the house just like swallows' nests fastened to the windows. If I hadn't him to take care of, I should think there was nothing for me to do."

Arnold listened to these naïve expressions of tenderness with an interest that was mingled with astonishment. The farmer's wife called a servant to help set the table; and at Moser's invitation, the young man approached the brushwood fire which had been rekindled.

As he was leaning against the smoky mantelpiece, his eye fell upon a small black frame that inclosed a withered leaf. Moser noticed it.

"Ah! you are looking at my relic. It's a leaf of the weeping-willow that grows down there on the tomb of Napoleon! I got it from a Strasbourg merchant who had served in the Old Guard. I wouldn't part with it for a hundred crowns."

"Then there is some particular sentiment attached to it?"

"Sentiment, no," answered the peasant; "but I too was discharged from the Fourth Regiment of Hussars, a brave regiment, monsieur. There were only eight men left of our squadron, so when the Little Corporal passed in front of the line he saluted us—yes, monsieur, raised his hat to us! That was something to make us ready to die to the last man, look you. Ah! he was the father of the soldier!"

Here the peasant began to fill his pipe, looking the while at the black frame and the withered leaf. In this reminder of a marvelous destiny there was evidently for him a whole romance of youth, emotion, and regret. He recalled the last struggles of the Empire, in which he had taken part, the reviews held by the emperor, when his mere presence aroused confidence in victory; the passing successes of France's famous campaign, so soon expiated by the disaster at Waterloo; the departure of the vanquished general and his long agony on the rock of Saint Helena.

Arnold respected the old soldier's silent preoccupation and waited until he should resume the conversation.

The arrival of supper roused him from his reverie; he drew up a chair for his guest and took his place at the opposite side of the table.

"Come! fall to on the soup," he cried brusquely. "I have had nothing since morning but two swallows of cognac. I could eat an ox whole to-night."

To prove his words, he began to empty the huge porringer of soup before him.

For several moments nothing was heard but the clatter of spoons followed by that of the knives cutting up the side of bacon served by the farmer's wife. His walk and the fresh air had given Arnold himself an appetite that made him forget his Parisian daintiness. The supper grew gayer and gayer, when all at once the peasant raised his head.

"And Farraut?" he asked. "I have not seen him since my return."

His wife and the children looked at each other without answering.

"Well, what is it?" went on Moser, who saw their embarrassment. "Where is the dog? What has happened to him? Why don't you answer, Dorothée?"

"Don't be angry, father," interrupted Jean; "we didn't dare tell you, but Farraut went away and has not come back."

"A thousand devils! You should have told me!" cried the peasant, striking the table with his fist. "What road did he take?"

"The road to Garennes."

"When was it?"

"After dinner: we saw him go up the little path."

"Something must have happened to him," said Moser, getting up. "The poor animal is almost blind and there are sand pits all along the road! Go fetch my sheepskin and the lantern, wife. I must find Farraut, dead or alive."

Dorothée went out without making any remark either about the hour or the weather, and soon reappeared with what her husband had asked of her.

"You must think a great deal of this dog," said Arnold, surprised at such zeal.

"It is not I," answered Moser, lighting his pipe; "but he did good service to Dorothée's father. One day when the old man was on his way home from market with the price of his oxen in his pocket, four men tried to murder him for his money, and they would have done it if it had not been for Farraut; so when the good man died two years ago, he called me to his bedside and asked me to care for the dog as for one of his children—those were his words. I promised, and it would be a crime not to keep one's promise to the dead. Fritz, give me my iron-shod stick. I wouldn't have anything happen to Farraut for a pint of my blood. The animal has been in the family for twenty years—he knows us all by our voices—and he recalls the grandfather. I shall see you again, monsieur, and good-night until to-morrow."

Moser wrapped himself in his sheepskin and went out. They could hear the sound of his iron-shod stick die away in the soughing of the wind and the falling of the rain.

After awhile the farmer's wife offered to conduct Arnold to his quarters for the night, but Arnold asked permission to await the return of the master of the house, if his return were not delayed too long. His interest in the man who had at first seemed to him so vulgar, and in the humble family whose existence he had thought to be so valueless, continued to increase.

The vigil was prolonged, however, and Moser did not return. The children had fallen asleep one after another, and even Jean, who had held out the longest, had to seek his bed at last. Dorothée, uneasy, went incessantly from the fireside to the door and from the door to the fire-side. Arnold strove to reassure her, but her mind was excited by suspense. She accused Moser of never thinking of his health or of his safety; of always being ready to sacrifice himself for others; of being unable to see a human being or an animal suffer without risking all to relieve it. As she went on with her complaint, which sounded strangely like a glorification, her fears grew more vivid; she had a thousand gloomy forebodings. The dog had howled all through the previous night; an owl had perched upon the roof of the house; it was a Wednesday, always an unfortunate day in the family. Her fears reached such a pitch at last that the young man volunteered to go in search of her husband, and she was about to awaken Fritz to accompany him, when the sound of footsteps was heard out-side.

"It is Moser!" said the peasant woman, stopping short.

"Oho, there, open quickly, wife," cried the farmer from without.

She ran to draw the bolt, and Moser appeared, carrying in his arms the old blind dog.

"Here he is," he said gayly. "God help me! I thought I should never find him: the poor brute had rolled to the bottom of the big stone quarry."

"And you went there to get him?" asked Dorothée, horror-stricken.

"Should I have left him at the bottom to find him drowned to-morrow?" asked the old soldier. "I slid down the length of the big mountain and I carried him up in my arms like a child: the lantern was left behind, though."

"But you risked your life, you foolhardy man!" cried Dorothée, who was shuddering at her husband's explanation.

The latter shrugged his shoulders.

"Ah, bah!" he said with careless gayety; "who risks nothing has nothing; I have found Farraut—that's the principal thing. If the grandfather sees us from up there, he ought to be satisfied."

This reflection, made in an almost indifferent tone, touched Arnold, who held out his hand impetuously to the peasant.

"What you have done was prompted by a good heart," he said with feeling.

"What? Because I have kept a dog from drowning?" answered Moser. "Dogs and men—thank God I have helped more than one out of a hole since I was born; but I have sometimes had better weather than to-night to do it in. Say, wife, there must be a glass of cognac left; bring the bottle here; there is nothing that dries you better when you're wet."

Dorothée brought the bottle to the farmer, who drank to his guest's health, and then each sought his bed.

The next morning the weather was fine again; the sky was clear, and the birds, shaking their feathers, sang on the still dripping trees.

When he descended from the garret, where a bed had been prepared for him, Arnold found near the door Farraut, who was warming himself in the sun, while little Jean, seated on his crutches, was making him a collar of eglantine berries. A little further on, in the first room, the farmer was clinking glasses with a beggar who had come to collect his weekly tithe; Dorothée was holding his wallet, which she was filling.

"Come, old Henry, one more draught," said the peasant, refilling the beggar's glass; "if you mean to finish your round you must take courage."

"That one always finds here," said the beggar with a smile; "there are not many houses in the parish where they give more, but there is not one where they give with such good will."

"Be quiet, will you, Père Henri?" interrupted Moser; "do people talk of such things? Drink and let the good God judge each man's actions. You, too, have served; we are old comrades."

The old man contented himself with a shake of the head and touched his glass to the farmer's; but one could see that he was more moved by the heartiness that accompanied the alms than the alms itself.

When he had taken up his wallet again and bade them good-by, Moser watched him go until he had disappeared around a bend in the road. Then drawing a loud breath, he said, turning to his guest:

"One more poor old man without a home. You may believe me or not, monsieur, but when I see men with shaking heads going about like that, begging their bread from door to door, it turns my blood. I should like to set the table for them all and touch glasses with them all as I did just now with Père Henri. To keep your heart from breaking at such a sight, you must believe that there is a world up there where those who have not been summoned to the ordinary here will receive double rations and double pay."

"You must hold to that belief," said Arnold; "it will support and console you. It will be long before I shall forget the hours I have passed in your house, and I trust they will not be the last."

"Whenever you choose," said the old soldier; "if you don't find the bed up there too hard and if you can digest our bacon, come at your pleasure, and we shall always be under obligations to you."

He shook the hand that the young man had extended, pointed out the way that he must take, and did not leave the threshold until he had seen his guest disappear in the turn of the road.

For some time Arnold walked with lowered head, but upon reaching the summit of the hill he turned to take a last backward look, and seeing the farm-house chimney, above which curled a light wreath of smoke, he felt a tear of tenderness rise to his eye.

"May God always protect those who live under that roof!" he murmured; "for where pride made me see creatures incapable of understanding the finer qualities of the soul, I have found models for myself. I judged the depths by the surface and thought poetry absent because, instead of showing itself without, it hid itself in the heart of the things themselves; ignorant observer that I was, I pushed aside with my foot what I thought were pebbles, not guessing that in these rude stones were hidden diamonds."

PRONUNCIATION OF PROPER NAMES

NOTE,—The pronunciation of difficult words is indicated by respelling them phonetically. *N* is used to indicate the French nasal sound; *K* the sound of *ch* in German; *ü* the sound of the German *ü*, and French *u*; *ö* the sound of *ö* in foreign languages.

ALGIDUS, *al′ ji dus*
ANJOU, *oN″ zhoo′*
ATHELSTANE, *ath′ el stane*
AYTOUN, WILLIAM E., *ay′ toon*
BANGWEOLO, *bang″ we o′ lo*
BECHUANALAND, *beck″ oo ah′ na land*
BOIS-GUILBERT, BRIAN DE, *bwah geel bayr′, bre oN′ da*
CEDRIC, *ked′ rick*, or *sed′ rick*
CHALDEA, *kal de′ ah*
DUQUESNE, *du kayn′*
FALERII, *fah le′ ry i*
FRONT-DE-BOEUF, *froN de buf′*
GHENT, *gent*
GRANTMESNIL, *groN ma neel′*
KHIVA, *ke′ va*
MALVOISIN, *mal vwah saN′*
MARACAIBO, *mahr ah ki′ bo*
MARESCHAL, *mahr′ shal*
NAOMI, *nay o′ mi*
NGAMI, *ngah′ me*
ONEIDA, *o ni′ dah*

OTAHEITE, *o tah he′ te*
PSALMS, *sahms*
RAKSH, *rahksh*
ROWENA, *ro e′ na*
RUSTUM, *roos′ tum*
SAGA, *say′ ga*
SEIUS, *se′ yus*
SEISTAN, *says′ tahn*
SENNACHERIB, *sen nak′ e rib*
SKALD, *skawld*
SOHRAB, *so′ rahb*
TARPEIAN, *tahr pe′ yan*
TONGRES, *toN′ gr’*
VENEZUELA, *ven e zwe′ lah*
ZOUCHE, *zooch*

Journeys Through Bookland